BLOWS
OF
CIRCUMSTANCE

by
ANN TURNBULL
and
JOSEPH WASE

WHITE MANE PUBLISHING COMPANY, INC.

Publisher's Note: This book is based on a true life story and told with permission of the principal characters. The names of certain minor characters have been changed to protect their privacy.

The lines from *Green Eggs and Ham* by Dr. Seuss are copyright by Dr. Seuss. Reprinted by permission of Random House, Inc.   All rights reserved.

Photographs of Dick Heidecker in police uniform in his early 30's, and of David with Dick and Shirley, around age 10, are used by permission of and copyright reserved to Olan Mills, Chattanooga, Tennessee.

The photograph of Coach Parker is used by permission of and copyright reserved to *The Carroll County Times*, Westminster, Maryland.

Printed by
Beidel Printing House, Inc.
63 West Burd Street
Shippensburg, PA 17257

For a complete list of available publications please write
White Mane Publishing Company, Inc.
P.O. Box 152
Shippensburg, PA 17257

Library of Congress Cataloging-in-Publication Data

Turnbull, Ann McKenrick.
    Blows of Circumstance / by Ann Turnbull and Joseph Wase.
        p.   cm.
    ISBN 0-942597-11-7 : $19.95
    I. Wase, Joseph Jay.   II. Title.
PS3570.U655B5   1989
813'.54--dc20   89-5821
                                                                                    CIP

PRINTED IN THE UNITED STATES OF AMERICA

For

DAVID WAYNE HEIDECKER

and all the people

who loved him

Dost thou look back on what hath been,
As some divinely gifted man,
Whose life in low estate began
And on a simple village green;

Who breaks his birth's invidious bar,
And grasps the skirts of happy chance,
And breasts the blows of circumstance,
And grapples with his evil star.

— *Alfred Lord Tennyson,*
"In Memoriam A.H.H."

TABLE OF CONTENTS

CHAPTER 1

September 1972

In the middle of an Indian summer night in Baltimore, the sound of insistent knocking startled Debbie Miller from sleep. Pulling a robe around her, she hurried anxiously to the front door. No one was there. She approached the back door warily. Her hand touched a curtain on the glass part of the door, and then froze. She could make out the silhouette of two uniformed policemen outside. It did not occur to her that a random encounter was about to change a number of lives forever.

Debbie Miller, twenty years old, was married to a Baltimore City police officer. Once before the police had called her at 3 o'clock in the morning to say that her husband, Dennis Miller, was at Mercy Hospital with a gunshot wound, come right away. Dennis recovered, but Debbie barely did.

"You tell the police, don't ever call me at 3 o'clock in the morning unless you're *dead*," she told Dennis. "Do you want me to have a heart attack?"

And now it was 3 o'clock in the morning, and two policemen were knocking on her back door.

She opened it. "Dennis!" she screamed. One of the policemen was her husband, very much alive and smiling sheepishly. Debbie had never seen the other man before. "What is it?" she yelled. "What's going on?"

The two policemen came inside. Dennis was limping slightly.

"It's okay, Deb," he said. "I had a little accident on my motorcycle, no big deal." He walked carefully through the small kitchen and sat down on the living room sofa, favoring his left leg. The other man followed him.

"Who's your friend?"

"This is my buddy, Dick Heidecker. He took me to the hospital already, I'm treated and released, here we are."

"Are you okay? Are you sure you're okay?"

1

"I'm fine, honey."

"Well." Debbie exhaled slowly. "You scared me."

"Give Dick some coffee," Dennis said. "We're tired."

"I don't drink coffee," Dick told her. "But I could go for a diet soda, if you have any."

Within a few minutes, the three of them were sitting in the Millers' living room drinking soda. The air conditioning in the small apartment hummed briskly even though this was September. After a cooler period around Labor Day had come a week of heavy, humid heat, the kind that for decades had characterized summers in Baltimore. The distant sounds of crickets and baby frogs penetrated the room, although every window in the ground-level garden apartment was closed tightly against the languid air. They produced a nocturnal chorus broken only now and then by noise of traffic so very late at night. Debbie Miller took a good look at her husband's colleague for the first time. Dick Heidecker was in his thirties, stood five feet ten inches tall, and weighed substantially more than two hundred pounds. He had a protruding gut and a receding hairline and was smoking a cigarette.

Debbie smiled perkily at Dick. "Thanks very, very much for bringing Dennis home." She was, ordinarily, a vivacious and outgoing person. Only five feet two inches tall, young and attractive, she was usually a bundle of energy. At 3 o'clock in the morning, she just wanted to be polite.

"Sure," Dick said. "It was just luck, really. I happened on the scene right after the accident."

"How did it happen?" Debbie asked.

Dick shrugged. "We don't know. He was off his bike, on the ground and not too conscious. He doesn't recall how he got that way."

"Was there another vehicle?"

"Not that we got any evidence of."

Debbie looked at her husband. "Dennis?"

"It's true, babe. I don't know." Dennis Miller had stretched out on the sofa by now. "Let me put it this way, if there was another vehicle I either never saw it or I forgot about it later. Call it a phantom vehicle if you want."

"Well. Do you know how much I appreciate that you didn't *call* me at 3 o'clock in the morning?"

Dick Heidecker laughed as if he had heard that line earlier in the evening. "Dennis told me," he said. "You got to get a little thicker skin, married to a city cop."

"How long have you been on the force?" Debbie asked him.

"Eleven years, since 1961," Dick said.

"Are you married?"

"Yeah, and my wife has a pretty thick skin by now."

Debbie laughed. "Do you have kids?"

"No, ma'am," Dick replied. "We'd like to have kids. I'm 33 years old and Shirley's 36. We haven't been able to have children. We've been looking to adopt one, but so far we struck out."

"Really?" Debbie asked. "Where have you looked?"

"Everywhere," Dick said. "We went to some agencies, but nothing happened. There's even a TV show about A Child is Waiting, some name like that, where they have children for adoption, and you call up. I called there a few times but it never worked out."

Dick drained his diet soda and stood up. He rubbed his belly nervously, a habit he had developed as his waistline expanded. Debbie asked, "What happened when you called there?"

"They gave me the runaround. Nothing ever came of it."

Debbie took Dick's glass into the kitchen and poured some more diet soda for him. "I work with children," she said, handing his glass back to him.

"Is that right?" Dick asked. "Where do you work?"

"It's called the Institute for Children. We have kids there who are emotionally disturbed, can't live in their families any more, or some of them don't even have families."

"What do you do there?" Dick asked.

"I'm just the librarian now," Debbie told him. "I'm going to school though, in hopes of becoming a real teacher there." She thought, here is a man who wants to adopt a child. I have a building full of children that nobody wants. What kind does he want? What size? What color?

She asked him.

Dick Heidecker began to rub his belly again. "Are you serious?" he asked. He was pacing now, drinking his diet soda.

Debbie said, "We have a whole institution full of kids. Most of them can't be adopted by anybody. Either they have families, or else they're so messed up they couldn't live in anybody's family. They'd burn your house down or run away or something. But we have one little boy who I think doesn't belong at the Institute. He's seven years old. I know he's available for adoption — he came to us through Social Services. He used to live with a foster family, but that didn't work out. They moved away. Now he doesn't have anybody. He's just there at the Institute wishing for somebody to take him home."

Dick stopped pacing. "Why is he at the Institute?" he asked.

"He probably has some emotional problems," Debbie said. "But the main reason is, there isn't any other place for him to be. He doesn't have anybody."

"What if I wanted to come out and see him?"

"You could come any time," Debbie told him. She thought a minute. "Shouldn't you discuss this with your wife, though?"

"Sure," Dick said. "But I already know how Shirley'll feel about it. We've been looking for quite a while."

He began to pace again, noticing for the first time that Dennis Miller had fallen asleep on the sofa while he and Debbie talked. Debbie laughed. "He does that," she explained. She pulled her robe tightly around her, abruptly realizing that she wasn't dressed. "And it's 4 o'clock in the morning!"

"Where is this Institute?" Dick asked.

"You know where Rosewood is?"

"Rosewood?" Dick stared at her. "I thought Rosewood was for retarded people."

"It is," Debbie explained. "But that's where our Institute is. We're not connected to Rosewood, but we're on their grounds. Do you know where it is?"

"Sure, in Baltimore County," Dick said. "I know right where it is. But do you mean you have a place for little kids that's sitting right in the middle of Rosewood?"

"You got it," Debbie told him.

Dick shook his head. "Okay," he said. "I'd like to come out there. What's the boy's name?"

"His name is David."

Dick Heidecker handed her his empty glass and said goodnight. As he and Debbie opened the door of the Millers' apartment, they could feel heavy pockets of humidity hanging in the air, pushing oppressively against their faces. Debbie watched Dick as he walked down the path to his police car. She closed the door and set the chain lock, then leaned against the door feeling very tired and suddenly grateful that this nice policeman had brought her husband home.

It was September, 1972.

CHAPTER 2

In The Beginning

On a cold day in December of 1964, a woman in her forties gave birth to a son at Johns Hopkins Hospital, one of the finest medical facilities in the world. Two days later, she took the child home to a squalid row house some eight blocks away in East Baltimore. She named the baby David Wayne.

He was her fifth child, and she was not married. They occupied a dilapidated rental property along with the woman's four other children of assorted ages, and three unrelated adults. No one in the home had steady employment, formal education, or any interest in David. By early summer, the household had come to the attention of the Department of Social Services, whose file soon contained a report characterizing David as undernourished and maternally deprived as early as the age of five months. The following Christmas, David's mother voluntarily turned the child over to social workers. On January 10, 1966, David officially became a ward of the Baltimore City Department of Social Services.

David was placed in his first foster home at the age of thirteen months. Although technically available for adoption, he was not considered adoptable because of severe emotional problems which were already manifest. While he had weighed seven pounds at birth, he was now dangerously small and physically undeveloped. When placed in a crib, he banged his head against the side over and over. The first foster family could not cope; another was found. There David exhibited frightening temper tantrums, slapping himself and becoming uncontrollably destructive of property. The second foster family couldn't cope, either. Social Services placed David in a children's hospital known in those days as Happy Hills, whose records reflected David's maternal deprivation in one or both of his foster homes. He remained in the hospital for three months.

The Department of Social Services could not locate any foster home in Baltimore to care for David. A family finally was found in the northwestern corner of Carroll County, some thirty-five miles away. Through a purchase of care arrangement, David became a ward of the Carroll County Department of Social Services. At three and a half, David went to live on a farm with Sam and Vinnie Wagner.

The farm which the Wagners owned lay in an extremely rural area towards the northwest, almost in Frederick County. Tucked behind an abandoned manufacturing plant, out of sight of the closest paved road, its few acres of inhospitable land provided subsistence for the Wagners. Parts of abandoned vehicles surrounded mature oak trees. Flowering shrubs and bushes brightened old tires; squirrels and raccoons darted through unused barrels and bits of furniture. There were no neighbors close by, and no zoning or other regulations to take notice of. The nearest small town was four miles away.

The Wagners were simple, God-fearing people who farmed and did odd jobs for a living. They had several grown children, and a revolving houseful of foster children for whom they were paid something more than $100 a month each. They occupied a large, broken-down farmhouse with several bedrooms, each of which contained more than one foster child. Sam Wagner left the house early each morning and returned after dark; part of his time was spent on the farm, and the rest out in the countryside performing odd jobs for money. Vinnie Wagner rose early each morning and spent her days caring for the house and those areas of the farm which she considered to be within her domain: the chickens, and some of the gardens. The foster children who were of school age walked down the dirt road to catch the yellow school bus each morning; after school, they worked on the farm. When David came to live with the Wagners, they were caring for four other foster children: three teen-age boys and a twelve-year-old girl named Sara.

David, not quite four years old, was short and very thin for his age. He had large brown eyes and straight and unruly sandy blond hair. He was only beginning to talk. He was unable to dress himself, and only partially successful at using the bathroom. He was put in a room with Sara, who was expected to watch out for him. Sara was a tall, plain girl who often seemed far away, but she usually had a warm smile for David. She rapidly became the first friend in David's life. He learned to say her name, and watched sadly each morning when she walked down the road to the school bus. While she was gone, there was little for him to do. There were few toys on the farm; Vinnie Wagner was occupied all day and had no time or inclination to play. At first, David would follow her around from task to task, seeking her attention; when none was forthcoming, he followed her anyway, looking at her from a distance. If he was quiet, as he often was, Vinnie had little to say to him.

David liked the animals on the farm, especially if they were little or helpless. He made friends with some of the chickens who ran around outside their chickenhouse cackling and squawking. Sometimes he tried to pat them, reaching out his hand until Vinnie yelled at him to get away. Once he found a chicken who was sick and carried it into the kitchen, where he stroked it gently until it died of its illness. Vinnie Wagner came in and found him with the dead chicken in his lap.

"Killer!" she hollered. "I told you to leave them chickens alone! Now look what you done!"

David shook his head. "No," he protested.

Vinnie Wagner grabbed David's arm and pulled him to his feet. She slapped his face. "Leave the animals alone!" she told him. "Don't touch them no more."

She heaved the dead chicken through the open door to the outside. David began to scream and throw objects around the kitchen. Vinnie Wagner put him in his room alone. She did that frequently. When she did, David threw things and banged his head against the wall. Sometimes he was ignored; other times, Vinnie came in and yelled at him or spanked him.

When the school bus brought Sara and the boys back to the farm each afternoon, David ran to meet them. The boys paid no attention to him, but Sara usually seemed glad to see him. She held his hand and talked to him for a little while until she had to begin her chores on the farm. Then David followed her around. She told him about her school, and sometimes sang to him. Once Sara brought home a picture she had made for David in her art class. She put David on her lap and pointed to things in the picture.

"Look, David, here's the sky," she showed him. "See how blue it is?"

David smiled at her. "Blue sky," he repeated.

"See the trees? I painted two trees in the picture, one for me and one for you. Do you see?"

"Trees," David said. He touched the one Sara had said was for him.

"That's right. Can you find the grass?"

David looked at the picture. He did not know how to find grass. He shook his head. "That's all right, I'll show you," Sara said.

She pointed to the grass. "Do you want to keep this picture?"

David smiled happily. He and Sara found a place next to David's bed and taped it to the wall. David touched the picture every day, saying "sky," "grass," "my tree." He asked Sara to make him another picture, but there were no art supplies on the farm; he would have to wait until she had another opportunity in school.

Sometimes Sara was cross with David, and told him to go away. Once, when she did that, he wandered off and was not found until nightfall; then Mrs. Wagner spanked Sara and yelled at David. That night, Sara cried and cried in their room and refused to talk to David, although he put his arms around her and tried to hug her. Later, David fell asleep on the floor with his clothes on. Usually, Sara helped him into bed. Vinnie Wagner had tried to teach him a prayer, but he didn't like it much. The prayer was about dying in his sleep, and it scared him. Mrs. Wagner got angry when he told her that, and demanded that he say it anyway. Most of the time she didn't come into his room when he was going to bed, though, and so he didn't.

Sam Wagner had little to say to David, or to anyone else. He came home late, often after dinner, and retreated somewhere. Now and then David approached him and stood watching. Once he said, "Hi."

Sam Wagner looked up at him, as if startled. "What do you want?" he asked.

"Hi," David repeated. He smiled.

"Kid, I'm tired," Sam Wagner told him. "Leave me alone, okay?"

David hesitated. He tried one more time. "Hi."

Now Sam was irritated. "Get the hell outta here!" he yelled. "Vinnie, where are you? Get this brat, will you?"

Vinnie Wagner hurried in and took David away. "Don't bother him," she cautioned.

"Why?" David asked.

"He's tired. Busy. He wants to be let alone."

David went off to find Sara.

Once there were kittens on the farm. David watched them each day with fascination. He sat near them, softly stroking one or two of the kittens at a time, humming to them. As they grew larger, he picked out a black and white one as his favorite and gave it a name: Kitty. He carried it about, patting it carefully, hugging it gently. Sometimes he was able to smuggle the kitten into his room and sleep with it, but Sara warned him to be careful, Mrs. Wagner wouldn't like it at all. David asked Sara why, but Sara had no answer; she said she didn't know. One day, David saw a dog attack the litter. One of the kittens was killed; the others, including Kitty, were injured. Vinnie Wagner put them in a box and told David to leave them alone.

"They're hurt," she told him. "Mr. Wagner will take care of them when he comes home."

David smiled. "Take care of Kitty," he said.

Sara shook her head, "You don't understand, David," she told him. "She means he'll get rid of them. He'll drown them."

Sam Wagner did. That night, David lay on the floor by his bed and banged his head and feet on the floor. Sara tried to comfort him, but he screamed with rage. He threw his own possessions, and Sara's, around the room, and finally tore from the wall the picture Sara had painted for him. He ripped it into tiny pieces which he scattered about. Sara began to cry, too.

"You shouldn't have drowned his kitten," she told the Wagners. "He loved it so much!"

The Wagners could not comprehend either the cause or the depth of David's grief. Sam Wagner threw up his hands. "The cats were injured," he said. "They were gonna die anyway. That's why you drown 'em."

"Then you could have let him die on its own," Sara insisted.

Sam Wagner stormed out of the room. The next day, Vinnie drove David to a doctor in Carroll County. The doctor looked at David and asked him and Mrs. Wagner some questions. Then he wrote out a prescription and handed it to Vinnie Wagner. "This should help," he told her.

Vinnie stared at the piece of paper in her hand. "I have to take this up with Social Service," she told the doctor. "I don't have money for medicine for these state children."

The doctor shrugged his shoulders and showed them out. Vinnie Wagner drove David back to the farm. He looked out of the window all the way back. It was only the second or third time he had left the farm since his arrival many months before.

Vinnie Wagner did not get around to communicating with her caseworker at the Carroll County Department of Social Services, and the prescription was never filled. A few weeks later, there were new incidents of temper tantrums and destructiveness. On one occasion, when the Wagners were unable to control David, Sam Wagner put him in a closet for an hour. "That oughta calm him down," he announced. But it didn't. From time to time, David went on rampages, hurling objects through the air or pounding his hands or feet or head against the furniture. Once some kitchenware was broken during such an incident. Vinnie Wagner, alone in the house with David, was at her wit's end. She took off her shoe and beat David with it, on his buttocks, his back, the backs of his legs. Later she was astonished to see traces of blood and to find that she had left marks on David. Some days later, when the marks were less visible, she got in touch with her caseworker. Vinnie Wagner told the caseworker that David was out of control.

They were referred to the Clinic for the Exceptional Child at the University of Maryland, and from there to the Carroll County Health Department Psychoneurology Clinic. This time, prescriptions were written for Dilantin and Benadryl, which were supposed to make David more controllable. Vinnie Wagner filled the prescriptions, but she often forgot to give David the medicine, and in any case she saw no improvement. Three months later, she stopped giving him the medication.

At five, David started kindergarten at an elementary school in Carroll County. A school bus picked him up at the farm and took him there. It was the first time David had been away from the farm on his own. David was overwhelmed by the school. He had no experience with other children his age, and lacked the most basic pre-school skills. He could not identify any letters or numbers, had had almost no experience with books, and had been provided with no information about the world. He had never sat down to a table with a box of crayons. He had never been part of a group listening to a story. He had not been on a swing or a sliding-board or a seesaw. He had never watched Sesame Street. He did not understand such concepts as taking turns or putting things away. He was unable to participate in an activity such as "show and tell." The school gave him a routine intelligence test and determined that he was in the "dull normal" range.

All around him, David saw children behaving in ways that he knew nothing about. They appeared to know things he didn't. Many of them had things that he did not. If the teacher suggested that the children bring a certain item from home, the others came to school with it; David had no idea how such things were acquired. Other parents came to the school to volunteer, to assist in special activities, to bring cupcakes and punch for special occasions; he had no one to do that.

What made school tolerable for David was his kindergarten teacher, Miss Kelsey. She was twenty-four years old and this was her second year of teaching. Not only was she kind and gentle, but she was, in David's eyes, beautiful. Tall and lithe, wearing brightly-colored clothes and narrow shoes with heels, she presented quite a contrast to Vinnie Wagner, who was short and stocky and generally wore overalls and workshoes. Miss Kelsey had shoulder-length blond hair that curled up on the ends, and wore lipstick and rouge. She had an open, friendly manner, and routinely hugged her little charges, nearly all of whom were away from home for the first time in their lives. She established limits and kept order, but so cheerfully that there were few complaints and scarcely any homesick children.

For David, Miss Kelsey was fantasy, a figment of his imagination who was actually standing before him. His strongest wish was to please her, to do as she asked so that her blissful smile would be bestowed upon him. Unfortunately, he was often unable to comply with her simplest direction, not for lack of trying, but because his absence of normal experiences made it impossible. Early in the year, David began to exhibit behaviors that were unacceptable for school. He refused to sit at a table to color; instead he broke the crayons. When Miss Kelsey sat next to him and put her hand on a crayon along with David's, he was able to draw lines, but as soon as she moved away, he would scream. When told to go outside and play, David was unable to put his coat on himself; he threw it on the floor instead. When Miss Kelsey picked it up and gently helped him on with it, he smiled at her, but when she moved along to help another child, he cried. On many, many occasions he threw himself on the floor and banged his head against a table, slapping himself and screaming in a way that frightened the teacher.

Miss Kelsey could see that David needed a great deal of extra attention, and she was willing to provide it, but she had twenty-one other five-year-olds to attend to, and there was only so much time in the day. She looked up David's record, which was skimpy, and found that he was a foster child. The Wagners were called in for a conference; only Vinnie showed up. Miss Kelsey spoke as gently as she could to Vinnie Wagner. She told her that David had serious behavioral problems which appeared to be emotional in nature, that he should be under the care of a pediatrician and that he probably needed medication. Vinnie Wagner shrugged her shoulders and said that David was a foster child, not her own, and she could not afford either the time or the money to get involved in this.

"I already raised my own children," she told Miss Kelsey, "and they all turned out good if I do say so myself. The children I have now ain't my own. I'm doing a favor for the state and the county, that's what."

Miss Kelsey nodded gravely. "Indeed you are, Mrs. Wagner," she replied. "I don't know what would happen to children like David if there were no families willing to take them in." She paused. "May I ask you how many other children you presently care for?"

"Four," Vinnie Wagner said proudly.

"Four, my goodness! And is David the youngest?"

"Yes, he is."

"You live on a farm, do you?"

"Yes."

"Are there any children David's age in the neighborhood, I wonder?"

"What neighborhood?" Vinnie asked. "We don't have no neighbors."

"I see," said Miss Kelsey. "And what does David do to entertain himself when he isn't in school?"

Vinnie looked at her suspiciously. "What do you mean?" she asked.

"Well, for instance, does he have access to books? Are there toys for him to play with?"

Now Vinnie Wagner was indignant. "Well, I don't know what you think!" she snorted. "Course there's toys. We don't have books, David can't read anyway. What is it you're asking me?"

Miss Kelsey smiled disarmingly. "Don't take offense, Mrs. Wagner," she said. "I know you want what's best for David. So do I. That's why I'm asking you these questions: the more information I have about David, the better I can help him."

Vinnie was slightly placated. "All right," she said. But she was plainly unwilling to answer any more questions. It didn't matter. Miss Kelsey already had a good picture of what David's life on the farm must be. Now it was her turn to be angry. She did not doubt that the Wagners were well-intentioned people, doing their best, but their best was grossly inadequate. They were limited, rigid, ignorant people, Miss Kelsey thought, who had no idea of what children needed, either in the way of affection or in terms of education. Now Miss Kelsey began to doubt the validity of David's intelligence test results. Clearly, he lacked normal experiences and exposure; how might that affect his test scores? Moreover, the school knew nothing about David's life before the Wagners. Miss Kelsey spoke to the school principal about David's situation. David was placed with a foster family, Miss Kelsey said, that was inadequate. Didn't the school have an obligation to notify the Carroll County

Department of Social Services? Wasn't there something that could be done?

The principal, a balding, rotund man who had been in public education for thirty years, listened patiently while he puffed on a thick cigar.

"I appreciate your concern, Miss Kelsey," he told her. "And I accept your opinion about the Wagners. They're probably terrible foster parents."

"They're outrageous!" Miss Kelsey said.

"I'm sure," the principal acknowledged. "But have you thought about how few qualified people exist who are willing to take care of other people's children? Especially ones with emotional or learning problems?"

"I don't know the answer to that," Miss Kelsey admitted.

"Well I do. Damn few, that's how many."

"I don't care," Miss Kelsey insisted. "There has to be somebody."

The principal snorted. "I can just about guarantee you that Social Services knows all about the Wagners, and how incompetent they are," he said. "What of it? Without the Wagners, David would be in an institution somewhere."

"Maybe he'd be better off," Miss Kelsey suggested.

"No. He's better off where he is." The principal gave her a long look. "You have to realize, Miss Kelsey, that life is not a textbook. Theory is different from practice, and life is full of compromises."

Miss Kelsey terminated the conversation. She felt patronized, put down, and helpless.

Back at the farm, Vinnie Wagner told David that if he didn't behave better, God would punish him, and so would she. Furthermore, they would have to give him back to the state. He was fortunate that she and Mr. Wagner provided him with a good home, she said; if he lost that privilege it was his own fault. David reached out and tried to touch her hand, but she pushed him away. He went to find Sara.

For the rest of the school year, Miss Kelsey gave David all the attention she could without slighting the other children. David's behavior did not improve much, but the school tolerated it out of sympathy for a child who obviously had severe problems and a poor family situation. Miss Kelsey noticed that although David had not made any friends at school, he had developed a relationship, of sorts, with two of the youngest, smallest children who were also friendless. She sometimes observed David walking with one of them in a protective manner, even getting into a fistfight with another boy who teased them. Miss Kelsey reflected on that. She had never known David to provoke a fight, although she had often seen him react to provocation by fighting. Miss Kelsey thought for a while, and then called Vinnie Wagner on the telephone to suggest that it might be beneficial for David to have a pet of his own, maybe his own dog. Vinnie said it was out of the question. She reminded the teacher that David was a ward of the state: "The state don't pay for dogs, you know."

Miss Kelsey gave David a book to take home and keep. It was one of the Dr. Seuss books, with large print and interesting, colorful pictures. She asked David if there would be anyone at the farm to read it to him. David said yes, he thought Sara would. Later that day, David showed the book to Sara and asked her to read it to him. She did, pointing out the various pictures and explaining what the story meant. David asked her to read it again. Sara did, but when David asked a third time, she told him he would have to wait until tomorrow. They found a safe place in their room to keep the book, and after that Sara read it to David every afternoon at least once. She began to notice that David was learning the story by heart.

In June, when the school year ended, Miss Kelsey told the children she would not be back the next year. She was getting married, she said, and her husband had a job in Connecticut, so they would be moving there. She would miss them all terribly, but they were going into the first grade anyway, where they would have a different teacher. She wanted them to know she would never forget them. Later, David came and sat on her lap and leaned his head against her shoulder. Miss Kelsey talked quietly to him for a long time, and finally kissed him on the top of his head and told him he would have to get on the bus, but he became so upset that she gave up on the bus and later put him in her car and drove out to the Wagners' farm. She walked David to the house, where he insisted on showing her his room. There they found Sara who, David said, had to read him the Dr. Seuss book while Miss Kelsey watched. As Sara read, David said the words along with her. Miss Kelsey gave David a hug and a kiss and told him she loved him. Then she asked Sara to look out for him.

Sara said confidently, "Yes, ma'am, I will."

Miss Kelsey turned and walked away. She was glad Sara was there, but she had no illusions. She knew that Sara was only fourteen years old.

In the fall, the school reluctantly allowed David to enter the first grade. Earlier, there had been talk of having him repeat kindergarten, especially in view of his positive relationship with Miss Kelsey, but since she was leaving anyway it seemed just as well to promote him. David, of course, was woefully unprepared in spite of everything Miss Kelsey had tried to do for him. He lacked reading readiness skills, and continued to behave in a disruptive and destructive manner. This time there was no Miss Kelsey to temper David's behavior; the first grade teacher was a woman in her fifties who was tired of teaching and brooked no nonsense. But if she was less idealistic than Miss Kelsey, she was also more assertive. Early in the year, she called the Wagners in for a conference, making it clear that both of them must appear. They did, reluctantly. The teacher told the Wagners that unless they put David on medication which controlled his behavior, the school could not continue to keep him.

She also asked for the name of their caseworker at the Carroll County Department of Social Services. That question frightened Vinnie Wagner, and she took David back to the Health Department for medication. This time, she tried to be conscientious about giving it to him.

For Halloween, the teacher told the children they could wear costumes to school. David asked Sara what a costume was. When she told him, he asked if he could have one. Sara hesitated. She knew they would never get one from the Wagners. That evening, when Vinnie Wagner was occupied, Sara took an old sheet from the closet. She tried to make a ghost costume for David. It wasn't very good, but David was thrilled; he had his very own costume to take to school. But in the morning, as David prepared to take the bus, Vinnie Wagner caught sight of the costume and demanded to know what it was. When told that Sara had cut up one of her sheets, she became enraged and beat both of the children. David rode to school on the bus without a costume, screaming and hitting the side of the bus. At school he had to be kept apart from the other children all day.

Several times over the next months, David wandered away from the farmhouse. He always started back when darkness came, but once he lost his way and had to sleep outside. When the Wagners found him, they beat him and isolated him even from Sara. The next day, David heard the Wagners arguing with each other because they had taken him to live there in the first place. He tried to climb into Vinnie Wagner's lap, but she made him go to his room instead.

By now, Sara had taken over much of the housework inside the farmhouse. She cooked, dusted, washed dishes, did laundry. David became accustomed to following her about, talking with her as she worked, and occasionally helping out. Sara showed him how to dust; David thought it was fun. Each of them would take a cloth, and they would dust together. Sara also showed him how to dry dishes, but she was reluctant to allow him to do too much for fear he would break something. David would stand beside her, begging her to let him help.

Sometimes Vinnie Wagner thought they fooled around too much in the kitchen. Late one afternoon in November, when the days were short in Carroll County, she came into the kitchen expecting to find dinner ready. Instead she found Sara laughing with David, piling up the stainless steel spoons and trying to teach David to count.

"Six!" David called out gleefully.

"No, David, that's five," Sara told him. "See, you counted this one twice."

David laughed. "Six," he insisted.

Vinnie Wagner strode across the kitchen where a pot of water heated on the stove. "What's this?" she demanded. "Where's dinner?"

"It's coming," Sara told her. "I don't have everything ready yet."

"Six spoons!" David shouted. He tossed the pile of spoons into the air. They clattered onto the floor, sliding and spinning in three directions at once.

Vinnie Wagner picked him up under his arms. "Quit it!" she yelled. "It's dinner time! Mr. Wagner done drove in just now and we don't have nothing ready to eat!"

"Put me down!" David shouted. "I want to count my spoons!"

Vinnie Wagner locked her fingers around David's tiny wrists and thrust his hands into the pot of hot water on the stove. "Shut up!" she yelled.

In a flash, Sara grabbed Vinnie Wagner's arm and yanked on it. She pulled David from Mrs. Wagner and held him. David screamed with pain. Sara ran cold water into the sink and plunged David's hands into it.

"Keep your hands in there, David," she whispered. "They'll feel better."

She took a rag from a pile on the floor to dry his hands with. Then she gently rubbed margarine on his hands. David sobbed against her chest and Vinnie Wagner stood like a statue as Sam Wagner suddenly walked into the kitchen.

"What's this?" he asked, looking around. "Where's dinner?"

Sara looked at him. "David got hurt," she told him tersely. "Mrs. Wagner's cooking tonight."

Once, near Christmas, David had a confrontation with Sam Wagner. It started when David asked if he could help around the farm. Sam spat in the general direction of the nearest trash receptacle.

"Work, huh," he said. "Course there's work. If you're big enough to work, I got plenty for you to do."

David looked at him with anticipation.

"What things?"

"Things outside," Sam told him. "Picking vegetables, feeding animals. Man things."

"I can do them!" David shouted. "Can I now?"

Sam looked at him with disdain. "Course not, you dummy," he replied. "It's winter. And it's dark. I'm talkin' about the spring, when there's things you can do that'll help out. You think work is a game or something?"

David looked disappointed. "No," he said.

"Then don't ask dumb questions," Sam told him. "Don't be so stupid."

David looked at him. "I'm not stupid," he said.

Sam Wagner took three steps across the room until he stood right in front of David. "Shut your mouth, kid," he said quietly. "Your sass is making me mad."

Behind them, Sara softly moved closer to David. She put her hand on his shoulder and silently walked him out of range of Sam Wagner. When they reached the safety of their room, she told him, "Don't ever talk back to Mr. Wagner. He'd as soon kill you as look at you."

David was perplexed. "Why is he so mean?" he asked.

Sara shook her head. "I don't know for sure," she said. "Maybe because we're state kids."

"What's that?"

"We're not their real children. We don't have any real folks."

David said, "Oh." He went over and picked up the Dr. Seuss book. "Let's read this," he said.

Although David was not very clear about what a state kid was, or, indeed, what a foster family was, other children in his class at school apparently were quite clear about it. Furthermore, they knew that David was a state kid who lived with a foster family. One day in January as David rode home from school on the bus, a group of older boys began to taunt him, calling him "orphan" and "foster brat." Heedlessly, David flailed at them with his fists. He managed to push one of them up against the emergency door and attempted to kick the door open while the bus was in motion. The driver became aware of trouble and stopped the bus. David had to be forcibly restrained and held by two older girls, at the driver's direction, so that the bus could continue. When David got back to the farm, he waited at the end of the dirt road for Sara's bus. But when it came, and Sara alighted, she told him she was busy with homework today and he would have to wait until later. David followed behind her, screaming at her to play with him; Sara, who was unaware of the events on the bus, told him no, not now. In the house, David got a pair of scissors from the kitchen and threatened Sara with them. She ran screaming from the farmhouse with David in pursuit, brandishing his weapon. That night, the Wagners called their caseworker and told her they could no longer keep David.

The Carroll County Department of Social Services initiated emergency proceedings to have David placed in an institution. On January 14, 1972, one month after David's seventh birthday, he was committed to the Institute for Children by emergency court order.

CHAPTER 3

RICA

David was delivered to an institution housed in two large buildings whose physical appearance lay somewhere between stark and grim. Known as the Richards Building and the Finesinger Building, they actually stood in the midst of another public institution, called Rosewood, for mentally retarded children and adults. The Richards Building, to which David was taken, was a very long, narrow two-story structure of red brick, with four white columns in front. It presented a disarming look of grandeur until one walked into the dingy lobby from which dark dilapidated halls spread out in three directions.

The first person to greet David was Cindy Pelham, a warm, black middle-aged woman whose job designation was "careworker." She took David by the hand.

"Come on, honey," she said. She took him up the stairs to the residential area known as the ward. David's "room" was a dormitory containing eight beds, eight small chests of drawers, and a poster on the wall. David sat on the bed Cindy showed him.

"This here is your chest," she said, pointing to one. "Let's put your clothes away."

She did, not commenting on the fact that he had few clothes and that those he had were in need of repair and alterations. Later David was to learn that Cindy had a sewing machine at her home which she sometimes used to mend clothes for the children at the institution. Today he knew only that she was nice to him.

"Who else sleeps in here?" he asked.

"Seven other boys, and they're most all bigger than you," Cindy told him. "You keep your eyes open and stay out of trouble. If there's anybody bothering you, you come and tell me."

"I will," David said. He felt relieved. He felt hungry, too. "Where do we eat here?" he asked.

"Cafeteria," said Cindy. "Come on, it's almost dinner time."

On the way, Cindy showed David the rest of the ward. There was a large bathroom with a number of showers. There was a recreational room, known as the "day room," with battered furniture and a TV. There were also several small, windowless rooms without furniture. David asked what they were.

"They's quiet rooms," Cindy said. "That's for if you're bad."

David didn't say anything. He followed Cindy downstairs to the cafeteria, where several dozen boys and a dozen or so girls converged noisily. David clung to Cindy. After the solitude of the Wagners' farm, this was chaos. But he was hungry. Dinner was a slice of meatloaf and mashed potatoes. Cindy put David at a table with other boys under ten. The boy next to him was an eight-year-old named Ernie.

"Hey," said Ernie, "you new today?"

"Uh-huh," David said.

"Well, where's your folks?" Ernie asked.

"Don't have any, only the Wagners."

"Who's the Wagners?"

"People I live with. On a farm."

"What did you do, run away?"

David shook his head. "Sara made me mad so I chased her."

"Are the people mad at you?" Ernie asked.

"I don't know."

"If they are you have to stay on weekends too, when everybody goes home."

"Everybody?" David asked.

"Just about," said Ernie. "There's nobody here on weekends."

David began to worry. He had not given any thought to his relationship with the Wagners. What if they didn't want to see him any more? What if they never came to visit? A social worker had explained to David that he would not live on the farm anymore, that after this he would stay at a place with lots of other children and plenty of people to take care of him. David could not tell whether this was good or bad. He had no sense of being glad to get away from Sam and Vinnie Wagner; what he felt most keenly was a loss as he left the home he had occupied for three and a half years — half his life — actually, for as long as he could remember. And he distinctly missed Sara.

He asked Ernie if Ernie had a family.

"Sure I do," Ernie said proudly. "I have a mom and two sisters."

"How come you don't live there?" David wanted to know.

"Because," Ernie said matter-of-factly. "My stepfather doesn't like me."

"Oh," David said.

"Anyhow, I go there every weekend. My stepfather goes away then."

After dinner, Cindy took charge of David again. Upstairs she introduced him to the other boys in his dormitory room. Ernie was one of them. Later they could play in the day room where the TV was, but the TV was broken. After a while, Cindy showed David where he could take a shower. When he was in his pajamas, she helped him into bed.

"Are you here all the time, Cindy?" David asked.

"No, honey, I'm evening shift," she told him. "I come from four o'clock in the afternoon til eleven at night. I'll be gone when you wake up, but another lady will be here. I'll be back at four o'clock tomorrow. You don't have to worry."

"Cindy?" David whispered.

"What, honey?"

"Is this a place where children stay forever?"

"Course not, silly. Children stay here till they're feeling better, and then their folks come and keep them."

"But I don't have folks. Just the Wagners, and maybe they're mad at me."

"Don't you worry," Cindy said firmly. "If they are, we'll have to look around for some new folks for you. They's folks in the world for everybody, somewhere."

In the night, David had to go to the bathroom. He couldn't find his way and he couldn't find Cindy, but somebody like her sat in a chair in the hall, and she helped David. He thought maybe things would be all right here.

David's new home, the Regional Institute for Children and Adolescents, known as RICA, began in 1958 as the Esther Loring Richards Children's Center. This state institution, administered by the Maryland Department of Health and Mental Hygiene, was established to provide in-patient psychiatric treatment for children with severe emotional problems. It originally occupied a single building, known as the Richards Building, on the grounds of Rosewood. In 1961, the newly-constructed Finesinger Building was added, and the name of the institution was changed to the Institute for Children. It continued under that name, at that location, until 1973, when it moved to the former site of St. Peter's Monastery in Baltimore City, and changed its name to RICA.

Like institutions everywhere, RICA continually evolved over the years, changing not only its name and location, but also its mandate, focus, and reason for being. RICA began as a place for short-term treatment, but later became a facility for long-term care; ultimately, by law, each child's stay was limited to two years. Most of the children came from difficult or inadequate family settings. Many had been abused. They came there, usually, through either the juvenile courts or the Department of Social Services. By the time of David's arrival, the program operated with a "team treatment" approach. Each child was to receive an individualized treatment program with specific and

The Richards Building at Rosewood, where David spent a year of his life.
Barbara Skarf

David in foreground at RICA. This is the earliest known photograph of David, age seven.
Barbara Skarf

final goals, and to be part of a "team" consisting of a doctor, psychologist, social worker, teacher, recreational therapist, and child careworkers.

David slowly settled into the routine at RICA. The youngest children spent half of each weekday in school, in the Richards Building. David was restless and disruptive in the classroom. Though he was seven years old, he could not read. He found it difficult to stay in his seat, and spent most of the time looking around, often darting from his chair or talking out loud. Sometimes he was isolated in one of the "quiet rooms." Obviously, under the circumstances, school could not be conducted in a normal way at RICA. The children learned, if at all, on a one-to-one basis. Because of their diverse educational backgrounds and informational levels, it was impossible to create a classroom of children who knew the same things and were ready to learn the same new things. School became a place in which the teachers did their best to keep order and impart at least some basic knowledge about the way to behave in civilized society.

Recreational therapy, art, or physical education occupied the other half of each weekday. Occasionally there would be a field trip to the Baltimore Zoo or some other attraction. In 1972, a twenty-year-old idealist with waist-length hair, Mel Klein, was the recreational therapist at the institution. (Fifteen years later, Mel Klein still worked at RICA, but as a psychologist with a Ph.D. and hair of normal length.) The setting was fine for recreational purposes. Rosewood was a sprawling complex of several dozen stone and brick buildings. Set high on a hill, it overlooked a suburban community in Baltimore County about a half mile back from the heavily-travelled Reisterstown Road. Later, garden apartments and a shopping center would be built on the sloping area between Rosewood and Reisterstown Road. In 1972, that was undeveloped land containing an occasional residence. Rosewood backed up to fields, woods and a pond. Mel Klein and the children spent hours fishing from the pond with rods made of sticks, string, and hooks, or climbing trees and vines.

David loved the time they spent outdoors. At the Wagners' farm, there had been acres of space, with climbing trees, places of interest, and various animals, but nearly all of its pleasures had been denied to David. He had seldom been permitted to roam the fields and explore, to climb and touch and collect, or just to play outdoors. Here at RICA, he could search the ground and brush and trees for hours, finding baby frogs or abandoned birds' nests; he could run and climb and shout, if he liked. Mel Klein encouraged the children to explore nature, to discover living things or dead things, to be free in the outdoors. He also helped them create a garden, showing them how to weed, plant and water until colorful flowers and a few simple vegetables sprang up and thrived.

Sometimes Mel took a small group to the pond. He showed David how to make a stone skip across the water. David loved it; he ran around searching for flat stones and bringing them to Mel.

"Is this one flat enough?" he demanded, showing one to Mel. "Will it work?"

"Try it," Mel said.

They did. It skipped beautifully. David yelled with joy. "I did it!" he shouted. "Let's do more!"

Sometimes they looked for particular kinds of birds. In the spring, the woods were filled with robins building their nests. Mel taught David how to tell a male robin from a female.

"See the bright red on the breast?" he pointed out. "That means you have a father bird there. The mothers aren't as bright."

"Why?" David asked.

"It's nature's way of protecting the birds," Mel explained. "It makes the mother robin harder to see, so nothing will hurt her and she can take care of her babies."

"Oh," David said solemnly. Then he suggested, "Let's look for blue-jays. They're all easy to see."

One day, Mel Klein took a group of boys in the woods to look for rocks and other treasures. David ran eagerly ahead, touching colorful leaves and overturning oddly-shaped stones.

"Look!" he called out. "Look what I found." Smiling triumphantly, he held up a small white rock with green moss around the edges. Suddenly he was approached by two ten-year-olds, Barry and Steve. Barry was an obese child with thick glasses and bad skin. Steve was a boy who had been turned over to the court system by his family who could not control him.

"So what, dummy," said Steve. "You only have a dumb rock."

"It isn't dumb!" David yelled. "It's pretty, look! Two colors!"

"It is dumb, and so are you," said Barry. "You stupid little kid. I could sit on you and you'd be dead."

"Just try it!" David shrieked.

"Then I will," Barry said, stepping towards David. He took hold of David's arm and twisted it behind him. David scratched Barry's fat arm with the stone that he held in his other hand. Barry screamed and pushed David to the ground. Steve kicked David in the side.

"Cut it out, cut it out!" David was screaming. The sounds brought Mel Klein, who broke up the fight. David sobbed in Mel's arms. "Look at my rock, Mel," he kept saying.

"It's great, David," Mel told him. "You found the best one."

David was quiet on the walk back to Rosewood. He held Mel Klein's hand, but he didn't have anything to say about the fight. He gripped his rock tightly in the other hand. When recreation time was over, he went to the day room and sat by himself. There wasn't much to do in the room, but there were a few torn coloring books and some crayon pieces. David began to color. He was not good at coloring inside the lines, but he liked to try. He began to think about the pretty picture Sara had made for him when he lived with the Wagners, the picture with the trees and sky and grass. He was sorry now that he had torn it up. He decided to make a picture for Sara, in case he saw her sometime. He tried to do a pond in the woods. The pond looked as if it stood on its end, but he didn't think Sara would mind. He colored the pond blue, although the one at RICA was really brown, not blue. He used the brown to color the trees. When he had finished, he put a "D" in the corner, for David.

He had just finished the picture when Cindy Pelham came to call him to dinner.

"Everything okay?" Cindy asked. "I hear you had a little trouble outside."

"I'm okay," David said. He smiled at Cindy and showed her the picture he had made. "Look what I did," he said. "This is for Sara, at the Wagners."

Cindy gazed appreciatively at the coloring. "Honey, that is wonderful," she said. "Do you want me to put that away for you, to save?"

David nodded. Cindy took the picture and ruffled his dirty blond hair. "Tough guy," she said. "Come on, I bet you're hungry."

She touched his arm affectionately, causing David to smile broadly and hug her around her waist. Cindy never failed to awaken feelings of warmth and security in David. As a careworker, she was one of the RICA employees having the greatest personal involvement with David and the others. A parent surrogate, it was she or a colleague who awakened David each morning, got him ready for the day, met his personal needs for clothing and minor first aid, got him bathed and to bed. The night shift careworker remained awake all night to comfort him from a bad dream, to prevent abuse by other children, and to help a lonely child fall asleep. For David, and many of the children, the careworkers were among the first kindly adults in their lives.

RICA was not a place where a child could make friendships in the ordinary sense. David was one of the youngest and least troubled boys ever to have been in the institution for a sustained period. But he was surrounded by children with emotional problems far worse than his, and some with serious physical disabilities as well: big boys who were bullies, children with motor disabilities who had been abused for years, boys who threatened suicide, started fires, or refused to speak, children who could not use a knife and fork at dinner. Activities which most children took for granted were difficult or impossible for many of the RICA children.

On cold or rainy days, the RICA children were permitted to use an indoor swimming pool in one of the Rosewood buildings. Mel Klein liked to take small groups of four or five and try to teach them to swim. Visitors sometimes saw him leading a group across the grounds, his long hair waving in the wind, small people following behind in single file, each one carrying a towel and swimsuit, oblivious to drenching rain or falling snow. Inside the pool area, Mel Klein called out the rules each time:

"Okay, there's not going to be any running in here. No running, no pushing, no horsing around. You walk around the side of the pool. You jump in only if I'm looking at you. You don't bother anybody else in the water. We don't have any splashing. Are you all with me?"

"Yeah!" the kids would yell.

And Mel would smile, knowing that sometime in the next forty-five minutes, every one of his rules would be broken by somebody.

David had never been in a pool before coming to the institute. Mel Klein was pleased to see that David liked the pool, even though he was so short he could barely stand in the shallow end. He was not a bit cautious — his favorite activity was to jump into Mel's arms from the side of the pool.

"Wait 'til I'm ready, David," Mel told him. "You gotta make sure I'm looking at you before you jump."

David laughed. "I want to surprise you, Mel," he said.

"No, David. A surprise like that could hurt both of us."

"Here I come!"

Mel began to teach David to swim. He held him around his waist while he practiced kicking and learned to move his arms. Soon David was able to swim four or five feet to the wall. Mel taught him to take breaths. Before long, David could swim the length of the pool.

Once in a while, Mel tried to organize a pool game or a relay race. It was difficult to accomplish because so many of the children were poor at following directions. There was also the ever-present possibility that somebody would have a temper tantrum in the middle of the activity. David did once, when another boy swam in front of him during a race. David climbed out of the pool screaming, "You got in my way! You got in my way!" He ran in circles around the side of the pool until Mel caught him and held him in his arms. Later, they resumed the race and David came in second.

"Not bad for a shrimp," remarked the boy who had incurred David's anger earlier.

"I'm gonna kill you!" David shouted, charging the boy with his fists. Mel had to restrain David again. He told the kids to get dressed, pool time was over.

The recreation room on the ground floor of the Richards Building held a number of dilapidated bicycles that had been donated to the institute. The building contained a very long hall that ran from the rec room at one end to the cafeteria at the other, with a lobby area which bisected the hallway. Sometimes Mel Klein permitted a small group of children to ride the bikes through the hall. He started each session with an attempt to establish some ground rules:

"Not too fast, guys. Don't hit the walls, and don't run into each other. And most of all —"

"I know, I know!" David interrupted.

"David?"

"Most of all, don't run over any visitors in the lobby!" David shouted triumphantly.

"Right!" Mel said enthusiastically, "David's got it." He lowered his voice. "Do any of you remember why we have to be extra careful in the lobby?"

"I do!" David yelled. "Because, what if you ran over somebody's grandmother who was coming to visit!"

The children giggled. Mel did the same routine with them every time. "That's right!" he said. "We can't be running over somebody's grandmother, can we? And who else? Is there anybody else we shouldn't run over?"

"Teachers!" another boy said.

"Teachers, that's right. No grandmothers, no teachers. Anybody else?"

David was jumping up and down with excitement. "The cafeteria ladies!" he yelled. "We can't run over the cafeteria ladies!"

"Right!" Mel said. "Tell me why!"

"Because then we won't have any lunch!" David announced.

"Okay!" Mel said. "Now get your bikes."

David always took the smallest bike, which was still too big for him. It was a broken-down two-wheeler with no brakes. David fell off of it incessantly, but he didn't appear to mind; Mel watched him climb back on over and over. Once in a while, David got mad at the bike.

"You stupid!" he yelled at it, kicking it.

"The bike can't feel that," Mel told him. "You'll just break it."

"It *is* broken," David said. "That's why I keep falling off."

That was partly true. The wheels were bent and the handlebars crooked — it would have been difficult for anyone to keep the bike from flipping over. Mel directed David to a bike that was slightly larger, but apparently in better condition.

"Try that one," he said.

David did. He had to stretch his toes to keep his feet on the pedals all the way around, but he had better success with this bike. Soon he was speeding up and down the hall, falling only occasionally.

"Good, David," Mel told him. "You didn't get any grandmothers, did you?"

"Nope, not even a cafeteria lady!" David called out as he sped down the hall. He liked the bikes almost as much as he liked the pool.

Except for an old record player at his kindergarten, where Miss Kelsey had sometimes played scratched records containing nursery rhymes, David had had no experience with music before coming to RICA. Mel Klein, an amateur guitar player, occasionally brought his instrument to work with him. Seated on an old wooden chair in the middle of the rec room, surrounded by kids sitting cross-legged on the floor, Mel taught them Burl Ives and other singalong tunes which some of the children, including David, came to love.

"Who wants to do I've Been Workin' On the Railroad?" Mel would ask.

"No, I want One Meatball!" David yelled.

"Meatballs? We just had lunch," Mel said, winking.

"No, the *song*, I mean!"

"How does it go?"

"You know it, Mel!"

"Tell me."

David sang in a little sing-song voice, "One meatball, one meatball, you get no bread with one meatball!"

Mel strummed his guitar. "Okay," he said. "Let's do it." Soon the room echoed with the sound of soprano voices raised in song, or at least generating a noise that was joyful, if not musical. Later they did There was an Old Lady Who Swallowed a Fly.

The routine at RICA included a general exodus each weekend as most of the children left the institution to spend two days with their own families or others. While not all of the children had families to receive them, most had someone — an aunt, or a foster parent. After lunch on Fridays, most of the activity was directed at getting the children ready to leave. Beds were stripped, clothes packed, faces washed. Children waited excitedly to be met, and the atmosphere in the institution became almost convivial. Likewise, Sunday evenings were a time of reunion at RICA, where children could exchange stories of their weekend activities and show off newly-acquired clothes or possessions.

These times were the hardest of all for David. From January until March, he did not leave the grounds of RICA. He was the only very young child to remain on weekends, and he spent those times following Cindy and other careworkers, quietly seeking companionship. By March, the doctor at RICA had prescribed Dexedrine for David to calm his hyperactivity and increase his attention span. The medication did have a positive effect. Coincidentally in March, the Wagners showed up to take David with them for a weekend. For the first time since his arrival at RICA, David was able to join in the anticipation of the others, to look forward to something special.

David was glad to see the Wagners, especially Sara. At the last minute, he remembered the picture he had colored for her, and retrieved it from Cindy, who had carefully saved it for him. When he thrust it joyfully at Sara, she hugged him and told him she loved it. The weekend went well for David. Vinnie Wagner apparently thought of him more or less as a guest, in her way, and left him alone. He spent the time with Sara, following her around, chattering, as she did her chores on the farm. Sara asked David if he liked it at the institution.

"Sure, it's nice there," he told her.

Sara nodded solemnly. She was almost sixteen years old by now. Her goal was to stay with the Wagners just long enough to finish high school; after that she could be on her own. She missed David, but she felt that he was better off away from the farm. She smiled at him.

"I'm glad you're okay," she said.

David spent two more weekends at the Wagners' farm. The next time he went there, the Wagners had moved out of their farmhouse into a trailer on the property, apparently intending to give the farmhouse to their married daughter. The trailer lacked space to accommodate all the foster children now staying with the Wagners, and therefore, David and Sara remained alone in the farmhouse overnight. David was frightened and upset, and the Wagners took him back to RICA one day early, on Saturday. There was only one more weekend with the Wagners, and then, in June of 1972, without notifying Social Services, the Wagners moved out of state, leaving their remaining foster children with their married daughter. David never saw any of them again.

After June, David knew he had no place to go on weekends, and not even the expectation of any place. He was consumed by this knowledge. He talked incessantly to anyone who would listen — Mel Klein, the social workers, the careworkers — about his wish to have a family of his own. He told Cindy Pelham:

"Guess what I want the most, Cindy?"

"What's that, honey?"

"I want a mom and dad who I can live with."

"You do?" Cindy said. "Well, will you settle for lunch instead? It's about that time."

David grinned at her. "I don't want lunch instead of a mom and dad, Cindy," he told her. "But I do want lunch."

They went off together to the cafeteria. Cindy knew that David had been told about the Wagners moving away, but she was not sure that he understood they were gone forever. As far as Cindy was concerned, David was better off.

"Don't nobody need that kind of family," she muttered to Debbie Miller, the librarian.

Debbie shook her head. "That's hard to say, Cindy. Maybe any kind of family is better than no family at all."

Cindy just said, "Huh!"

Cindy was not the only one at RICA to question the suitability of the Wagners as foster parents or their commitment to David. The entire staff agreed with her. In fact, however, RICA had no authority to effect a change.

The foster care program in the State of Maryland was run by the Department of Social Services, but RICA staff members were employed by the Department of Health and Mental Hygiene. The bureaucratic structure was such that RICA lacked the power, as well as the right, to find other parents for David. That was the job of Social Services, where things moved, if at all, through channels that were jealously guarded against invasion by another state agency.

To Mel Klein, who spent part of every weekday with David, the situation was outrageous. "This kid is so plucky," he told a co-worker. "He clings to you like an abandoned waif. But he doesn't quit." Mel and the others found themselves in the hapless position of watching David deteriorate after the Wagners disappeared, while, some of them believed, Social Services plodded slowly around in its morass of rules, regulations, policies and paperwork — shifting, shuffling, struggling in the magnitude of red tape that threatened to strangle whatever life the agency might once have possessed.

Many of the RICA personnel took a special interest in David, not only because he was so young and little, but also because they found him an appealing, lovable child, in contrast to many RICA children who were difficult to like. Further, David's low tolerance for frustration required frequent intervention by the staff. He also was starved for affection so that any overture, however slight, was accepted and reciprocated. Once in a while, Debbie Miller found the time to read to David. Although the RICA library was stocked mostly with hand-me-downs and discards, its supply was copious compared to the nonexistent reading material at the Wagners' farm. There were few books of pre-school level, but Debbie found some, including a couple by Dr. Seuss, which she discovered were David's favorites. Debbie liked them, too, because, she realized, most of them were not about families and therefore would not remind David of his status. Debbie would put him on a chair next to her and point to the colorful pictures as she read with exaggerated feeling to entertain him. David would turn the pages for her, laughing gleefully at the funny parts, listening quietly when Debbie lowered her voice to a whisper for the serious parts, finally exploding with applause as Debbie shouted:

"I do so like
green eggs and ham!
Thank you-
Thank you,
Sam-I-am."

David would scream with pleasure: "Green eggs and ham? That makes me sick!"

And Debbie would kiss him on the top of his sandy blond hair and say that was all for now, they'd read another story soon.

It was in September, 1972 — three months after the Wagners' disappearance from Maryland without notice — that Dennis Miller's motorcycle accident brought Dick Heidecker to the Miller home at 3 o'clock in the morning.

CHAPTER 4

Dick and Shirley

Richard Thomas Heidecker was born in Baltimore on May 31, 1939, the second son and younger child of Henry and Pearl Heidecker. Dick's father worked as a Baltimore City policeman for twenty-eight years, a good part of which he drove a paddy wagon. Dick's mother was a homemaker who, Dick always believed, favored his older brother. Dick and his brother were raised in a traditional home with a good deal of physical discipline which, however, failed to dampen Dick's high spirits or change his fun-loving personality. As a small child, Dick was closest to neither his mother nor his father, but to family friends and neighbors named Harold and Ollie Houghton. The Houghtons actually met the Heideckers on the beat — when Ollie, having trouble with a tenant, opened her front door and called for help, to which Patrolman Henry Heidecker responded. The two families became lifelong friends, and Ollie Houghton, known to Dick as Aunt Ollie, became the strongest maternal influence in his life.

Dick grew up in Baltimore in the years that followed World War II. It was a simple era, in a racially segregated city, before the advent of television, ubiquitous air conditioning, the beltway that would surround the city by 1960, or suburban sprawl. Although Baltimore is a city on the water, the water in those days consisted of a working port rimmed with industries, shipyards, piers and slums — the most glamorous enterprise near the water was McCormick Spice, with a gigantic vanilla bottle on its roof; the glitter of Harborplace and two hundred thousand dollar condominiums was thirty years away. City houses in those days were rowhouses, laid out block after block, some with white marble steps, others with formstone fronts, all edged with sidewalks that stretched to streets which held far fewer dangers than they would in the future. The city blocks were interspersed with green parks, refuges from monotonous streets and summer humidity — some, like Druid Hill Park, with rolling hills and great spaces, and others, without names, only a square block of grass for a picnic or a makeshift game of ball. Children walked to school and played in their neighborhoods in safe innocence that city planners in the 1980's could barely recall, let alone recreate.

As a small child, Dick spent many hours with Aunt Ollie, who had no children of her own and seemed to attract other people's. On many occasions she could be seen escorting a crowd of five or six children to the nearby park, or on a more ambitious excursion. Once in a while she took Dick horseback riding or swimming or to the zoo. Often she let him paint or color at her kitchen table while she cooked and did her housework; he loved to talk, and Aunt Ollie was a good listener.

The Houghton family owned substantial acreage in Carroll County, some thirty miles west of Baltimore, which would belong to Harold and Ollie one day. There was a big old house on the property where Harold and Ollie frequently stayed on weekends. They often invited friends, including Dick and his family. Their land spanned both sides of a winding country lane called Gillis Road. A large hill of wildflowers and shrubbery, surrounded by many acres of woods, grass and wildlife, stood on the north side of the road. An unused dirt lane traversed the hill and disappeared somewhere beyond its crest, among the trees. To Dick Heidecker, living in the city, the Houghtons' place in the country was the most beautiful spot on earth. While the adults feasted on beer and seafood, played catch outside or listened to the radio inside, Dick liked to climb the hill, following the remnants of the dirt road as far as he could, pushing his way through virgin underbrush, climbing trees, searching for wildlife, collecting rocks. When he was eight years old, Dick told Aunt Ollie that he wanted to live in a house on top of the hill one day. Aunt Ollie smiled and made him a promise that he could have that part of her land whenever he was ready.

By the time Dick Heidecker was in high school, his propensity for practical jokes and general mischief was getting him into trouble with the school authorities. He got his driver's license and proceeded to go through old car after old car, accidentally totalling them or causing more damage than it paid to fix. He rode a motorcycle for a while, and learned to smoke cigarettes and drink beer — two habits that he retained for life. In the tenth grade, he quit school and went to work for a venetian blind company, putting shades together. Later he worked as an apprentice typesetter while he joined the Army Reserves, eventually going to Fort Knox, Kentucky for six months. In the summer of 1957, Dick was sent to Fort Lee, Virginia, for Army summer camp. A friend in the Reserves, who lived in Pennsylvania, asked Dick to join him in his home town after summer camp was over.

"There's a girl you should meet," the friend urged. "She's a girlfriend of my girlfriend. We can all go out together."

At age eighteen, Dick Heidecker was game for anything. Moderately tall, he had sparkling blue eyes and, in those days, a full head of light brown hair. His face was gentle; some people called it a baby face. Dick was on the heavy side then, but not really fat. The Army had hardened up his body and strengthened his muscles. He loved to tease, but he had a quick smile to soften his raucous sense of humor. After summer camp, he acompanied his friend to Pennsylvania for a blind date.

"This better not be a dog," he told his friend. "I don't ordinarily drive two hundred miles for a date."

His friend laughed. "You don't usually drive anywhere because you don't usually *have* a date," he ribbed. "Trust me."

"Huh," said Dick. "What's this girl's name, anyway?"

"Her name's Shirley," his friend told him. "Shirley Weaver."

Shirley Ann Weaver, born May 21, 1936, was three years older than Dick Heidecker. She was the third and youngest child, and only daughter, in her family. They lived in a small rural village known as Pennsylvania Furnace, located next to State College, Pennsylvania, the site of Penn State University. Shirley's father, with only an eighth-grade education, operated his own automobile repair shop for a time, and later worked for Penn State. Shirley's mother, the oldest of twelve children, had had to leave school to help out at home. She was an accomplished homemaker who taught Shirley to sew and cook and bake. Shirley graduated from high school and went to work for Navy ROTC as a clerk typist. She continued to live at home with her parents.

One of Shirley's friends had a boyfriend in the Army Reserves. One weekend in August, 1957, she told Shirley that her boyfriend was on his way to Pennsylvania with a friend from the Army, and that the four of them were going on a double date. Shirley said, "Fine." That night she was introduced to Dick Heidecker. The two couples set out for a drive-in movie with Dick and Shirley in the back seat.

Dick Heidecker took a good look at Shirley, who was five foot four and perky with short, dark hair and a farm fresh complexion. Dick liked what he saw. He spent the next part of the evening regaling Shirley with tales of his exploits in high school and the Army.

"In music class, the teacher always wanted to sing the Battle Hymn of the Republic and we wanted to sing Dixie, so we made up our own version of Battle Hymn of the Republic."

"Really?" Shirley asked. "With dirty words?"

"No, clean words, but they wrecked the song for old Miss Snodgrass, so I got thrown out of music."

Shirley, who had led a very straight life compared to Dick's, was fascinated. If Shirley seemed high class from Dick's point of view, Dick was the height of sophistication to Shirley.

"What else?" she asked him.

"Well, in shop one day, our teacher was picking up tools and we rolled the chassis over and he couldn't take a joke. So I got thrown out of shop, too."

"What classes were you still in?" Shirley wanted to know.

"English, but I laughed through the romantic poetry. Every time we did a poem by one of those romantics, Shelley or whoever, the teacher got all misty-eyed and I burst out laughing."

"Did they throw you out of English class, too?"

"No, I quit. I was afraid we were heading for Shakespeare."

Two hours into the evening, Dick asked Shirley to marry him. Ten seconds later — according to Dick — Shirley said yes.

They could not get married right away, of course. Shirley's parents had not even met Dick, and when they did, they would expect an engagement of reasonable duration. For the next ten months, both of them continued to live with their parents, two hundred miles apart. They carried on a long-distance courtship, with Dick driving to Pennsylvania nearly every weekend. On June 21, 1958, they were married in the Presbyterian church in Pennsylvania that Shirley and her family attended. Dick's family was Roman Catholic, but Dick had not been a practicing Catholic for years.

At first, Dick and Shirley moved in with Dick's parents in Baltimore. Dick worked as a typesetter and Shirley found a job as a clerk in an office in downtown Baltimore. Both Dick and Shirley hated living with the senior Heideckers, but the price was right. They saved their money, and within a few months they had their own apartment. Neither of them liked living in the city. Shirley was used to fields and grass, and Dick continued to dream about the hill in Carroll County. Nevertheless, they took advantage of some of the activities that a city had to offer, and went to movies, parades, wrestling matches. Sometimes they drove out of town to the stock car races. In many ways, this was a happy time for Dick and Shirley. They fought sometimes, often when Dick had had a lot of beer to drink, but they were young and unencumbered: they were making money, they had their own place, and they had no family responsibilities. They had two cars, then and always, because Shirley liked to be independently mobile.

Shirley got to know the Houghtons, and soon became as close to Aunt Ollie as Dick was. By this time, Aunt Ollie had inherited the land in Carroll County, and now owned a little over thirty acres. The big old house had burned down, but soon after Dick and Shirley got their own apartment, the Houghtons built a small brick house there and moved into it. Their house was close to the road, actually at the bottom of the big hill; Harold said they chose that spot because he didn't intend to shovel snow at his age and he didn't want to walk down the hill to get his mail. Dick and Shirley spent many evenings and weekends with Harold and Ollie in the new brick house on Gillis Road. Dick delighted in showing Shirley all of his childhood haunts on the hill, or all of them he could find; sometimes he would swear that some important landmark had moved, or disappeared. He nearly drove Shirley crazy as he tried to reconstruct the way things were. Shirley told him that only concrete stayed the same; everything in the country shifted around from time to time.

As soon as Dick turned twenty-one, in 1960, he joined the Baltimore City police force. He was bored with typesetting, he told Shirley; he needed adventure. It turned out that he loved police work. Initially he was assigned to Southwestern District; after two years he moved to Northwestern on Reisterstown Road. Every day brought a different activity, a new experience. There was no predictability, no sameness to the job. Along with everyone else on the force, Dick changed shifts every other week, working midnight to 8, then 8 to 4, and then 4 to midnight. He liked that part of it, too; it was impossible to get stuck in a routine.

Dick's job became a perpetual adventure. Sometimes he was assigned to foot patrol, which meant walking a beat; he did that in a neighborhood on the west side of the city, and later in an inner city community, both of which had become high crime areas. At other times he rode in a radio car with another police officer. Both jobs were action-packed. On the beat, he came to know the neighborhood residents, and to expect their support. But he once was threatened with a butcher knife on the sidewalk, once stood at the wrong end of a double-barreled shotgun in an abandoned house, and in general learned to stay alert. In the patrol car, his job was to respond to emergency calls; this provided excitement. He was called to the scene of nighttime break-ins, armed robberies, a bank hold-up, street fights, and domestic assaults. Sometimes he arrived in time, sometimes it was a false alarm, and once in a while he got there too late. There was one night in which he witnessed seven dead bodies, all but two from unrelated incidents: homicides, a fatal traffic accident, a suicide. It was, as he told Shirley, life in the big city.

On December 14, 1964, Dick and his partner were on duty in Radio Car 602 at 7:55 a.m. when the car in which they were riding was struck from behind by an oil company truck on Reisterstown Road. Dick suffered a whiplash injury, with neck and back contusions, which left him with low back pain that not only disabled him for weeks and months at a time, but ultimately led to his special disability retirement from the police force twelve years later. He was off from work initially for two and a half months; in the twenty months that followed the accident, Dick lost 434 days from work. During that time, he received his regular pay from the City of Baltimore, which in 1964 amounted to $13.25 per day and by 1966 had increased to $16.11 per day. But the impact on his general health was serious and permanent. Dick had been overweight for most of his life; now it was more difficult for him to stay active, and the pounds increased. His medical records began to describe him as "obese." He continued to do foot patrol and car patrol duty when he was physically able, but more and more he found himself assigned to duty at the station house, or in one of the criminal courtrooms in Baltimore City. He enjoyed being in the courtroom, because the cases interested him. Duty at the station house was not as much fun, except that once in a while he was permitted to be the acting desk sergeant, although he was never actually promoted to sergeant. Eventually he sued the oil company whose truck had hit him, and settled the case out of court for $25,000, of which, after costs and legal fees, he retained around $12,000.

Dick and Shirley had tried to have children ever since their marriage. At first, because they were so young, there had been no sense of urgency. But as time passed, and Shirley did not become pregnant, they became anxious. Shirley went to a doctor, who did extensive tests. He told her she had a hormone deficiency that would make it difficult for her to conceive. It was theoretically possible for her to get pregnant, he said, but it wasn't likely. Shirley was distressed.

"What can I do?" she asked.

"The only advice I can give you is to keep trying," the doctor told her.

Shirley left his office in tears. Both she and Dick had strong ideas about the kind of parents they hoped to be. Neither was entirely satisfied with his or her own upbringing. Dick, in particular, was close to no one in his family. He had always felt like a stepchild, or a charity case, as he put it, of his own parents. Shirley's childhood memories were far more positive, but she felt that her parents had been too strict and unyielding. She and Dick wanted to have several children. It was weeks before she could bring herself to tell Dick what the doctor had said.

They talked about adoption. Both of them were willing to pursue that avenue, but neither of them looked forward to whatever procedure or red tape might be required. They decided to continue to try to conceive for a while longer — in 1965, Shirley was still in her twenties, although just barely. That year, she got a new job as a stock clerk for Webster Clothes. Like Dick, she had found a career; Shirley was to remain at Webster's for many years, slowly advancing to better and better positions.

By 1966, Dick and Shirley felt financially secure enough to consider building a house up on the hill in Carroll County. Over the years, Aunt Ollie had reiterated her promise that Dick could have the land when he was ready. She said the same thing to Shirley. That winter, Dick and Shirley spent a weekend at the Houghtons' house. After they had dinner and watched television, Dick broached the subject.

"Aunt Ollie," he said, "remember when I was little and I told you I wanted to build a house up on the hill, and you said I could when I was ready?"

"Sure do," Ollie said.

"Well, I'm ready now," Dick continued. "I want to know how much you want for the land up on the hill."

"How much?" Aunt Ollie appeared to consider that. Finally she said, "I'll tell you. One dollar."

Dick said, "No, I'm serious now."

"I'm serious, too," Aunt Ollie told him. "That's my price."

Dick looked over at Harold. "Is she?" he asked.

Harold's eyes twinkled. "Don't ask me, you know she's the boss," he answered.

Dick looked back at Aunt Ollie. "You mean you'll give us the land, is that it?"

Aunt Ollie looked surprised. "Give it? What do you mean, give? You don't give something away if there's a cash price, do you?" She sounded indignant.

Dick said, "Aunt Ollie, I never meant for you to *give* that property to me. I always intended to pay for it, you know that."

Aunt Ollie looked at him. "Dickie," she said, "I got over thirty acres of land up here. I'm getting old, and I don't have no children. What's all this for? To go to the state or some relatives we don't care for when we die? The way I look at it, there's no use to having anything unless somebody can use it. We're as close to you and Shirley as we are to anybody." She paused. "And this way, we'd have a neighbor, too."

Dick rubbed his stomach. He looked over at Shirley, and back to Aunt Ollie. "Thank you," he said.

Now Dick and Shirley needed to find a builder to construct their house. Harold knew of one, and they went to see him. Dick and Shirley drew him a picture of what they wanted. The door would open into the living room. There would be a bedroom on either side, and a bathroom, and straight ahead would be the dining area, with the kitchen off to the side. Everything would be on one floor. The outside walls would be constructed of cinder blocks which, they were told, were much less expensive than bricks or other materials. They could always improve the house later on, the builder said, or add to it; they had the land, which was the main thing, and the next step was to get a house built so they could live in it. Dick and Shirley agreed. They paid the man a deposit to get started.

The construction of their new home became the focus of their lives for the next three months. At every opportunity, they drove out to Carroll County to see what progress had been made. Shirley called Aunt Ollie every day to find out what was happening. The builder had to improve the road up the hill, too, which would be their driveway. It was not to be paved, but the builder worked on the roadbed and added some gravel for traction. It rose steeply up the hill from Gillis Road, winding slowly to the right in the direction of the new house. Dick and Shirley financed the $5,800 construction cost with a bank loan which became a ten-year mortgage.

In the summer of 1967, Dick and Shirley and some fellow policemen moved all of their possessions out of the apartment in the city onto Dick's pick-up truck, which Dick then drove to Carroll County. Shirley followed in her car. At the top of the hill, Dick's friends helped him carry their furniture inside. When the truck was empty, everything was accounted for, but the house was a mess. Dick and Shirley looked at each other. Then they walked down the hill to the Houghtons' to get a bite to eat. Afterwards they set up the furniture in their bedroom and spent their first night as permanent residents of Carroll County.

If their new house was less than imposing, the view from their front door was breathtaking. In the 1960's, Carroll County remained an overwhelmingly rural county, cloaked with dairy, grain and cattle farms, corn and wheat fields, and orchards. It stood in the Piedmont region, an area of rolling hills with a temperate climate of four distinct seasons. This was the same county in which the Wagners' farm was located, but the two properties were at opposite ends, separated by more than twenty miles. Dick and Shirley lived in the southernmost section. Their post office address was Woodbine, a tiny village which spans the Patapsco River. The view from the top of their hill was framed by woods, country roads and streams, with only an occasional house dotting the landscape in the distance.

The link from southern Carroll County to urban civilization was Maryland Route 26, also known as Liberty Road. It spanned all of southern Carroll County, and crossed into Baltimore County at the bridge over the Liberty Reservoir, in the Patapsco River watershed. The road began in the country as a two-lane highway, but widened as it headed east, ultimately becoming four lanes lined with fast food, gas stations, strip shopping centers and radar traps. It was this road that Dick and Shirley drove every day to and from their jobs. Their house was about two miles off Liberty Road. For Dick, the drive to work was around thirty miles; for Shirley, closer to twenty. Neither one of them minded the drive in the least.

Dick and Shirley had never liked living in the city. In July and August, the heat and humidity were often heavy and oppressive. To Dick, overweight and intolerant of hot weather in general, required to wear a police uniform eight hours out of twenty-four, the annual heat in downtown Baltimore was part of the reason he had moved to the country in 1967 — that, and the rising crime rate. The racial tension in Baltimore City that culminated in violence after the murder of Martin Luther King, Jr., the April after their move to Carroll County, proved to Dick that he had done the right thing. It was true that he worked an eight-hour shift in the city every day or night, but at the end of the shift he could leave it all behind until the next day. Dick used to say that his favorite part of the day came on his way home from work as he passed through Randallstown in Baltimore County — the last large population center as he headed west — and drove into the country. Shirley felt the same way.

View from the top of the hill on Gillis Road. The back of Aunt Ollie's house can be seen at the bottom of the hill in the foreground. This picture makes the house seem closer than it is. *Candace Wase*

With the new house completed, Dick and Shirley settled into their new life. At first it was fun to have friends come over. Dick invited some city policemen and their families to cook out on the hill. Shirley cooked dinner for one or two couples from Webster's. But not being particularly gregarious, they gradually developed a routine that revolved around the two of them. Shirley worked regular hours and arrived home around dinner time each evening. If Dick was working the morning shift or the midnight shift, she cooked dinner for the two of them. If he worked 4 to midnight, she had dinner alone. When Dick was there, they watched television on winter evenings, or Dick went bowling. On weekends, and on summer evenings, they worked outside. Shirley was good with flowers; soon the hillside bloomed with color. Dick cleared out the parts of the land that were overgrown, and transplanted small trees to better locations. They made a vegetable garden. They worked on the long gravel driveway that washed out in every serious storm. Dick bought an

18-foot flagpole and put it in the ground at the top of the hill, in front of the house. He ran an American flag up the pole and flew it all the time.

They continued to spend many evenings with Harold and Ollie, but now they could alternate locations: sometimes Dick and Shirley went down to the red brick house, and other times Harold and Ollie came up the hill. Whenever that happened, Harold Houghton arrived huffing and puffing and told Dick how glad he was that he had been smart enough to put his house at the bottom of the hill instead of the top.

"You old fool, you're just jealous," Ollie would say, and she and Shirley would go off to pick vegetables.

Aunt Ollie showed Shirley all the important places in southern Carroll County. The closest real town, sixteen miles away, was Westminster, the county seat — a town of about 8,000 with an historic main street and a courthouse dating back to 1837. There was no county police force. The fire departments were volunteer. Private wells and septic tanks supplied water and sewage disposal. The first public library had opened in 1965. The local newspaper, *The Carroll County Times*, published six times a week, not on Sundays. The food stores were not supermarkets, but small grocery stores run by elderly couples, some of whom still extended credit to people in the community by writing their names and balances in a notebook. Shirley learned where those stores were, but she also shopped at supermarkets along Liberty Road on her way home from work. There were flower shops, delicatessens, even furniture stores and pet shops, sometimes in unlikely places off the beaten track.

Dick and Shirley found a Methodist church to attend. Although Shirley had been raised Presbyterian and Dick had been raised Catholic, neither of them had any particular attachment to the church of his or her childhood. Carroll County, they discovered, was populated with quaint country Methodist churches. The closest one to their home was Ebenezer United Methodist, a picturesque little white church on Woodbine Road with four white columns in front and a country cemetery alongside. Dick was not enthusiastic.

"You need a church when you have a family," Shirley told him. "We're a family now."

Dick acquiesced. Neither of them became regular churchgoers, but they met some people and Shirley felt more a part of the community.

Not long after the move to Carroll County, two incidents in the line of duty exacerbated Dick's physical problems. While in the Baltimore City courthouse, Dick helped a jail guard subdue a prisoner who attempted to escape; Dick twisted his back as he and the guard carried the 240-pound prisoner to the lockup. The following week, as Dick was on duty in a courtroom in the same building, a convicted felon who had just been sentenced attempted to throw a chair at the judge. Dick and two jail guards wrestled

Dick Heidecker in police uniform in his early 30's. *Courtesy Olan Mills*

with the convict and subdued him; Dick hurt his back again. He lost more time from work. The police force continued to send him to various doctors and specialists. All of them advised Dick to lose weight. Some of them prescribed medication. None was able to relieve his pain on a permanent basis, but Dick refused to let the pain control his life. He didn't trust doctors anyway, didn't think they knew what they were talking about, and usually paid no attention to their advice. He went to a doctor when he had to, but the rest of the time he acted as if the problem did not exist.

Shirley told him he was a cross between Superman and a big baby. "First you want me to wait on you hand and foot because your back hurts, then you go out and chop down a tree," she complained. "Why don't you make up your mind?"

"I have made up my mind," Dick told her. "I like you to wait on me, and I like to chop down trees."

Shirley would not have admitted it, but in her heart she did not object to waiting on Dick. Like Dick, she had been raised in a traditional home in which waiting on her man was part of a woman's job. Shirley liked to think she was far more liberated than her own mother. Indeed she was. She was independent in the sense of being able to take care of herself, and could be quite outspoken when the spirit moved her, but nevertheless she considered it her responsibility to keep Dick happy and comfortable. Fortunately, she was energetic and efficient, and required less sleep than most people, for this often meant cooking meals for him at strange times because of his work schedule. Dick was absolutely helpless in the kitchen, Shirley used to say. He would have difficulty making himself a cheese sandwich if he were starving, and could find the refrigerator only for the purpose of extracting a cold beer or diet soda, his two favorite drinks. It also meant cleaning up after him and keeping the house supplied with things he needed, all of which Shirley was willing to do.

"It's because you're so good at it," Dick liked to say, teasing her.

"You better look out that I don't get tired of it," Shirley would tell him, knowing full well that she never would.

By 1968, Dick and Shirley had been married for ten years. Shirley was thirty-one. She felt that life was pretty good except for their inability to have children. By now, Shirley was positive that she would never conceive. She and Dick had begun to make serious but unsuccessful efforts to find a child to adopt. Shirley had called a couple of agencies, who told her there were almost no white infants available for adoption. People were keeping their babies born out of wedlock, or were having abortions. The only children available any more were black — and there weren't many of those, either — or children with serious handicaps. They could put their names on a list, if they liked, but there would be a long wait, and there might be nothing at the end of it.

Shirley called some religious agencies, but nothing came of that, either. She and Dick were not Catholic. They weren't Jewish. Shirley got the impression that those agencies really had no babies, either. The possibility of adopting a foreign child never occurred to them.

Shirley began to be consumed by the fear that she and Dick would never have a child to raise. She knew that Dick was just as anxious. But the Heideckers were private people, not given to discussing their feelings with others. Shirley could go so far as to talk to Aunt Ollie about her desire to have a child, but she could not talk to people who might be in a position to help her find one. Neither could Dick. After a while, they stopped talking to each other about it, and just continued to live their lives.

CHAPTER 5

David Wayne Heidecker

In September of 1972, when Dick Heidecker learned from his random encounter with Debbie Miller that a child was available for adoption, he and Shirley inquired at once about what needed to be done so they could meet David. Debbie Miller promptly contacted David's social worker. Legally, the Heideckers had to qualify as foster parents before they could have David in their home. If they did qualify, and if they kept David successfully for six months, then adoption could be considered.

The first step was the "foster home study," which required extensive interviews by a social worker. The Heideckers had to answer questions addressing their backgrounds, values, and intimate lives. Had their childhoods been happy? Was there sibling rivalry? Did their parents argue? How did Dick feel about his failure to graduate from high school? What was the status of his physical health? Would his job in the police department keep him away from home too much? What did they expect from a child? Was there an extended family? What about Shirley's job? What did she think about setting limits for children? Would she be able to help a child with schoolwork? Would they expect a child to do chores around the house? How did they feel about buying clothes and other necessities for a foster child? What were their religious beliefs?

Dick was offended by the personal nature of some of the questions, but he answered them.

"Lucky for them I want a child so much," he told Shirley. "Otherwise I'd tell them to go shove it."

He almost did when the questions turned to their inability to have children. What specialists had they been to? Were they given fertility tests? Did Dick know what his sperm count was?

"Jesus!" he exploded after the social worker left. "Do they think I don't know how to do it?"

Shirley was equally offended, but less volatile. She bore the additional burden of knowing that had she been able to conceive, no one would be asking any questions.

Then came the home inspection. There were certain regulations and guidelines that had to be adhered to, the social worker explained somewhat apologetically. One rule was that a room in which a foster child slept must have a window. The second bedroom in the Heideckers' house had no window. The origin of the rule, said the social worker, probably was the need to ensure that children were not kept in closets. Of course, the room at the Heideckers' was much larger than a closet, and was very nice, the woman said; obviously, the rule was silly in their case, but nevertheless, all of the regulations had to be followed. Dick and Shirley had a simple solution. They switched the furniture in the two bedrooms, and commenced to occupy the windowless room themselves. They joked about it later. Dick would call out, "Hey, I'm tired, let's go in the closet." Or he would say sarcastically, "It's a regulation, my hands are tied."

Early in November, the social worker called to tell the Heideckers that the foster home study was complete.

"You have qualified to become foster parents," she announced cheerfully.

Dick's desire to say "No shit!" to the social worker was overcome only by his desire to adopt a child. The time had come for him and Shirley to meet David.

At RICA, David had been told only that there was a couple who wanted to meet him. On a cold Sunday afternoon when most of the other children were out with their families, he followed Cindy Pelham around as he restlessly awaited their arrival.

"Is this my family, Cindy?" he asked her.

"No, David, they ain't your family," she told him firmly. "They's just some folks who want to come out and see you."

"Maybe they'll *be* my family," David insisted joyfully.

Cindy looked at him. "Honey, you better calm down," she said. "How do you know you'll even like these people? How do you know they'll like you? Don't get your hopes all excited."

"I know they'll like me," David persisted.

"Well, I'm sure they will."

"I know I'll like them!"

"I hope so."

"Are they here yet?"

"Soon. Will you help me change the sheets on this here bed?"

"Okay."

When Dick and Shirley Heidecker saw David for the first time, they both noticed two things immediately. The first thing was that this short skinny little boy, with big brown eyes, sandy hair, and two front teeth missing, supposedly one month away from his eighth birthday, looked like a six-year-old. The second thing they both noticed was that David was the cutest child they had ever seen.

David spoke first. "Hi," he said optimistically.

Dick took a step forward. "Hi, David," he said. "I'm Dick Heidecker. This is Shirley."

He shook David's hand. Then Shirley did. David grinned at both of them. Dick was wearing his police uniform; he was pleased to see that David did not appear to mind. Dick looked for a place to sit. This first meeting took place in the front hall of the Richards Building. The agenda was that Dick and Shirley were to spend an hour or two with David there. If they liked each other, they could take him off the grounds for dinner the next time. If they still liked each other, they could take him home for a weekend after that.

The lobby was practically deserted on this cold Sunday afternoon in November. It was furnished with a tattered sofa and two mismatched chairs that looked like charitable contributions from a large family. A threadbare rug partially covered the floor. Only a framed announcement of RICA's regulations decorated the walls. Dick and Shirley sat down on the sofa with David between them. David looked expectantly at Dick, who groped for the right thing to say. He tried to remember what interested him at the age of seven or eight. Finally he asked if David liked pets.

"What kind of pets?" David wanted to know.

"Animals," Dick explained. "Dogs and cats, animals like that."

"Sure!" David said enthusiastically. "Do you have any?"

"Yup," Dick told him. "We have three dogs at our house."

"Three dogs!" David yelled.

"And a cat," Shirley added.

"Wow!" David said.

"Oh, you think that's something?" Dick asked. "We have a goat, too."

"A goat? Oh, boy! Can I see it?"

Dick winked at him. "Pretty soon, I bet."

David asked, "Do you have any more animals?"

"We have ducks," Shirley said. "Do you like ducks?"

David wasn't sure about that. "I don't know," he said.

They were quiet for a minute. David looked around at the depressing lobby. Then he jumped to his feet and asked Dick and Shirley if they wanted to take a walk outside. Dick glanced at Shirley. It was about thirty-four degrees outside, but they both said, sure. They put on their coats and stepped outside.

"Wanta see the pond?" David asked. "We have a really neat pond here. I even fished there."

"Catch anything?" Dick asked.

"Well, once I did. But we threw it back."

David led the way along a winding, unorthodox route, talking excitedly, pointing out landmarks as they went. "See that tree? I climbed it once and fell out. See this scar on my knee? That's what happened. See those vines? You can swing from there in the summer. I used to do it all the time."

David chattered happily, showing them one thing and another. Before long, he was holding hands with both Dick and Shirley. He led them to the pond, half running, half skipping, until they could see it through the trees. "There it is!" he shouted. "See?"

At the edge of the pond, David found a flat stone and skipped it across the water. He asked Shirley if she could do it; she said she couldn't. Dick tried, but his stone sank. David laughed.

"I can show you," he insisted. "Want me to teach you?"

"Can we wait for a warmer day?" Dick asked.

"Okay," David said.

They started back. Other children were beginning to return from their weekends with their families. The lobby became busier and noisier as the sun went down. David alternately talked excitedly and sat quietly, with an air of reserve. It was time for Dick and Shirley to leave. They asked David if he would like them to come back the following weekend, maybe take him somewhere.

"Oh, boy, will you?" David answered.

"Sure," Dick told him. "Do you want to come?"

"Yeah!" David yelled.

Shirley said, "We'll see you then, David." She shook his hand again.

David smiled tentatively at her. "Bye, Mom," he said.

Shirley, taken aback, glanced over at Dick. Dick winked at David. "So long, kid," he said. "See you soon."

David said, "Bye, Dad."

Dick gave him a playful punch on the shoulder. Then he and Shirley walked outside and got into their car. Dick lit a cigarette for himself, and one for Shirley, as they sat in silence for a few minutes. At last Shirley said, "Did you like him?"

Dick reached for her hand. "Yeah, I did. You, too?"

Shirley nodded silently. She said, "Yes. I liked him a lot."

Later that week, at the request of the RICA staff, Dick and Shirley returned to the institution to meet with staff members and learn more about David. David's "team" now consisted of his teacher, careworkers, psychologist, psychiatrist, and two social workers — one from RICA and the other from the Department of Social Services. The psychologist told Dick and Shirley that David had been neglected as an infant, that he had spent time in several foster homes, and that he had never known a family who could meet his needs.

"Why?" Dick demanded.

"Because his emotional problems undoubtedly began in infancy," the psychologist told him. "His records show this going back to before his biological mother gave him up."

"We believe it was her neglect that caused the initial problems," the psychiatrist interjected.

The psychologist said, "We have David on medication now to help him control his behavior. There have also been times when he has had to be confined to a 'quiet room.'"

Shirley said, "He doesn't act emotionally disturbed to me."

"He won't, most of the time," the psychologist agreed. "But if David finds himself in a situation where he feels threatened, or even frustrated, he can act out in anti-social ways. I want you to know that from the start."

"Maybe what he needs is a family," Dick volunteered.

Barbara Skarf, David's RICA social worker, smiled warmly at Dick. Barbara was a recent graduate of the University of Maryland School of Social Work. Her RICA experience was her first job. She had always felt strongly that David was misplaced at the institution.

"You'll find David adorable," she told Dick and Shirley. "He is a child without any meanness in him. And you're right that what he needs is a loving family."

But other members of the team, most of whom agreed with Barbara, wanted to make sure the Heideckers had all the facts before beginning their relationship with David. The psychologist handed them a report which he had prepared recently. Shirley read:

> On the ward David was initially aggressive, hyper-active, hostile and stubborn. He was in fights four to five times a day and wore his battle scars all over him. Although he is small, he is willing to fight with any child, regardless of size. In March, David was placed on Dexedrine, with dramatic results. He became less hyperactive and aggressive and related more easily. He is still moody in the morning but as the day goes on, he is more friendly and cooperative. His attention span has increased, and he can play by himself for periods of time. He is well liked by adults and relates well to them. He enjoys their affection, being able to accept and handle it. Although he does mischievous things, he does not do hurtful things and gets along well with other children. David is enuretic three to four times a week. He talks about the Wagners, would like to return to them, and becomes quite sad when they disappoint him.

The report went on to say that David's behavior in the classroom was less of a problem, that he needed individual attention for learning, but was not aggressive or difficult to handle. The report stated that David showed no signs of depression or psychosis, but that he had a poor self-image and "has not had an opportunity to develop trust in people." The report concluded, "His sensitivity to separation from his foster parents was noted, as well as his great wish to be part of a family."

The report brought tears to Shirley's eyes as she thought of forlorn little David's past. She looked earnestly at the psychologist.

"When can we take David out?" she asked.

"Sunday," he told her. "You can take him out to dinner if you like."

"We like," Dick said.

That Sunday, when Dick and Shirley arrived at RICA, they were greeted by David's hurling himself at them and hugging them, first Dick and then Shirley.

"Hi, Dad, hi, Mom," he announced enthusiastically.

Dick and Shirley took David to a McDonald's for dinner. When they asked David what he wanted to eat, he asked what kind of things they had there; he said he had never been to a place like that before. Dick ordered him a big cheeseburger and a large order of french fries with a chocolate milkshake, and David ate it all. Shirley asked David if he would like to visit their home next weekend. David was wildly enthusiastic. Could he see their animals, he wanted to know? Would he be able to feed the dogs? Could he play with the goat? Was there a room for him to sleep in? Did they have any toys? How long could he stay? Was it very far?

Shirley did her best to answer David's questions. Then Dick showed him a magic trick with two nickels, and let him keep the nickels. David said he had never had money before. It was time to go back to RICA. David put the two nickels in his pocket and put his hands in Dick's and Shirley's as they walked out to the car. Back at the institution, Dick and Shirley kissed David good-bye in the front hall.

The following Friday afternoon on the ward, most of the children were getting ready to be picked up for the weekend. Cindy Pelham and the other careworkers packed suitcases, stripped beds, and attempted to calm excited children. Shouts of anticipation echoed through the hall as adults' directives fell on deaf ears. In the midst of the activity, Debbie Miller came upstairs to help David get ready for his first weekend away from the institution in five months. David had no suitcase, but Debbie carried a large brown paper bag which she filled with David's clothes. David followed her around the room that he shared with seven other boys, pulling at her clothes.

"Are my mom and dad here yet?" he demanded.

Debbie looked at him. "David, the Heideckers are not your mom and dad," she told him firmly. "At least not yet."

"They are too!" David yelled.

"Okay," Debbie said. "But don't you want to wait until you visit their home, make sure you like it there?"

"I'll love it there!" David shouted. "They have three dogs and a cat and goat and some ducks."

Debbie stared at him. "Really?" she asked.

"Yup! And a room just for me, too!"

Debbie laughed. "Okay, sport," she said. "I guess you're right. You'll love it there."

At three o'clock, the adults herded noisy children downstairs to be greeted by their families. Debbie Miller carried a bulging brown bag in her right arm as she gripped David firmly with her left arm.

"Don't get away from me, now," she told him. "This is chaos down here."

This was not part of Debbie's job, but she had a special interest in this case. As they reached the bottom of the steps, she saw the Heideckers in the hall, eagerly awaiting David's appearance. Two months had passed since her brief encounter with Dick Heidecker in the middle of the night, but she had no trouble recognizing him. He was rubbing his stomach. It was the first time Debbie had seen Shirley Heidecker, who stood beside Dick with a nervous smile on her face. Debbie felt David break loose from her grasp. She watched him dash across the room and hurl his arms around Dick's thick waist. She walked over to the Heideckers, where David, by now, was hanging onto Shirley.

"Hi," she said tentatively, reluctant to disturb this scene that looked as if it had been sketched by Norman Rockwell. "I'm Debbie Miller. You must be Shirley Heidecker." Shirley smiled at her. Debbie handed her the brown bag. "We didn't have a suitcase for David, I'm sorry."

"This is fine," Shirley said. She took the bag.

Dick looked at Debbie carefully. "So this is what you look like with your clothes on," he said. Debbie blushed. Dick winked at her. "Thanks," he said seriously. He looked down at David. "Ready to go?"

David nodded happily. He waved good-bye to Debbie, who watched him walk out the door with Dick and Shirley, holding their hands. Unaccountably, Debbie felt tears welling up in her eyes. She felt ridiculously like a successful matchmaker.

David jumped up and down in the car as they drove to Carroll County. As Dick finally made the turn into his gravel driveway, he said, "This is it, now. Hold onto your hat until we get to the top."

"What hat?" David asked. "I didn't bring any hat."

"Just teasing, David," Dick explained. "Stick around and you'll learn a lot about teasing. It's fun."

David was hanging out the car window by now. "Look, I see the house!" he shouted. "Is that it?"

Dick made the sharp right turn at the top of the hill and pulled up towards the house. "That's it," he said. "Let's go in."

David leapt from the car in wild anticipation, leaving Shirley to remember the brown bag. As they stepped inside, David stopped in his tracks, looking all around. Finally he said, "Wow!"

Dick and Shirley looked at each other. Then Dick said, "This is our house, David. Want to come in?"

David ran through the living room, into the kitchen. He stopped and looked around. "Where's the quiet room?" he said.

Shirley looked quizzically at Dick, who said simply, "There's no quiet room in our house."

David looked around some more. "This is neat," he said. "Where is my room?"

Shirley showed him. It was the bedroom with a window, containing a bed and chest of drawers and a table and chair. On the table, Shirley had placed a box of crayons, paper, and a stuffed bear. David said, "Is this for me?"

Shirley said, "This is your room for you to stay in while you're here, David. We got the toys for you to play with."

She picked up the brown bag and took out the clothes Debbie Miller had packed. She noticed that all of them were old and worn. She put them in the chest of drawers without comment. "Come on," she said. "Let me show you where the bathroom is."

The Heideckers' house was constructed without partitions between the living room, dining room, or kitchen. Thus, Dick and Shirley and David could all be together while Shirley cooked dinner. Dick turned on the television set, which was a large screen color TV. He was surprised again to hear David say, "Wow." He wondered how long it had been since David had seen television. They watched a rerun of Leave it to Beaver. David said he had never seen that show before. He climbed into Dick's lap. Dick was surprised at how light David felt. He put his arms around him as they watched the show.

At dinner, David was suspicious. Shirley had made fried chicken and rice with gravy and peas. David liked the chicken, but he wasn't sure about the rice and peas.

"Is that a vegetable?" he asked warily.

"No, it's mud," Dick told him. David gave him a startled look. "Teasing, remember?"

David smiled. "Oh yeah. I forgot," he said.

"It really is a vegetable," Dick said. "But it won't bite you. Not if you bite it first, anyhow."

David took a bite of the peas. "Okay," he announced. "I'll eat it."

He ate everything on his plate and drank a glass of milk. Then he had chocolate ice cream. After dinner, as it began to get dark, he and Dick went outside. David noticed the flag and asked Dick what it was.

"That's the American flag, buddy," Dick told him.

"Why do you have it there?" David asked.

"Because I'm an American," Dick said. "That flag stands for our country."

"But why do you have it?" David persisted.

"Because we live in the greatest country in the world and I'm proud of it," Dick said.

David said, "Oh." Then he asked, "Can I be an American too?"

Dick laughed. "Sure thing," he said. "You already are."

David looked around and quickly saw a dog, two cats, and the goat. "Are those your animals?"

"They're our pets," Dick said. "Yours, too."

David could hardly believe his eyes. He fed grass to the goat and patted its head, and then he and the goat took turns chasing each other. Dick stood by, watching and rubbing his stomach. It occurred to him that his back was probably in for some abuse this weekend.

Later, he and David went inside, and the three of them watched some more TV. When she thought it was time for David to go to bed, Shirley asked him if he wanted to take a shower. He said he did. She turned it on for him and left him a towel. A little while later, David came into the living room with the towel wrapped around him.

"I'm done!" he announced happily. "Where's my pajamas?"

Shirley got the small, ragged pair he had brought with him, and led him to the spare bedroom. When he was ready, she helped him brush his teeth. Then she realized they had no children's books to read him.

"How about if I tell you a bedtime story?" she asked.

"What's a bedtime story?" David asked curiously.

"It's a story that someone reads you or tells you when you're about to go to sleep," Shirley explained. "Do you want me to tell you one?"

David nodded. Shirley racked her brains to think of a story. Finally, she remembered Goldilocks and the Three Bears. As she got into the story, Dick came into the room to play the role of the father bear. Rubbing his stomach, he bellowed his lines in a loud deep voice. David loved it. As soon as he caught onto the story line, he took over the role of the baby bear. Soon he was speaking in an exaggerated high voice. *"And who's been sleeping in my bed?"* He thought it was the most fun he had ever had.

On Saturday, Dick and Shirley put David in the car and drove down Liberty Road to the nearest shopping center. They took David into a children's clothing store and bought him new jeans, a shirt, underwear, and pajamas. Afterwards, they went into a toy store and told him to pick out something. David picked out three things; they bought them all. Then they went home and let David explore the property. The weather was cold, but David was undeterred; he ran around the hill with the animals and climbed a couple of trees. Later, Shirley made him some hot chocolate and rubbed his shoulders. They had dinner and watched TV.

On Sunday, Shirley picked out a little suitcase for David to use. She packed his new clothes in the suitcase, and one of his new toys.

"Let's keep the rest of your toys here, for next time," she suggested. "Then you'll have them to play with when you come back."

"When can I come again?" David asked.

"We hope next weekend," Shirley told him. "Would you like to?"

"Yes!" David shouted. He ran around the house, touching everything he could. Outside, he said good-bye to the animals and chased the goat one last time before climbing into the car. As they headed back to RICA, he kept popping up to look out of the window, trying to recognize landmarks he had seen on the trip out.

At the Richards Building, they were greeted by Cindy Pelham.

"You tell the Heideckers good-bye," she urged David. "Say, thank you, Mr. and Mrs. Heidecker."

David threw his arms around Dick's waist. "Good-bye, Dad," he said.

Dick put his hands on David's shoulders. "Bye, son," he said. "See you next Friday."

David hugged Shirley. "Good-bye, Mom," he said.

Shirley hugged him back.

On Monday, Dick called Debbie Miller. "We want to take David next weekend," he told her. "In fact, we want to take David for good, as soon as they'll let us."

Debbie was not surprised. David's weekend with the Heideckers had become the talk of the institution. David had arrived on the ward with his new suitcase, wearing new clothes, bringing new pajamas and toys. He had a broad smile on his face and talked all evening about the house, the hill, his room, the food, the dog, the cats, the goat, Goldilocks and the Three Bears. No one at RICA had ever seen David so happy. His euphoria lasted until Tuesday, and then he began to mope around and ask how many days it was until Friday.

A routine was established. Every Friday, Dick Heidecker arrived to pick David up. Each Sunday, he and Shirley brought David back, always carrying something new. David talked all evening about his weekend; early in the week he lapsed into depression. By Friday he was "hyper," as Debbie put it, waiting for Dick.

"Where's my dad?" he would demand. "When's he coming for me?"

"He'll be here, David," Debbie or Cindy would tell him.

"But why can't I stay there all the time?" David would persist.

"Be patient, David. It'll happen."

December 15, 1972, was David's eighth birthday. It fell on a Friday, making it possible for Dick to pick him up at RICA on that day. That evening they had a birthday cake with candles. If it was not the first birthday cake David had ever had, it was the first one he could remember. Aunt Ollie and Uncle Harold came up the hill to celebrate. The little house on Gillis Road was filled with presents to delight an eight-year-old boy; there would have been more except that Shirley said they should keep some for Christmas, which was only ten days away.

Ollie and Harold, like Dick and Shirley, had become attached to David. Aunt Ollie told Dick that David reminded her of him, except that David was so scrawny. They all noticed that David had acquired Dick Heidecker's habit of rubbing his stomach. It looked hilarious when David did it, because Dick's stomach protruded over his pants, while David's was perfectly flat. Aunt Ollie liked to hold David on her lap and tell him about Dick's childhood.

"I have a lot of stories to tell you about your father," she said.

Everybody, especially David himself, now referred to Dick and Shirley as David's parents. David urged, "Tell me now! I want to hear!"

Aunt Ollie smiled and told him about the time Dick sat in her kitchen doing finger painting and knocked over the royal blue paint onto her linoleum floor.

"What happened?" David wanted to know.

Aunt Ollie chuckled. "Before we could get a rag, my white Siamese cat walked right through the paint and kept on going. The next thing I saw, there's little blue footprints all through my kitchen, into the dining room, and up on my good sofa in the living room. And the cat's going crazy trying to get that paint off her feet."

"What did you do?" David wanted to know.

"I put the cat in the bathroom right quick, and we wiped the paint off her little paws with an old towel. But I never did get rid of all those footprints."

"How come?"

"Well, I had a yellow and white sofa in those days. I took every kind of cleaner there was and I worked on it, but forever after, if you looked close, you could see those little blue specks that was the cat's footprints."

"What about the kitchen floor?"

"I had one tile that was always a little blue," Aunt Ollie said. "People used to notice it. They thought it must be blueberry, from a pie I made. It never did come off all the way."

"Tell me another story," David begged.

Aunt Ollie smiled. "Next time," she said. "We have lots of time."

"Then will you make a blueberry pie for me?"

"Tomorrow," she promised.

Three days later, the Heideckers were told that when they brought David to their home the following weekend, they did not have to bring him back. David's DSS social worker, in consultation with the RICA staff, had decided that David could live with the Heideckers. Legally, Dick and Shirley would be David's foster parents. If all went well for a period of six months, they were told, then adoption could be considered. So long as they continued as foster parents, they would receive slightly over $100 a month from the State of Maryland.

On Friday, December 22, 1972, the Heideckers packed up David's belongings at RICA and brought David home. Strung across the house on Gillis Road was a large sign proclaiming: "Welcome Home David." As David leapt from the car and ran joyfully to the house, Dick and Shirley followed with his things. Shirley carefully arranged all of David's possessions — most of which had been supplied by Dick and Shirley over the past weeks — in his room, and then they had a special dinner. David was "hyper," as Dick and Shirley sometimes described him. He had been discharged from RICA with a two-week supply of Dexedrine and a prescription for more, but Dick and Shirley observed that the medication did little to calm him down, particularly tonight. They didn't mind. David was often loud, energetic, careless, but neither Dick nor Shirley had ever seen him behave in a way that was mean or malicious. If a few things got broken along the way, neither of them cared.

After dinner, Dick told David to stand up straight against the bathroom door frame. Dick put a ruler horizontally across the top of David's head, and made a mark on the door frame with a pencil.

"This shows how tall you are," he explained to David. "We'll do that every month, and see how much you grow."

David looked at the pencil mark. "I bet I'll grow really fast!" he shouted.

In the weeks they had known him, the Heideckers had seen many facets of David's personality. After the first couple of weeks, when David ceased to be on his "best behavior" all the time, they witnessed temper tantrums and fits of rage; the first one came on a Sunday evening when it was time to return David to the institution. There were more incidents, some when David was not allowed to do something he wanted, and others when he became frustrated by his own inability to accomplish a task. Dick and Shirley were understanding of David's frustration level. From their perspective, they saw an eight-year-old child who looked six, who could not read, did not know most of the letters of the alphabet, could not write numbers or tell time, could

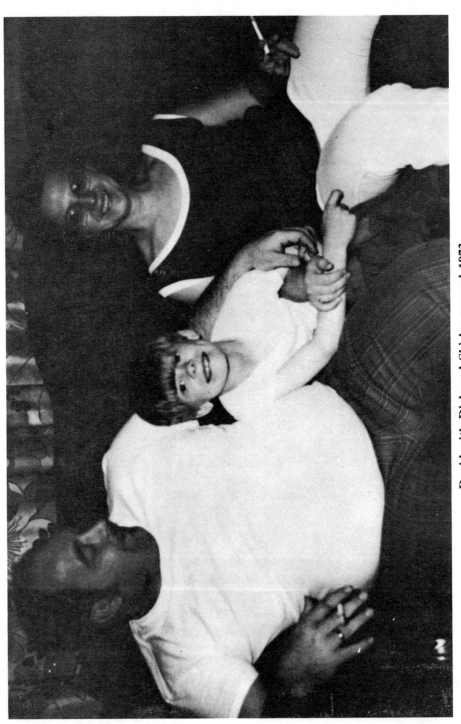

David with Dick and Shirley around 1973.

not tie his shoes. Although the Heideckers had had limited experience with children, they knew that these were things an eight-year-old should be able to do. Both of them blamed David's past. They had already seen that David had missed out on many experiences that other children take for granted: birthday parties and holiday celebrations, bedtime stories, children's television programs, trips to McDonald's. They also knew about the physical abuse and neglect which had characterized his stay in other foster homes. When Dick Heidecker thought about David's past, he was filled with silent rage. There were times when he imagined himself finding the Wagners on a lonely road and beating them up. He fantasized sometimes about what he would say to David's biological mother if he ever met her. To Shirley, David's background was a source of profound sadness. She could hardly bear to think of David's never having a birthday cake. She looked forward to the opportunities she would have to make it up to David.

David's first Christmas with the Heideckers, which came three days after his permanent arrival there, became an extravaganza. They had a tree, decorations, lights, presents upon presents. Shirley took David to visit Santa Claus at a shopping center in Westminster. They bought huge Christmas stockings to hang on the wall. David picked out candy canes and lighted angels to take home. He helped Dick put colored glass balls on their tree while Shirley baked cookies and the radio played Christmas carols. If it was a typical middle-class American Christmas, it was the first one David had ever experienced. He could not even recall the previous Christmas which he had spent on the Wagners' farm just before his commitment to RICA.

On Christmas morning, Dick and Shirley allowed themselves to be awakened in the early hours so that David could begin the job of opening his many presents. Later, Shirley cooked breakfast and the Houghtons came up the hill to join them. After Christmas, Dick and Shirley took off from work for a few days. The family spent the time together, assembling toys, walking in the woods in the cold, playing in the snow when it came. When the ball at Times Square fell at midnight to usher in 1973, David watched it on television for the first time in his life.

Not long after Christmas, David's social worker from the Department of Social Services paid a visit to the Heideckers' home. She explained that since David would be living in Carroll County, he would be reassigned to a social worker from Carroll County. She told Dick and Shirley that the new social worker would pay a visit every month or so, just to make sure that everything was fine, and that she would be in charge of the adoption, too, if they decided to proceed with that.

Dick told her, "There's no if about it. We would adopt David tomorrow if the system would let us."

The social worker smiled patronizingly at Dick Heidecker. "There are reasons for the system's rules," she told him. "All of us hope that things work out here for David, but to be very honest with you, Mr. Heidecker, it would not surprise me if David were back at RICA by the spring."

Dick stared at her in disbelief. "What do you mean?" he asked.

The social worker looked at the ground. "David has a lot of problems, Mr. Heidecker," she reminded him. "Sometimes I'm not sure you appreciate that."

Dick glared at her. "Know what I don't appreciate?" he demanded threateningly.

Shirley poked him. "We understand what you're saying," she said to the social worker. "It's just that we don't agree with you."

The social worker shrugged. This would be her last visit to the Heideckers' home anyway. She turned and left. Dick blew smoke from his cigarette in her direction, but she didn't notice.

Dick tried to explain to David why he did not like social workers. "They're do-gooders," he said. "That means they think they can save the world."

"Can they?" David asked.

"Of course not. They make it worse because of their silly rules and regulations. That's because they're over-educated. They go to school a lot, but when they finish they don't really know anything."

"Why not?"

"I guess because they study do-gooding and rule-making instead of anything useful. Besides, they don't talk English. They speak jargon instead, which is just a lot of fancy phrases that don't mean anything."

"Why do they talk that way?" David wanted to know.

"To impress people." Dick rubbed his stomach. "See, if they talked English, people might figure out that they don't know anything. This way, the folks they're talking to think the social workers know something that they don't. It scares people, intimidates 'em."

"But do they help anybody?" David insisted.

"Well, maybe once in a while, by accident," Dick told him. "But mostly they make things worse. They're the same people that let hardened criminals out on the street, them and the mental doctors. They come into court and tell the judge that this poor slob who just killed three people shouldn't be in jail because he had an unhappy childhood and now he can't help it. So the judge lets him out, and he kills more people. That's one of the other things that social workers do that I don't care for, especially after I risk my life to lock that criminal up in the first place."

"Oh," David said. He had never realized that social workers did all that damage. He had always thought they were nice ladies who tried to help but never seemed to succeed.

Early in January, Shirley Heidecker's father came to live with them. Mr. Weaver was in his seventies, with severe arthritis that made it difficult for him to walk. He had sold his home in Pennsylvania Furnace and now divided his time among the homes of his three children. This was Shirley's turn. At first, he slept on the sofabed in their living room. Soon, however, David volunteered to take the sofabed so that Grandpa, as he called Mr. Weaver, could have David's room. Dick and Shirley asked David if he were sure he would not mind giving up his room for a while. David said he was sure; he thought it might be an adventure to sleep in the living room. He and Shirley's father worked it out so that David could keep all his things in the bedroom, but the old man could sleep in the bed.

In January, David entered the second grade at a public elementary school in Carroll County. David was insistent that the school know him as David Wayne Heidecker, rather than by the name of his biological mother, which he had used all his life. Dick and Shirley asked the school. It was agreed that although they had to use David's legal name on their records, he could use the name Heidecker, and be addressed as such, in the classroom. David was placed in a special class with only ten children in it, where remedial help was available every day. He had not been in a regular public school for a whole year. He found it difficult to sit still, and often frustrating to do the work. Within a week he had challenged the teacher's authority, gotten into a fistfight with another boy who called him a shrimp, and gone into a rage in the hall when some other children blocked his way. Dick and Shirley were called to the principal's office for what was to be the first of many such sessions. Shirley's inclination was to explain David's background by way of mitigation. Dick's was to hang tough and act as if David had not done anything wrong. When they left the school, with David in tow, both Dick and Shirley had encircled David's shoulders with their arms and were speaking to him in conciliatory tones. They knew school was tough, they told David; sometimes other kids picked on you, or the teacher did; but it was important to try to get along, even if that made you feel angry inside; otherwise you would spend all your time being in trouble and you couldn't be on the playground having fun. David listened to Dick and Shirley. He knew they were his security. He told them he was sorry about getting in trouble, he would try to do better.

Some problems could be dealt with on a simpler level. When David was teased by a classmate because he was unable to tie his shoes, Shirley took him to the store and bought shoes with buckles; Dick began to teach him how to tie laces. When David came home frustrated because he could not make all his letters, Shirley bought workbooks and helped him with the alphabet. Dick made up a game: "A is for awful, that's what we think of the kids who make fun of us. B is for bomb, that's what we'll do to the teacher if she bothers us. C is for cuss, but we won't do that in school, okay, David? D is for *darn*, that's the worst word we're gonna let the teacher hear us say." David squealed with laughter and climbed onto Dick's lap.

The school schedule worked out nicely for the Heideckers. A yellow school bus came along Gillis Road each morning and stopped at the foot of the driveway. Shirley watched as David ran down the hill and either got on the bus or waited at Aunt Ollie's until it arrived. In the afternoons, when the bus brought David home, Dick was often there, depending on which shift he was working. If he wasn't there, David could stay with Aunt Ollie until Shirley came home before dinner, or he could go up the hill where Shirley's father would be. Late in the afternoon, Shirley would get home and cook dinner.

David's behavior problems continued at school, but they were tolerable. Sometimes they happened at home, too. Dick and Shirley established a routine of chores they wanted David to do, such as taking care of the animals and keeping track of his own possessions. Sometimes David balked at this; once he had a temper tantrum and told Dick that nobody could make him do that work. Dick Heidecker, weighing in the neighborhood of 230 pounds, kept a straight face as he told David they could just wait it out. He and David sat in chairs across from each other until David, finally tired of sitting, announced nonchalantly that he might as well do a few little jobs as die of boredom. Other times, David refused to sit down for dinner, or turn off the television, or go to bed; Dick and Shirley usually could end the confrontation by talking, and if they couldn't, they waited it out.

In addition to receiving a home visit from the DSS social worker once a month, the Heideckers were supposed to report to RICA from time to time. In January of 1973, RICA moved from the grounds of an institution for retarded people, where it had been for fifteen years, to its own building in Baltimore City. The building had once housed a monastery, known as St. Peter's, which had moved away in the 1960's. The State of Maryland had acquired the property and had renovated it. Surrounded by 35 acres of land, the building was red brick, three stories tall, standing high on a hill so that one could see the downtown Baltimore skyline from third story windows. If the Richards Building at Rosewood was bleak, the new RICA, known to the staff as "St. Pete's," was bucolic by comparison. The institution purchased all new furniture at the time of the move. Each room was designed for two children, and contained two beds, bureaus, and closets. The classrooms were located on the basement level. The building could have been mistaken for a private academy, were it not for the bars on the windows of the lower floors.

It was to this location that Dick and Shirley returned to RICA as David's foster parents. They met with various staff members to discuss David's situation. How were things going? Was David adjusting to his school? Did the medication help? Dick and Shirley gave acceptable answers. The staff appeared pleased with David's adjustment. A RICA report dated March 7, 1973, concluded: "Mr. and Mrs. Heidecker are impatiently waiting out a six-month period in order to adopt David."

As winter gave way to spring, the hillside on Gillis Road burst into bloom, as it always did, and the trees became green again. David delighted in playing outdoors. He discovered a dozen climbing trees, and soon developed a pattern of running to Shirley with blackened hands and skinned knees, asking for bandages. He explored and got to know every inch of the property around the house, including the woods out back that were still owned by the Houghtons. There was also Houghton property on the other side of Gillis Road, at the bottom of the hill, with an old wooden shack on it that attracted David. Dick and Shirley told him he could cross the road, which was still just a country lane with very little traffic, if he asked them first so they knew where he was going and if he stopped at the edge of the road, looked both ways, and could not see any cars in either direction. Once Dick saw David dash across the road without looking. He hollered for David to come up to the house and made him stay inside for the rest of the day. David yelled at Dick, but Dick yelled back. After that, David usually stopped and looked.

Dick, who remained an avid sports fan despite his bad back and his fat stomach, got a softball and began to play catch with David. He discovered at once that David had had absolutely no experience with a ball; still, it looked as if he had an aptitude. Dick would throw the ball underhand, aiming precisely for David's hands, shouting, "Watch the ball, keep your eye on the ball!" As David began to get the hang of it, they got a bat and practiced hitting. That took longer, but David learned to make contact with the ball. Soon Dick found himself running around on the hill, his back aching, as he chased balls.

There was a little league in Carroll County with teams for eight-year-olds. Dick found the team for his community and agreed to be an assistant coach. He and David began to go to practices. Dick observed that David's lack of experience put him behind the other boys initially, but David was beginning to catch up. He loved it, too. Shirley came to the games whenever her work schedule permitted, and she kept his little white uniform as clean as it could be. After a game, David would run to Dick, calling, "How'd I do, Dad? How was I?"

And Dick would say, "Not bad, son, not bad at all." After a game, they often cooked out at the top of the hill.

One weekend afternoon, they sat at the picnic table having lunch when a social worker from Carroll County drove up the hill. The Heideckers had never seen this one before. After David had come to live with them, he had been assigned to a new social worker from Carroll County, but she had left the Department of Social Services by spring. David had been assigned to another worker, Miss Lerner, who was now walking across the top of the hill. She introduced herself and announced that she had come for a monthly home visit. Shirley invited her to sit down at the picnic table and offered her a hamburger, which Miss Lerner declined. Then Shirley introduced her father, who was at the table. A conversation followed about David's baseball games and his progress in school.

Miss Lerner looked across the table at Shirley's father and asked him politely if he lived nearby. Dick and Shirley realized at the same moment that the next question would be about who was sleeping where in the house.

Shirley said, "No, my father lives in Pennsylvania. He's just visiting us today."

"Really," Miss Lerner remarked. "Did you drive here?"

"No, no," Dick said, observing his father-in-law's cane leaning against a tree. "No, he took the train."

"Train?" Miss Lerner asked. "What train comes near here?"

"Oh, the train," Shirley said. "Yes, it comes to Baltimore. We picked him up there."

Mr. Weaver, who was hard of hearing, continued to eat his hamburger as the conversation went on around him.

"I'm interested," Miss Lerner said, "because I'm originally from Pennsylvania myself, and I'm wondering whether there's a way I can visit my family without driving. Where did you get on the train, Mr. Weaver?"

Dick said, "Philadelphia" at the same moment that Shirley said "Allentown." Miss Lerner looked from one to the other. Then she leaned across the table towards Shirley's father. "Mr. Weaver," she said loudly. "Where do you live?"

Shirley's father looked up from his hamburger, trying to make out who this young woman was and what she wanted to know. Before he could open his mouth, David, who had caught on, kicked him in his bad leg. Old Mr. Weaver shouted with pain.

"Ow!" he yelled. "David, what are you doing?"

Miss Lerner stood up uncomfortably. "I think we're about finished," she said. She added apologetically, "I am supposed to look around the house, though."

David jumped up from the table, ran inside, scooped up his grandfather's bottles of medicine and stuffed them in his pockets. He glanced around. Everything else looked all right. He heard Miss Lerner coming in.

"Come on, I'll show you my room," he said. He took her into the bedroom, now occupied by Mr. Weaver, and pointed out his various possessions. Miss Lerner made a peremptory inspection and said good-bye. As she drove down the driveway, Dick and Shirley and David burst out laughing. Shirley's father was mystified.

"What's funny?" he demanded. "And why'd David kick me before?"

"Nothing, Dad," Shirley assured him. "Everything is fine."

Dick and Shirley did not tell Miss Lerner that they had taken the affirmative step of discontinuing David's medication on their own. David had been on Dexedrine since before he came to live with them. Neither Dick nor Shirley thought the medication did any good, and it had the negative side effect of making David feel different from other children. And so, one day in the summer of 1973, they just stopped giving him the medicine. Neither of them noticed any change in David's behavior.

Before the end of the school year, David learned to read. He was immensely proud of himself, and so were Dick and Shirley. Shirley had bought some "I Can Read" books to help him along. David took pleasure in struggling through the pages aloud until he got to the end, but if the struggle became too difficult he threw the book across the room and screamed. Once he told Shirley, "People think I'm dumb, but maybe I'm not." Dick and Shirley were both quite sure that David was anything but dumb. They had seen the results of tests taken in David's early childhood, which labeled him as "dull normal," but neither of them believed it. They could see that David was alert, energetic, and apparently bright. In fact, Shirley asked the school to test him again, and was told that he would be retested at the normal time, but that had not yet occurred.

As the school year came to a close, Shirley's father went to live with one of her brothers, and not long after that, he died. David moved back into the bedroom. When summer came, Shirley decided that Aunt Ollie, then in her seventies, was not up to caring for David all day. She found a family nearby whom she paid to watch David at their home while she worked. In the mornings, when she left for work, she dropped David off; he played with the children who lived there until the end of the day, when Shirley picked him up on her way home. Some days, when Dick worked the midnight shift, he watched David at home. On weekends, Shirley spent time planting and tending flowers on the hill. David liked to help. He wanted to know the names of the various flowers, and hooked up the hose to water them. Later he had water battles with anyone who would play; sometimes it would be Shirley, but only on a very hot day if she had on old clothes. By now David had a few playmates from his baseball league and from school; often he had a companion to climb a tree with him or rescue an injured bird. A few times the Heideckers went to a public swimming pool in town. Dick and Shirley were surprised to find that David could swim. He liked to ride in the car with Shirley, too. Sometimes she took him grocery shopping, and he helped out by finding items on the shelves. Once he created a scene in a grocery store when Shirley said he could not eat potato chips before lunch, and she had to seek the assistance of the store manager to remove David from the store and get him into her car. At home she smacked his bottom one time and confined him to his room, but later she relented when David hugged her and said he was sorry.

By now, Miss Lerner, like her predecessor, had left the Carroll County Department of Social Services, and David had been assigned to a new social worker. Dick Heidecker described this one as the nosiest social worker he had ever met. She was an older woman, with three children of her own, she told the Heideckers. Not only did she want to know everything that was happening with David, but she also liked to give advice based on her own experience as a mother. Dick had become increasingly impatient with the system. David had been in their home for six months, but nothing was being done about the adoption. He began to suspect that the constant turnover in social workers was part of the reason.

"Oh, no, Mr. Heidecker, that's not the reason," Mrs. Javits, the new social worker, assured him. "Personnel has nothing to do with it."

"Then what does?" Dick asked her.

"It's our feeling that we should go slow on this one," Mrs. Javits told him. "Better safe than sorry, as they say."

"Maybe you're better safe than sorry," Dick retorted, rubbing his stomach, "but I'm damn sick and tired of this runaround. Is there any legal reason why we can't adopt David right now?"

"Realistically, Mr. Heidecker, you cannot adopt David without the approval of my agency, and we have not given that approval."

"Why haven't you? Is there something wrong with my home?"

"Not at all," Mrs. Javits said. "The problem is with David. DSS must be sure that David can flourish in your home before there is an adoption."

"What do you mean, flourish?" Dick demanded. "Look at him. Does he look happy to you or not?"

"Yes, he does," Mrs. Javits admitted.

"Do you want to know how much he's grown since he came here?" Dick asked. "Five or six inches, something like that. We have it marked on the bathroom door. Do you want to see it?"

"Oh, I'll take your word for that," Mrs. Javits said.

"And do you know that he's learned to read this year? Do you know that?"

"I'm very glad," Mrs. Javits said.

"Then why do you want to talk about flourish?" Dick asked. "Why don't we just make it legal?"

"Mr. Heidecker," Mrs. Javits said, "have you ever thought about what would happen if the adoption went through, and afterwards David became such a problem to you that you could not control him? Have you stopped to ask yourself what position you would be in if you wanted to give David back after you had adopted him?"

"Give David back?" Dick thundered. "Are you crazy?"

Now Shirley stepped in. Her opinion of social workers was not much better than Dick's, but she was capable of being more tactful. She was also more fearful of the consequences of alienating the social worker.

"He means that we have no intention of giving David back," she said. "We don't have any problems with him that we can't handle, and we want to keep him."

"Has David had problems in school during the last 30 or 60 days?" Mrs. Javits asked.

"Nothing serious," Shirley said. "We had to go up and see the principal once or twice for things, that's about it."

"What kind of things?"

"Little things, talking back to the teacher, not doing his work, things like that."

"Do you ever have trouble at home having David carry out his responsibilities?"

"Once in a while, just normal things."

"Like what?" Mrs. Javits persisted.

"Sometimes he doesn't want to take care of his things, or he forgets to carry out the trash. Stuff like that."

Mrs. Javits peered earnestly over her glasses. "Have you tried a reward system?" she asked.

Dick looked suspicious. "What's that?"

"Let's say there are certain things you expect David to do. You make a chart, maybe a nice, colorful poster, and you list the jobs you want him to do. Then you make columns for the different days. Whenever David fulfills his responsibilities, you can put a gold star in the column for that job for that day. Or you can use other colored stars, such as a nice bright red or emerald green. Then the child feels rewarded for doing his tasks, and he wants to do them. At the end of the week, he's looking at a nice picture with pretty stars on it, and he feels successful. Do you see?"

Dick looked at Mrs. Javits as if she had taken leave of her senses. "Gold stars?" he repeated.

"Right," Mrs. Javits said enthusiastically.

"And you say they don't have to be gold, they can be red or whatever?"

"Yes."

Dick shook his head. His desire to spit on the floor was almost overwhelming, but he restrained himself. "Mrs. Javits," he said, "I've heard a lot of things, but I've never in my life heard of anything as crazy as what you just said."

Mrs. Javits did not appear offended in the least. "That's because it's a new idea to you," she announced. "You haven't heard about the reward system before. Why don't you give it some thought?"

"I already did," Dick told her. "But you don't want to know what my thoughts were."

"Well, it was just a suggestion," Mrs. Javits said cheerfully. "If you don't wish to try it, why that's up to you, of course."

"Thank you," Dick said sarcastically.

One Sunday afternoon in August, Dick discovered that David had forgotten to feed any of the animals that day. Dick told him to go do it. David refused. Dick said that in that case, David could stay in his room until he changed his mind. David picked up a plastic toy and threw it at Dick, who caught it in mid-air. Dick told David to stop. David picked up another toy and threw it. Dick Heidecker lost his temper. He put a chair in the middle of the room, sat down on it, put David across his knee and walloped him. When it was over, David ran out of the house, wildly, at first, in circles, and finally down the hill to Aunt Ollie's house. He crashed through the front door and stopped. Aunt Ollie sat in her rocking chair. Startled, she looked up to see David with tears streaming down his face.

"Davey?" she said. "What is it?"

David ran to her and put his arms around her neck. "Aunt Ollie, Aunt Ollie!" he cried.

She hugged him and held him for a long time without asking any questions. Finally she said, "Do you feel better now?"

David nodded. "I love you, Aunt Ollie," he said.

"You know, it's getting on to be dinner time," she said. "Maybe you ought to go back for supper."

"No," David said adamantly.

"Well, I can give you some here, if you like," she offered. "Only your mom and dad'll be wondering what happened to you, won't they? They might be worried about you."

"My dad's mad at me," David explained quietly.

"Mad at you? I bet he isn't by now, though. I bet he isn't mad at all."

David looked at her. "Do you think?"

"I'm sure," she said. "You can go on back."

"Okay," David said.

Up on the hill, Dick Heidecker struggled with a mass of feelings. Parents had been doing what he had just done for centuries, since Biblical times at least, and many people thought it was the right thing to do, even necessary. Certainly it had been done to him on many occasions, with no ill effects. But David's childhood, until now, had been anything but normal. David was not a child who had grown up in a middle-class household, with all the trappings that American children were used to, including a family who loved him. He had been abandoned, neglected, and abused, and to that day carried scars on his back from a beating in a foster home. Was it right to use physical discipline on a child with that background? Dick wondered if he had been forced to spend too much time around social workers — perhaps he was beginning to develop their philosophy. He tried to intellectualize. Once, while on duty in a courtroom, he had heard a judge observe that while he couldn't always explain the difference between discipline and abuse, he knew which was which. Dick agreed with that. Just because David had been abused as a little child, Dick told himself, was not a reason to refrain from discipline now. Knowing that, somehow, did nothing to diminish the pain Dick was feeling.

When David came home, he and Dick hugged each other. Dick figured that David had gone down to Aunt Ollie's. He was secretly glad that Aunt Ollie was there to lend comfort to David, as she had many times to him in his own childhood. Dick reflected on the fact that families were made, not necessarily born, since to him, his family included Aunt Ollie and David, neither of whom had any genetic connection to Dick or to Shirley. One of the happy by-products of their having David was David's wonderful relationship with Aunt Ollie which, to Dick and Shirley, served to cement the three generations.

David did, indeed, like to visit Aunt Ollie. She was almost always home, and she often had something good for him to eat. David loved to run down the winding driveway as fast as he could and crash inside the door to Aunt Ollie's house, shouting a happy greeting and often startling Aunt Ollie awake from an afternoon nap.

"Aunt Ollie, I'm thirsty!" David would yell. "Do you have lemonade?"

And Aunt Ollie would rouse herself and say. "Davey, you startled me. Can't you come into a person's house more quietly?"

David would look hurt. "What do you mean?" he would yell. "Am I too noisy for you?"

Aunt Ollie would smile and pour him a glass of lemonade. Sometimes they sat out back on a glider and felt the cool country breeze. Other times, Aunt Ollie sat in her big rocking chair and held David on her lap.

"Come on, Aunt Ollie, tell me another story about my dad!" he would say.

Aunt Ollie would just smile and say, "Well, let me think. Maybe I can remember just one more."

Once she told David about a day she had taken Dick horseback riding, nearly thirty years before. The memory made her smile.

"You should have seen him, Davey," she told him. "Here he was, a little boy younger'n you, and the horse we had was great big."

"What color was it?" David wanted to know.

"Black, I think. Black with a little white on it. It had a name like Midnight, or Black Beauty, something like that."

"Was he scary, Aunt Ollie? Was the horse really scary?"

"I'll say he was!" Aunt Ollie chuckled. "That horse was so scary, he scared *me*. And you know there isn't much that scares this old lady."

"Except thunderstorms, Aunt Ollie. I know you're scared of thunder and lightning."

"Well, that, maybe," Aunt Ollie admitted. "I don't like thunderstorms much, that's true. But that's about all that scares me, except for this big old horse I'm telling you about."

"Was my dad scared, too?" David demanded.

"He sure was, honey. He was scared half to death. But he didn't want to show it, you see. So he let the man help him up to the saddle, and then he held onto those reins for dear life."

David was almost breathless. "What happened?"

"Well, the horse started out to walk, kind of slow, you know, and your daddy got a little bit braver. I think he sat up straighter and held on a little looser. Then that horse began to move a little faster. Well, your daddy was still in the saddle, so that made him braver still. In fact, he let go the reins with one hand and waved at me, and he yelled, 'Aunt Ollie, look!' And that did it."

"Did what, Aunt Ollie? Tell me!"

"That old horse began to gallop. And just about then, your daddy lost his balance and fell plumb off of that Midnight."

"Did he get hurt?"

"Shucks, no! He landed on a soft patch of grass with some leaves on top, as I recall. Why, he jumped right up! And guess what he said next?"

"What?"

"He said, 'Aunt Ollie, I want to ride some more!' Can you believe it?"

"Wow!" David shouted. "Did he get back on, Aunt Ollie?"

"No way," she said. "He wanted to, but I wouldn't let him. I told him, 'Dickie, we're gettin' outta here. I had enough of this Midnight.' Well, Dick began to holler and carry on, saying he wasn't scared of no horse, and finally I had to take his hand and practically pull him away from there."

"Did you ever take him riding on a horse again?" David wanted to know.

"Oh, my, yes," the old lady said, with a smile. "Many a time. But we always got a smaller horse, at least until he was quite a bit bigger. Oh, my, I took him lots of times."

"Aunt Ollie, will you take me?" David wanted to know.

She smiled at him. "Oh, no, honey, I couldn't. I'm too old for that now. But I bet your dad will, or your mother."

"Yeah!" David burst into a wide grin. "I'll ask them today!" He paused. "Aunt Ollie?"

"What, honey?"

"Will you tell me another story about my dad?"

"Not today, David. We'll save the next story for another day."

"Please, Aunt Ollie!"

"No, don't bother me about it. I'll give you a fresh baked cookie, how's that?"

"Okay."

Afterwards, David would ask Dick if the stories were true. Dick would laugh and say maybe so, maybe not.

"Depends on the story," he told David. "Was I tough in the story?"

"Yeah!"

"Was I brave and strong?"

"You sure were!"

"Then that story's true."

David laughed. He had caught on to Dick's teasing. "Dad, she told me a story yesterday where you weren't a bit tough!"

"Is that so?"

"Yup. You were real scared and crying."

"Then that story definitely is not true," Dick announced.

"Ha, I made it up!" David yelled. "I made it up and I fooled you!"

Dick winked at him. "Come on outside, let's throw a ball around," he said.

They ended the summer with a day trip to Gettysburg. It was a trip made to order for David, who could run aimlessly through the battlefields and make as much noise as he liked. They even took a helicopter ride, which was a first for Dick as well as David. Dick, who was petrified, encircled David with his arms and held him tight, while David yelled with pleasure. Later they spread out a picnic on an old Army blanket. David reminded Dick and Shirley that they should save some dessert for Aunt Ollie, who had decided not to come. He carefully wrapped some to take back to her. At home, David jumped out of the car at Aunt Ollie's house, clutching her cake. He delivered his package and then, with a wave to his parents who waited patiently in the car, David took off running up the gravel driveway, happily trying to calculate how fast he could do it, with his shirt flapping in the wind.

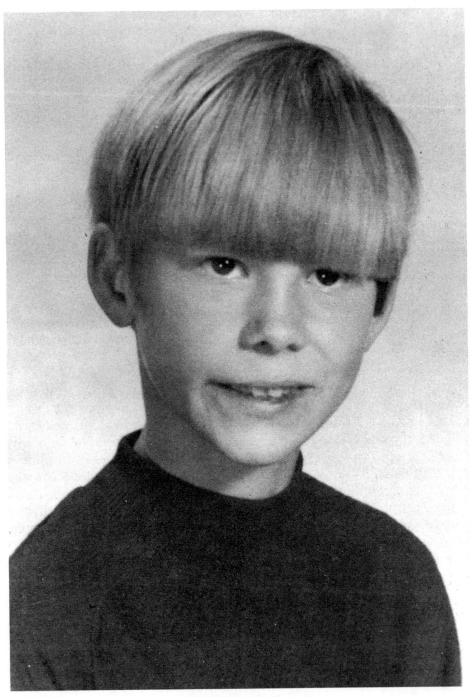

David in 2nd or 3rd grade.

CHAPTER 6

Mainstream

"You know what they say about institutional food," Shirley said indignantly to Aunt Ollie. "But this is ridiculous!"

She had just measured David on the bathroom door frame and learned that he had grown nine inches since December. Not that she was surprised — she and Dick had noticed that David grew at a rate that seemed incredible, and now, as he prepared to enter third grade, he had outgrown all of his clothes.

As David grew taller, he hardly seemed to fill out much. His feet got bigger, but the rest of him stayed skinny — or lean, as Dick liked to say. He did look older. His two front teeth had come in, and his face no longer looked hollow. Dick said it was the look of an athlete, and signed him up for a junior football league, which Dick also assisted in coaching. David took to football right away. Now he and Dick spent their free time throwing a football around the top of the hill, with Dick shouting, "Run! Look where you're going! Run!" In fact, as Dick had begun to notice, David ran unusually fast. Dick wondered if track might not be another sport for David in future years.

Third grade began inauspiciously for David. His teacher was a humorless, heavy-set woman whose physical appearance reminded him of Vinnie Wagner. David's feelings about the Wagners had undergone dramatic change over the past two years. While he lived on their farm, they were the only family he had, and really the only family in his memory. He accepted them, therefore, as children do, despite their neglect and mistreatment of him, and ultimate abandonment; he had even missed them when he went to RICA. But after coming to live with the Heideckers, and having a standard of comparison for the first time, David began to realize just how badly the Wagners had treated him. Certainly there was much he had forgotten, having left the farm just after his seventh birthday, but none of what he could remember, except for Sara, was positive. He recalled going to school without a Halloween

69

costume, and he definitely remembered at least some incidents of physical abuse, particularly the beating with Mrs. Wagner's shoe that left scars on his back. He also had memories of long, dull days with nothing to do. Mr. Wagner had almost faded from his mind.

The sight of David's new teacher brought feelings of rage to David. Looking at her made him remember things he didn't want to think about. Sometimes she seemed to act like Vinnie Wagner, too. David thought she was authoritative, mean, and without a sense of humor. She did not tell funny stories to the children, or ask them what they liked to do. In fact, she did not appear to enjoy her job at all. David thought she acted as if she were supposed to make the students miserable.

Early in the fall, David went into a rage in the classroom which manifested itself by his throwing a chair in the direction of the teacher. So serious was this incident that it was described in a social worker's report as "an outburst involving homicidal threats to surrounding adults, profanity, suicide threats, tearing and throwing objects." The school transferred David to another elementary school in the community, to which bus service was also available, and six days after the incident, Dick and Shirley took him to a pediatrician who prescribed Dilantin and Phenobarbital. At the doctor's recommendation, they took David to the Carroll County Mental Hygiene Clinic, where family therapy was recommended. Because this was a public clinic, however, therapy could not begin for three months.

Things did not go a great deal more smoothly in the new school, although there were no reports of "homicidal threats." David was involved in frequent fistfights, many incidents of defiance of authority, and some scenes in which he threw, tore, or destroyed property. On some of those occasions, Dick and Shirley were called to the school. Dick continued to take a "boys will be boys" attitude, while Shirley tried to explain about David's background. At home, they talked seriously to David about his behavior, trying to make him realize the possible consequences of his actions, but they were not punitive. Dick even suggested that some of the responsibility should be borne by the various teachers or administrators — an approach of which the RICA staff strongly disapproved. RICA was now watching the situation with some alarm. If David could not control himself, he could not remain with the Heideckers.

At home, David had good days and bad. One minute he might be tossing a football around the hill with Dick, and the next, throwing rocks at his father. In the morning he could cheerfully feed the animals and clean up the yard, and by afternoon he could scream at Shirley that he hated her. Once Aunt Ollie threatened David with Uncle Harold's belt if he didn't learn to control his mouth; David was quiet for a minute, and then hugged Aunt Ollie and asked her for a cookie. Most of his rages and temper tantrums could be controlled by Dick and Shirley, who put him in a chair and talked to him until he became calm. One thing they all knew about David was that he never stayed mad for long, never held a grudge. After a scene it was not hard for him to apologize, to tell Dick and Shirley that he loved them.

Shirley decided to start David in Sunday School. She and Dick had belonged to the Ebenezer United Methodist Church on Woodbine Road for several years, but they seldom attended. Shirley thought this should change, now that they had David. She was usually unable to persuade Dick, but most Sundays she helped David put on his best clothes, and they drove off together. David could not recall ever having been in a church before, although Vinnie Wagner had talked a lot about God. When David told Shirley that the God Mrs. Wagner told him about didn't sound very nice, Shirley assured him that the Wagners had it all wrong.

"God isn't somebody to be scared of," she told David. "God is love. He loves everybody."

"Oh," David said. He kept remembering parts of a prayer that Vinnie Wagner had made him say. It had something in it about being dead, David told Shirley. Shirley said just to forget about that, and she taught him a new prayer that was happier. She enrolled David in the children's Sunday School at Ebenezer. He seemed to enjoy it. Once in a while she kept him in the church with her. When that happened, David was well-behaved; he learned to find his way around the hymnal and the prayer book, and smiled with pride when Shirley praised him.

In October, David asked Shirley about Halloween. At age eight, going on nine, David thought that Halloween meant a costume; he had never heard about "trick or treat." When Shirley explained it to him, David was ecstatic. Shirley carefully made him a clown costume that he could wear to school on Halloween. The third grade had a little party; Shirley sent in cupcakes for all the children.

That evening, when Shirley got home from work, she took David trick or treating. Driving up Gillis Road towards the scattered houses that were there, she explained to him again what to do.

"First you knock on the door," Shirley told him. "When somebody comes, you say Trick or Treat! Say it real loud, so they can hear you. Then they'll give you candy or a cookie, or maybe an apple, and you say, Thank you very much."

"What if they don't give me anything?" David wanted to know.

Shirley smiled. "They will," she assured him.

"What if they're mean to me?" David persisted.

"They won't be," Shirley said. "But if anything happens that you don't like, just come back. I'll be waiting for you in the car, all right?"

"Okay!" David said enthusiastically.

The first house they came to, about a mile up the road, was lit up hospitably and looked like a good place to begin. It was the home of Bob and Joyce Langhage, a family whom Shirley did not yet know. David climbed out of the car and ran excitedly to the front door, where he rang the bell insistently. Joyce Langhage opened the door and looked at David expectantly. David looked back at Mrs. Langhage. He had suddenly forgotten what it was he was supposed to say. Horrified, he kept staring at Joyce, stammering and trying to think of the words. Joyce helped him out.

"Are you here for trick or treat?" she asked kindly.

Relieved, David exclaimed, "Yes! Trick or treat!"

Joyce handed him a homemade candy apple. "Well, here's your treat," she said cheerfully.

David looked at it. He turned to leave, then remembered and turned back. "Thank you very much!" he called out. He ran like lightning to Shirley's car, and jumped in.

"I did it, I did it!" he yelled. "Look, Mom, look what I got!"

They drove on, stopping at other houses. Now David could remember the magic words. They continued until he had a large bag of treats, and then started for home.

"Did you like it?" Shirley asked.

"Wow!" David said. "It's almost like Christmas!"

At home, he eagerly shared his booty with Dick, who said that maybe they should do this every night, then they wouldn't have to shop for food anymore.

"Can we?" David asked.

Dick winked at him. "We'll do it again, sport," he said. "Next October."

On December 15, David was nine. He had been with Dick and Shirley for nearly a year. They planned a birthday party at Pizza Hut. Shirley invited a dozen boys from David's third grade class and his little league and football teams. One of her brothers, who then lived in Australia, was in town and came too. So did Aunt Ollie and Uncle Harold Houghton. There was a huge array of presents, followed by pizza, cake and chaos. Dick and Shirley looked at each other as gangs of noisy nine-year-olds raced past. Was this why people had birthday parties in public places, they wondered, to prevent destruction of their own homes? When the party ended, David helped them load his presents into the car.

"That was fun!" he yelled. "Can we do it every year?"

"Don't get ahead of yourself," Dick said, rubbing his stomach. "Christmas is ten days away."

Right after Christmas, the Heideckers were told that there was an opening at the clinic for them to begin family counseling. Dick told Shirley it would be a waste of time, but Shirley said it might help move the adoption along if they went. She and Dick explained to David that they were going to talk to a counselor who could help him feel better. What they did not realize, until the sessions started, was that David was a pro when it came to counselors. At RICA he had learned what answers were expected, and he gave them. Each time they went, David talked confidently to the counselor, but afterwards Dick and Shirley saw no improvement in his behavior. On their fifth visit, Dick and Shirley were amazed to hear David and the counselor engaged in deep conversation about the nature of responsibility and self-control; when David told the counselor that he always tried to count to ten when anything made him mad, they just looked at each other. The conversation became even more amazing when David, less than two hours after the session, had a massive temper tantrum during which he threw a toy racing car through his bedroom window, breaking the glass.

"Damn it!" Dick hollered. "What was all that crap you told the counselor today?" David's disarming smile failed to disarm Dick this time. "I'm about ten seconds away from giving you something to yell about," he continued. "You want me to count to ten?"

He stormed into the kitchen, where Shirley was cleaning up the dinner dishes. "I'm through with that counseling," he announced. "We've gone five times, and every time we go David gives them some story about how he's gonna act. Then we come home and what does he do?"

Shirley lit a cigarette. "He does what he damn well pleases," she said casually.

"So why are we wasting our time there?"

"We'll stop going," Shirley said.

They did. It was the middle of winter, when snow and ice made travel difficult anyway; Shirley made excuses to the counselor for the next couple of weeks, and after that she just stopped calling. Nobody ever mentioned it again.

When spring came, David knew what to expect. He had seen the hillside bloom the year before; this year he was ready. He helped Shirley plant flowers, and had some ideas of his own about a garden. When Dick suggested that he and David plant a semi-circle of pine trees around the rim of the hilltop, David was thrilled. Back in the woods, he and Dick found dozens of young pines, under a foot high, that could be transplanted. Painstakingly, they dug them up, one at a time, and carried them to the hilltop. Dick did most of the digging. Carefully, they put each baby tree in its hole and patted the dirt around it.

"One day those trees will be taller than you," Dick told David.

"Even taller than you?" David wanted to know.

Dick laughed. Despite David's size when they met him, his growth rate had been such that Dick now expected him to grow taller than six feet. "Even taller than me," he said. "And there won't be those spaces between them. That'll fill up as the trees grow."

"Can we still see the sunset?" David asked anxiously.

"Oh, sure. We'll just look across the tops of those trees and see anything we want."

When the school year ended and David's little league season was over, Dick and Shirley took a week off from work and drove to Niagara Falls with David. It was David's first vacation. He loved it. They stayed in a motel and enjoyed all the tourist activities they could pack into a week. When they rode under the falls on the Maid of the Mist, Dick tightened his fingers around David's arm and never let go. They brought a carload of toys and cheap souvenirs home to Carroll County, with David chattering all the way about the trip.

Two days after their return, Dick heard about a family nearby who had a Shetland pony for sale. He and David went up and took a look. The pony was tiny, a miniature in black and white, but large enough for David to ride. David put his arms around the pony and refused to let go.

"Dad, can we get it?" he asked. "Can we keep him, please?"

Dick asked the people how much they wanted for the pony. Thirty-five dollars, he was told. Dick hesitated, puffing on his cigarette. Thirty-five dollars was a lot of money, he said, and they would have to buy feed, too. The people offered to throw in a saddle and some feed. Dick gave in. Next they had to provide a shelter for the pony. Dick bought a portable shed at Sears and put it together.

Shirley asked David if he had a name for the pony. David thought a minute.

"I know!" he called out exuberantly. "I'll name him Midnight!"

"Midnight?" Dick said. "Where did you get that name?"

David laughed. "From the horse you fell off of when you were little, Dad!"

Dick shrugged. "Okay, rub it in," he said. "But you oughtta know one thing — the horse I fell off of was a whole lot bigger than this little Shetland."

"Yeah, I know," David said.

The pony had belonged to a family of children who rode him mercilessly. He was easy to ride, even for David, who had never ridden before. David learned to put the saddle on and soon could be seen riding proudly across the hilltop. Dick and Shirley explained that he was responsible for taking care of the pony. He had to be fed twice a day, and his shelter had to be kept clean. David listened earnestly. He would take care of Midnight, he promised. Most of the time, he did. Once in a while, at bedtime, he would jump to his feet, shouting that he had forgotten to feed Midnight; he would run outside and do it. Dick and Shirley were pleased to see how responsible David was with the animal, and also how kind and loving he was towards him. Often they saw him hugging the pony, talking gently to him, reassuring him in a thunderstorm.

David completed the third grade at the school to which he had been transferred, but at the end of the year Dick and Shirley were told that David could not return to the public school system. The Carroll County Board of Education told the Heideckers that David's behavior was so disruptive, and his ability to control himself so limited, that he needed special help. He would not be readmitted to the public schools, they were told, until a professional assured the Board that David could follow directions and behave.

The RICA staff was quite concerned. Despite assurances from Dick and Shirley that everything was fine, there were obviously serious problems. Thus far, the DSS reports had been positive. But when DSS learned about the problem in the public school system, anything could happen. After all, the Department had the power to remove David from the Heideckers' home and to return him to RICA, or to place him anywhere else at all. From the point of view of the RICA people, the Heideckers were the best thing that ever happened to David; whatever problems he manifested were in spite of Dick and Shirley, certainly not because of them. Still, nobody could predict how DSS would look at it.

The RICA staff had a solution. They had an arrangement with an independent school known as Lida Lee Tall, which was run by Towson State University in Baltimore County. The arrangement was that certain RICA children, who were able to function outside of the institution on a day-to-day basis, were bussed to Lida Lee Tall for classes each day. The program at Lida Lee Tall was designed to deal with the special needs of these children. If David came back to RICA each Monday to Friday, the staff said, he could go to Lida Lee Tall and then spend weekends with the Heideckers.

Shirley hit the roof. There was no way, she told Dick, that David was going to spend a single night at that institution. After he had made so much progress in a year and a half, it would all be for nothing if he had to go back there to sleep. David had grown a foot and learned to read and write since he had come with them. Did anybody think they were going to give all of that up and put David back where he came from? She told the RICA staff that David was not going to sleep there for any reason, on any basis, ever.

RICA came up with another idea. Was Shirley willing to drive David to and from RICA every weekday? If so, he could take the bus to and from Lida Lee Tall, but still go home with the Heideckers each evening. This approach was unorthodox, they told her, but it might work. Shirley asked why she couldn't take David directly to Lida Lee Tall every day; it was closer to their home than the institution was, and then David wouldn't have to ride the bus. No, she was told. The RICA-Lida Lee Tall program was supposed to be for children living at the institution; they were already making an exception to accommodate David. But he would have to depart from and return to RICA each day. Shirley reluctantly agreed. She would leave home at 7 in the morning with David, drop him at RICA about 45 minutes later, and then drive to her job at Webster Clothes, which was another 15 minutes from the institution. When her workday was over, she would go back to RICA, pick up David and drive him home to Carroll County. They would arrive home around 6 o'clock.

David hated the bus ride, and complained about it incessantly to Dick and Shirley. All the kids on the bus were nutty, he said, and everybody at Lida Lee Tall thought he was one of them. Dick and Shirley said they were sorry, but there was nothing they could do about it. They explained to David that if he did well at this school, and especially if he behaved well, he could go back to a regular school next year.

David progressed rapidly at Lida Lee Tall. The program was structured and had a built-in reward system for good behavior. Over the course of the school year, David developed more self-control than he had ever had before. He turned ten in the middle of the year. By Easter, even Dick and Shirley, who had never made a point of noticing David's problems, could see a difference. Aunt Ollie remarked to Shirley that she had never seen David so calm.

"He's not such a wild Indian any more," she added. "Are you giving him some new medicine?"

Shirley shook her head. "No, we're not giving him anything," she said. "Those medicines never did much for David. He's just getting older, Aunt Ollie."

Aunt Ollie smiled. "Age don't cure everything," she said. "If he was still in the institute he'd be the same age, but he wouldn't be like this, would he?"

David's social worker from Carroll County — a successor to Mrs. Javits, who had left her job — seemed pleased with David's progress, despite the setback of his having to leave the public school system. That spring, when she came by for a visit, Dick and Shirley asked her about the status of David's adoption. What was taking so long, they wanted to know? David had been with them now for over two years. They got the same tired response, which by now was completely unsatisfactory. Even David got into the discussion this time.

"When am I gonna be adopted?" he demanded to know.

The social worker appeared taken aback. "Well, I don't know exactly, David," she smiled. "These things take a lot of time."

"That's what you all say!" David replied. "It doesn't have to take a long time, though."

The social worker promised to look into it.

At Lida Lee Tall, David was tested for aptitude and achievement. Dick and Shirley were told that the school placed no credence in the tests from David's very early childhood which put him in the "dull normal" range. David was normal, they were told, but not dull; he actually tested slightly above average. Dick announced bluntly:

"We told everybody that all along. We always knew it."

Shirley nodded. "It's obvious," she said confidently.

At the end of the school year, a report from RICA concluded:

> "David was rated daily for his morning and afternoon behavior on such items as verbal and physical interactions with peers, politeness, care in handling of material objects, following instructions of staff, remaining in designated area, etc. Any misbehaviors that David engaged in were considered minor. There was infrequent misbehavior in the dining room, occasional occurrences of not remaining in the appropriate area, occasional (once or twice a month) incidents of not following directions, a few fights during his entire stay at RICA. David's behavior at RICA was, on the whole, excellent."

David was discharged from RICA on June 6, 1975. The administration at his old elementary school had changed by now, and he was scheduled to return there for fourth grade. He had lost a year in the progression, but he would be back in the public school system.

Dick and Shirley bought David a bicycle that summer. Dick told the Carroll County social worker that this was part of the reward system that everybody recommended: David had done well in school and so he deserved a prize. The social worker nodded approvingly, thinking to herself how much progress the Heideckers were making as parents, not understanding that Dick was pulling her leg. In fact, Dick and Shirley bought things for David because they wanted to, and for no other particular reason. They had been known to bring him presents to cheer him up when he got in trouble at school, to give him candy if he didn't care for the dinner Shirley had made, to let him skip school because he didn't feel well but allow him to play outside. Harold Houghton once remarked to Ollie that the Heideckers broke every rule of good parenting.

"Whatever it is you're s'posed to do to raise kids, they do the other," he said.

Dick and Shirley with David, around age 10.   *Courtesy Olan Mills*

"That's true," Aunt Ollie agreed, "but you can't hardly argue with success."

The bike replaced the Shetland pony, which David had now outgrown. They agreed to give it to some friends in the country who had younger children. David gave Midnight a final embrace, and handed him over to the new family.

"Take good care of my pony," he cautioned, feeling sad. He turned to Dick and Shirley, "At least I won't have to feed my new bike," he added optimistically.

David had as much fun with the bike as he did with the pony. Dick laid down rules about how and where to ride, but he did so skeptically. He and Shirley knew that David was a dare devil who loved risks and challenges, that caution was not a part of his personality.

"There's one rule that's the most important, David," Dick told him sternly. "That rule is, do not get killed. All the other rules are less important."

David grinned, rubbing his stomach. "I'll be careful, Dad," he promised.

Actually, as Dick and Shirley predicted, he was anything but careful. Dick was secretly proud of David's approach to life. Shirley knew with quiet certainty that that quality was what had enabled David to survive his early years. Nevertheless, they worried that David would injure himself. One afternoon, as Dick drove home from work, he saw David riding towards him, both hands high in the air, in the middle of Gillis Road. Dick told Shirley later that if there were a white line dividing the road, David's bike would have been right on top of it. Dick jumped out of the car and hollered at David to get up to the house. There Dick announced that he was taking the bike away. Tears and promises followed; by the next morning, Dick had given in.

In the fall, Shirley and David set out one Saturday to shop for school clothes. As they drove up Gillis Road, Shirley swerved to her right to avoid a dog and struck the mailbox of the house there. It was the same house where David had first gone trick or treating. She and David got out of the car. A little boy about David's size sat in the yard holding a basketball. His mother, Joyce Langhage, opened the door and came outside.

By the time Shirley finished explaining about the mailbox, and saying she would pay for the damage, the two boys appeared to have struck up a friendship. They sat in the grass, a few feet apart, tossing the basketball back and forth between them.

Joyce said, "It looks as if our boys are getting acquainted. Chris, this is — what's your boy's name?"

"David," Shirley told her. "David Heidecker."

"Chris, this is David. David, that's Chris." Joyce turned to Shirley. "Would you like to come in for a cup of coffee?"

Shirley did. She was unnerved by the close call, and David seemed content with his new friend. She sat in Joyce's kitchen and drank coffee as Joyce told her about their family. They had lived originally in a community in another county, and had two children — Chris, who was eight, and Holly, who was three. In 1973, the telephone company where her husband Bob worked had transferred him to Carroll County, and they had decided to move to the country. They had bought their lot on Gillis Road and had hired a contractor to build this house. Bob had done a lot of the work himself, to keep the cost down. It was a modern brick one-story house with a basement, and at that time was the only house in view on that side of the street. There was a dairy farm across the road. They had never regretted the move for a single day, Joyce said; she only hoped that Carroll County would never become too developed.

Shirley learned that Chris and David were about to enter the fourth grade at the same elementary school. Shirley explained to Joyce that David was old for his class because of his background. But the two boys appeared to be making friends with one another. When Shirley went to leave she told the boys they would be going to school together, and pointed out to Chris the direction of their home. David asked if he could ride his bicycle up to Chris's house later on. Shirley said she thought it would be all right.

This chance meeting spawned a long friendship between David and Chris and their families. The two boys soon developed a pattern of calling each other on the telephone to say, "Wanta play?" or, "Can you sleep at my house?" Because they lived only a mile apart on a country road, their homes were accessible by bicycle. In addition, they both rode the same bus to and from school. It was possible for both of them to get off the bus at the same house, play for a while, and then be picked up or driven home by somebody's parents.

It was fortuitous, perhaps, that their meeting came at a time when David's most severe emotional problems were behind him. His fourth grade year was the best year he had had so far. No longer in a special class, he became a part of the mainstream for the first time. Although there were incidents of misbehavior, including a verbal assault on a teacher and several fistfights with classmates, all of the incidents were considered to be within acceptable limits. There were no suspensions, and no talk of transferring David to another school or out of the public school system. His report card for that year showed satisfactory progress in every subject.

If the Langhages had any qualms about David's conduct, they never expressed them. Bob Langhage was a personable, outgoing man with a generous heart and a love of people. He told David that they had one rule in their house, and that was that you behave yourself.

"You're welcome here whenever you want to come," he told David. "Come up and play with the kids, stay for dinner, spend the night. But you have to behave yourself."

At first, the boys spent more time at the Langhage home, because Chris's parents would not allow Chris to ride his bike as far as the Heideckers'. David loved to go to the Langhages' house. Joyce was a homemaker who did not go out to work. She was forever making doughnuts or cookies or soup, and she was glad to take requests. Nor did she mind if David walked into her kitchen and helped himself to whatever he saw in the refrigerator. As the boys got a little older, Bob and Joyce finally permitted Chris to ride his bike to David's house. After that, the boys began to spend about equal time at each house. If there were more people at the Langhages', there was more space at the Heideckers' — they had the big hill, and acres of woods behind the house. David had a tire swing at his house; Chris had orchard trees at his. The boys often pitched a tent on the grass in front of the Heideckers' house and slept there all night. There were trees to climb, and Dick had installed a basketball hoop. It was possible for the boys to camp out there, then peddle their bikes up to Chris's house for breakfast, and then ride back to climb a tree behind David's house.

The boys had vastly different personalities. David was noisy, energetic, and athletic. Chris was quiet and decidedly not athletic. His parents thought they were a good combination; Chris tended to quiet David down a little, and David was able to bring Chris out. Sometimes, however, their interests were divergent. The Heideckers were big on sports; the Langhages weren't. Chris and his father liked boy scouting, but they were unable to interest David in that. Most of the time, the boys just played at whatever they happened to think of. They had noisy water battles in the Langhages' back yard or played a quiet game of monopoly on a rainy day.

Once in a while they fought. One day, Joyce Langhage saw both boys get off the school bus at her house, fighting as they stepped down, and shortly after that rolling around on the grass as they punched at each other. Joyce walked outside.

"What do you boys think you're doing?" she demanded. They paused in their fight and looked up at her. "You boys are each other's best friends," she continued. "If you fight, both of you are going to lose a best friend."

The boys were silent for a minute, and then David said, "Oh, all right." He stood up and brushed himself off. Chris got up beside him. David started for the house as he said, "Do you have anything I can eat, Mrs. Langhage?"

The Heideckers were pleased at the relationship, too. David had had playmates before, but Chris was a friend. David was forever dreaming up something else that he and Chris could do. Once, they cleared out some brush and set up their tent in the woods behind the house. They stayed there all night, but the next day they both broke out with poison ivy. Another time, they thought it would be fun to sleep in the shack which was on Aunt Ollie's property, across the street on Gillis Road. They ran down the hill to Aunt Ollie's and barged through the door, as usual.

"Aunt Ollie!" David called.

She was in her kitchen making cookies. "Hello, boys," she answered.

"Aunt Ollie — what is that I smell?"

Aunt Ollie's eyes twinkled. "Don't know what you mean, Davey," she said. "What smell?"

"It's cookies!" David yelled. "Can we have one?"

"In a minute," she said. "They're too hot just now." She looked at the boys. "Is that what you came by for, to rob me of my cookies while they're too hot to handle?"

"No, we have an idea," David told her. "Aunt Ollie, can we have that shack that's across the street on your property?"

"What do you mean, have it? Have it for what?"

"For a playhouse, you know. To play in and sleep in."

"Well," she said, "I think you ought to take that up with your folks. I don't mind, but to tell you the truth that shack is probably pretty dirty and all. Let your dad take a look at it and decide. If he says yes, then it's yes."

"Thanks, Aunt Ollie! I'll go ask him right away!"

David turned to go. Chris said quietly, "Are the cookies ready yet?"

"Yeah, I forgot! Can we have our cookies?"

"Here, and don't burn yourselves," Aunt Ollie said.

The two boys dashed out the door with cookies in both hands and took off running up the hill.

The shack had stood on Aunt Ollie's property long before she moved there. It actually looked like a tiny house, which is probably what it had been at one time. When David and Chris got to the top of the hill and told Dick what they wanted, he put the boys in his car and drove down the driveway to Gillis Road.

"Come on, let's check it out," he said.

The three of them walked over to the shack and opened the door. David had been inside before, but not for quite a while. As they opened the door, a malodorous stench hit them in the face.

"Phew!" Dick said. "That stinks."

David and Chris giggled. "What is it, Dad?" David wanted to know.

"What do you think it is?" Dick asked him. "I bet you can figure it out."

"It's dog-do!" David shouted. He and Chris were now doubled over with laughter.

"Well, it's something-do," Dick acknowledged. "I don't know what did it, but whatever it was, it sure did it!"

"Can we clean it up and sleep here?" David demanded.

Dick looked around. The shack had windows that could be opened. He went inside and opened them. There appeared to be nothing dangerous inside, although to him it was anything but inviting; on the other hand, he realized that he was not being invited to stay.

"I guess you can," he said. "But you really have to clean it first. It'll be a lot of work, you understand."

"We don't mind!" David shouted. "Do we, Chris?"

"Nope," Chris agreed. "We don't mind."

They spent the day working on the shack, going up and down the hill for supplies, carrying a broom and a bucket and rags, going across to Aunt Ollie's for water. Dick came down once to check on them; it was unbelievable that they could think this was fun. Finally, they had the shack in decent shape. It wasn't perfect, Dick thought, but it wouldn't kill them, either. He told them to collect flashlights and sleeping bags; they could come down after dinner.

The boys stuck it out all night, but it wasn't as much fun as they expected. A lingering odor was still present; they had to leave the windows open for air, and it was cold. They also found that it was scarier in the dark structure than it was in a tent; more shadows, maybe, or unexplained sounds. After that night, they went back to camping out in Chris's boy scout tent on top of the hill.

When school let out for the summer, the boys had each other's companionship throughout the lazy days of June, July, and August. On the 4th of July, Dick and Shirley took both boys to a picnic with fireworks and band music, and Dick, who was not inclined towards making speeches, nevertheless took the opportunity to remind David and Chris that they were privileged to live in a free country. The boys took him literally, joyfully spending the rest of the summer at leisure. They became proficient explorers on their bicycles, finding every back road and country lane in the area. They waded in the stream that trickled down near the Heideckers' house from the Gillis Falls. They rode and ran and climbed and swam, and sometimes just laid around, mostly together, savoring their free time, living each day as it came. They plotted harmless schemes, often succeeding in persuading Joyce to bake them something special or Shirley to drive them to a store.

On September 9, 1976, as David entered fifth grade, the Circuit Court for Carroll County declared David to be the adopted child of Richard and Shirley Heidecker, and changed his legal name to David Wayne Heidecker. This event did not happen by itself. Fed up by the interminable delays, Dick finally had called an attorney, who promptly filed a Petition for Adoption. Whatever opposition existed in the Department of Social Services disappeared. Almost four years had passed since Dick and Shirley had met David.

The Heideckers celebrated with a special dinner and a cake. Chris Langhage was invited, along with the Houghtons. Dick attempted to make a little toast:

"To my son," he said, lifting his bottle of beer in the air. "It's about time."

David giggled. He knew all about the adoption procedure. Under Maryland law, he had been required to sign the adoption papers because he was over ten years of age. He mimicked his father by raising his paper cup of chocolate milk, and said:

"Now you can't ever give me back."

Shirley looked at Dick. There had never been a moment, in the period of nearly four years they had had David, that either one of them had ever entertained the thought of giving David back. There had been times of frustration and anger, and certainly great anxiety, but never rejection. Yet, David had sometimes accused them of wanting to take him back, or expressed fear that they would return him to the institution. That was part of the reason that Dick and Shirley had become anxious to expedite the adoption, so that David's fears would be allayed. Now they had succeeded.

Shirley put her arms around David and hugged him. "We're stuck with you," she said. She kissed him on top of his head.

Shortly after David entered fifth grade, Dick retired from the police force. His medical problems had continued unremittingly. There had been several more minor injuries in the line of duty as Dick had had to restrain or capture prisoners, and the summer before he had fallen from an eight-foot ladder at his home. After that, he was placed on limited duty status, which meant that he worked the day shift and spent most of his time in the station house. This relieved his symptoms slightly, but was not a solution. In 1976, Dick applied for special disability retirement. The chief physician of the medical section of the Baltimore City Police Department wrote a report containing a diagnosis of "cervical and lumbosacral discogenic disease, obesity." After a brief hearing on October 7, 1976, Dick's application was granted and he retired from the Baltimore City Police Department with his pension. He was thirty-seven years old.

Dick was unemployed throughout most of that school year. Shirley was deeply concerned about the psychological effects of early retirement on Dick. Although he seldom said anything about it, she knew how much his job had meant to him. First of all, it was fun. He had not had to sit at a desk most of the time, or look through files all day, or stand behind a counter from morning until night. He had been able to go to work each morning — or afternoon or evening — not knowing what might happen, where the job might take him, whom he might meet. And secondly, for a man without much ambition and with very little education, the job as a police officer had given Dick a sense of respectability that he might not have found in any other job available to him. As much as he complained about the discomfort of his police uniform, especially in hot weather, Shirley knew that the act of putting it on bolstered his self-respect every time he did it. Now all that was in the past.

For David, Dick's unemployment meant that one of his parents was always home for him when he got off the school bus. He would jump off the bus, run up the hill, and crash into the house before heading for the refrigerator and talking animatedly to his father. Sometimes Chris would come home with him, and the two of them would play together for hours until Dick drove Chris home. Sometimes they took the bus directly to the Langhages', and played there until David called for Dick to pick him up. Shirley came home to cook dinner, and afterwards David did his homework. For Dick, it was the extra time with David that made his retirement tolerable — enjoyable, even.

That spring, David noticed something about Mrs. Langhage. He was used to seeing her almost every day, but something about her seemed different. She looked fat.

"Mrs. Langhage!" he said. Then he stopped. His mother had told him it was impolite to mention things like people being fat. Maybe he shouldn't say anything. He closed his mouth.

Joyce Langhage was looking at him expectantly. "Yes, David? What is it?"

"Nothing," David said. But he continued to stare at her.

Joyce looked down at her waistline. "Are you noticing my maternity dress?" she asked.

"What's that?" David wanted to know.

"I'm wearing a special dress because I'm pregnant." she told him. "I'm going to have a baby."

"Have a baby! That's fantastic!"

Joyce smiled. "You think you'll enjoy that, do you?"

"Yup! I love kids. I wish we had a baby at our house."

"Well, you can visit here whenever you want. This can be your baby brother, too, if you like. Or sister."

"Thanks, Mrs. Langhage!"

David was so excited he could hardly wait to tell Shirley. He rode his bike home and told his mother about the expected baby. "It can be mine too!" he said. "Mrs. Langhage said so!"

Late in the spring, Dick found a part-time security job. He worked for several automobile dealers in Baltimore County, checking the lots at night. The job could not begin to compare with his career as a police officer, but it gave him something to do and some extra money; besides, it enabled him to be home in the afternoons with David, and to drive him to his little league practices which were beginning again. When the school year ended, and baseball was over, they all took a trip to Florida. The Heideckers had friends in St. Petersburg where they stayed for a few days, and then drove over to Orlando and took David to Walt Disney World. David tried to sit in the front of every ride, and begged Dick to accompany him, despite Dick's futile protestations that a wrong motion against his back could cripple him forever.

"But it's fun, Dad!" David insisted.

"Yeah, I know," Dick said. "What do I need with my back anyway?"

He gave in, as usual, and stood in line for an hour to spend two horrifying minutes on Space Mountain before they packed up the car and headed home to Carroll County.

CHAPTER 7

Middle School

David turned thirteen in sixth grade. He and Chris now attended a middle school in Carroll County, where they would spend the next three years. Although many of the students came from David's elementary school, many of the others came from different schools and knew nothing at all about David or his background. David told Shirley he wanted everything to go right at this school.

"I don't want anybody calling me a juvenile delinquent," he said. "Now I'm just David Heidecker."

He continued to spend time with Chris and his family. Joyce had given birth to Amy, in whom David took delight. After school, he liked to take the bus to Chris's, where he would walk in the back door and call out quietly:

"Mrs. Langhage? Is Amy awake?"

Joyce often let David hold the baby, and sometimes feed her. He would sit carefully on the sofa, with Amy cradled in his arms, his back hunched over as he leaned down to talk to her. Joyce was amazed to observe this patient, gentle side of David. As noisy and careless as he was the rest of the time, he was quiet and careful with the baby, making sure not to frighten or disturb her. Amy seemed to love him, too. She smiled at the sight of him, and reached out for his hands.

"See, Mrs. Langhage? She likes me!"

The Langhages continued to welcome David in their household, although once David broke their rule about behaving himself. On a rainy Sunday, as he and Chris and Holly Langhage played Monopoly in the basement, David lost his temper when he landed on Boardwalk, owned by Holly, with a hotel on it. He flipped the board through the air, scattering the cards and money pieces around the room while Holly, who had been on the verge of victory, began to wail. Bob Langhage came downstairs to investigate.

"David?" he said, incredulously. "Did you do that?"

"Yes," David admitted.

"Clean it up," Bob Langhage said sternly. "Put everything back in the box right now and go on home."

David looked defiantly at Bob Langhage for a moment. Then he said, "Okay." Quietly, he moved around the basement, picking up the pieces, and put them away. He left without saying anything and jogged home, where he found his mother in the kitchen.

"Home so early?" she asked.

David shrugged. "I got in trouble," he said. "I got mad at the game we were playing and threw the stuff around the room." He dropped onto the living room sofa, his long legs hanging over the arm.

"What did the Langhages say?" Shirley wanted to know.

"Mr. Langhage told me to clean up the game and go home."

"So what did you do?"

"I did what he said."

Shirley smiled sympathetically. She handed him a cup of hot chocolate and rubbed his back. "You're wet from the rain," she said. "Let's change your shirt. Maybe you'll want to call the Langhages later and let them know you're sorry."

David took a large drink of hot chocolate. "Yeah, I probably will," he said.

Instead, he put on his slicker and walked down the gravel driveway and up Gillis Road, in the rain. He knocked on the Langhages' front door apprehensively. When Bob opened it, David said he had come to apologize.

"Can I come in?" he asked sheepishly.

Mr. Langhage let him in.

"Oh, Amy's up!" David said, striding across the living room to the sofa, where Joyce sat with the baby on her lap. "Can I hold her?"

Soon he was sitting on the Langhages' sofa, feeding their baby. When Holly came in, David told her he was sorry about the game.

"You really won, Holly," he said. "You would've wiped me out with that hotel on Boardwalk."

Holly smiled forgivingly. Bob turned on the TV and found a basketball game for everybody to watch.

Harold Houghton died that spring. Before his death, he gave Dick and Shirley seven more arces of land. It wasn't a gift, Aunt Ollie insisted, because the price was one dollar an acre, and besides, they made Dick pay the cost of getting the deed drawn up and recording it in the Carroll County Land Record Office in Westminister. The baby pine trees that Dick and David had transplanted years earlier had grown to heights of twelve and fifteen feet, creating an evergreen border in a semi-circle along the rim of the hill. Those trees roughly marked the original boundary of the Heideckers' property. Now Dick and Shirley owned the whole hill, all the way down to the Houghtons' back yard. It was a good feeling, Dick said, knowing you owned land in a place that meant something to you.

For Aunt Ollie, having Dick and Shirley as neighbors gave her peace of mind that money could not buy. Getting up in years, she was determined to stay on in the country as long as she could handle things. Shirley explained that to David.

"Aunt Ollie's getting older, David," she told him. "She'll need some help from us, keeping her company, taking care of her house, things like that."

"I will!" David said enthusiastically. His family had always been accustomed to stopping in at Aunt Ollies's frequently. Now Shirley made a point of going at least once a day. David, too, increased his visits. Often he stayed and helped her put away the dishes, or straighten up; a few times he pushed her vacuum cleaner around the living room for her. Once in a while, Aunt Ollie recalled another story from Dick's childhood to tell David. She still baked cookies, but it took her longer.

One night in May, as Dick and Shirley and David watched television after dinner, they heard the sound of thunder. Dick said the forecast was for violent storms. David jumped up and headed for the door.

"Where you going?" Dick asked. "You don't want to go out in this weather, David?"

"Dad, Aunt Ollie's scared of thunder storms," David protested. "She's down there all alone."

"Oh," Dick said. He watched David run out of the house, carelessly leaving the door ajar. As Dick walked over to close the door, he looked outside to see David disappear through the pine trees, running towards Aunt Ollie's house at the bottom of the hill.

As the storm progressed, David and Aunt Ollie turned up the volume of her television set in an effort to drown out the sound of thunder. They played cards as David explained loudly that if you see lightning, it won't hurt you.

"It's a scientific fact, Aunt Ollie," he said authoritatively. "It's the same with thunder, too. If you can hear it, it can't hurt you."

Aunt Ollie smiled. "Thunder can't hurt you whether you hear it or not," she told him. "My mind knows that. It's my heart that don't know it."

As the hours passed and the storm continued, David said he would just as soon sleep there. Aunt Ollie gratefully made up a bed for him on her living room sofa and David called home to tell his parents. He fell asleep with the TV flickering softly across the room. The next morning, as rain gave way to tentative sunshine, Aunt Ollie made him the biggest breakfast he had ever had.

"I'll come any time, Aunt Ollie," David told her cheerfully. "Just call me if you need me."

"Thanks, Davey," the old lady whispered. She gave him a long hug.

David completed sixth grade with a B in every subject, except for a C in science and A in music. Dick and Shirley were pleased and proud, despite a notation on David's report card of eleven absences, at least half of which had to be from playing hookey.

"So what?" Dick said to Shirley. "I hooked school half the time, not to mention all of eleventh and twelfth grades."

Shirley looked at him skeptically. "David doesn't have to do everything you did," she reminded him. "Maybe we'd like him to graduate high school."

Dick nodded confidently. "He'll do it."

Seventh grade started out with a bang when David came home early in the fall and told Dick the principal had hit him.

"What do you mean?" Dick asked.

"Dad, he punched me!" David said. "He walked up to me and he punched me!"

"What were you doing?"

"Well, actually I was in the middle of a fight with some guys," David said. "But it wasn't my fault. See, one guy called me a name, and another guy knocked my books out of my arms. So I had to slug 'em."

"I guess I better go up there," Dick said.

"Yeah, well, I forgot to tell you," David added. "I brought a note for you. They want you to come up."

Dick and Shirley and David met with the principal. As they were ushered into the office and invited to sit down, Dick reflected that the room looked like every principal's office he had ever seen. Medium-sized, cluttered, containing one window and decorated with pictures of the man's family, it was furnished with plywood bookshelves and fake leather chairs. The principal sat behind a large desk which was designed, Dick assumed, to insulate him from those who sat on the other side, while intimidating the students. He pushed a large unbreakable ashtray in the Heideckers' direction as Dick and Shirley lit cigarettes. Then he told them that he had just happened to come along as David was beating up two other students.

"I had to hit David to stop the fight," he added.

Dick puffed on his cigarette. "What about the other students?" he asked. "Did you hit them, too?"

"No, I didn't," the principal explained patiently. "You see, the other two boys were being assaulted by your son. My goal was to stop the fight. There was no reason for me to hit the other boys."

"David says the other boys started it," Dick said. "How come they're not here with their families?"

The principal shifted in his big chair. "Mr. Heidecker, I don't know who started the fight," he admitted. "It might have happened as David says.

The only thing I wanted to do was stop the fight, and to do that I had to stop David, because whoever may have started the fight, David was clearly winning it.''

"Okay," Dick said. He put out his cigarette in the ashtray and leaned slightly in the direction of the principal. "Look," he continued. "I know David loses his cool sometimes. If people pick on him, he fights them. I know you have to stop the fights. If you have to hit David to do that, you have my permission." He paused. "That is, you have my permission to hit him one time."

The principal looked startled. "Sir?"

"One time," Dick reiterated. "Once. If you hit him more than one time, you do it at your own risk." Dick turned to David. "David? If this man has to hit you one time to calm you down, you take that punch, you understand?"

"Yes, Dad," David said.

"You take that punch, but you don't take the next one," Dick continued. "If the principal hits you more than one time, then you hit him back."

The principal looked at Dick with alarm. "Mr. Heidecker, I don't think —"

"You break his arm if you have to," Dick said to David. "Break his leg."

"Mr. Heidecker!"

"Break his neck, if that's what it takes. You understand?"

The principal got to his feet. "Mr. Heidecker, that kind of talk is irresponsible," he said angrily. "You are telling David things that could be very dangerous."

"Dangerous to you," Dick retorted. "I'm telling him to protect himself because I'm getting damn sick and tired of being the only parents called up here whenever there's any trouble."

"What do you mean?"

"I mean, if you have a fight in your school with three kids in it, then there's three kids and three sets of parents ought to be here, aren't there?"

"Maybe, maybe not," the principal said. "It all depends."

"Depends on what?" Dick asked belligerently. "I was a police officer for sixteen years. I spent a lot of that time on the street, and some of it in the courthouse. Know what I learned?"

"What?" the principal asked warily.

"There's never just one side to anything," Dick told him. "There's as many sides as there are people in it. That's why you don't just ask one side what happened, you ask everybody. And you don't put all the blame on somebody without hearing from everybody."

The principal looked from Dick to Shirley to David. Then he said, "Mr. Heidecker, Mrs. Heidecker, I want to thank you for coming by. You too, David. I'm glad we were able to clear the air here."

He walked around the desk and put out his hand. Dick shook it reluctantly. The principal opened the door to his office and graciously encouraged the Heideckers to exit. On the way home, David was quiet.

"What's the matter?" Dick asked him.

"Dad, I don't know if you should have said that stuff to the principal," David said.

"Why not? I was standing up for you."

"Yeah, I know. But I have to live with him for the next two years."

Dick chuckled. "You're gonna find out that living with him will be a whole lot easier after this," he told David.

David was skeptical, but Dick proved to be right. After that, if there were problems at school, the Heideckers found that they were not the only ones called in. There were no more reports from David that anyone was hitting him.

That winter, David began to accompany his father on his job occasionally. Dick still worked as a security guard for several automobile dealers, checking their lots after hours. On Friday nights he worked from eleven at night until seven in the morning. David liked to come along once in a while. He sat in the front seat of Dick's car, chattering to his father and playing with the radio. At the car dealerships, Dick waited in the car while David got out and checked the vehicles to make sure that keys had not been left inside and that they were locked. Once or twice, David found a set of keys, and ran excitedly to tell his father. One time, they thought they heard someone sneaking around late at night. Dick locked David in the car and went to investigate. David protested loudly — he wanted to come, too. Dick found nothing, and later he always claimed that David scared the thief away, yelling and screaming that he wanted to go look for the thief.

As they drove around the lots, Dick told of adventures from his days on the police force. "Once I got a call for a B and E," he said. "Breaking and entering. So I pull up in front of this house where the call came from, and my partner and I get out of the car and walk up to the front door."

David fiddled with the radio as he listened to Dick. "What happened?" he asked.

"Four big guys jumped out of the bushes, I put one hand behind my back, and beat 'em up," Dick said.

"Come on, Dad!"

"Well, it didn't happen quite like that," Dick admitted. "See, we get up to the door, and we see there's a window on the ground floor, looks like it goes to a bathroom, and it's broken. By now we got our guns drawn. My partner thinks he hears a noise inside the house, and he crouches down in the bushes and he hollers, 'Police, freeze!' "

"Who was it, Dad?"

"We waited, and we didn't hear anything. Then all of a sudden was this scrambling noise, like, and a raccoon jumped outta the window onto the ground."

David laughed. "What did you do?"

"My partner like to wet his pants," Dick said. "It's a miracle he didn't shoot that raccoon. It just run off, and we let it go. Then we knocked on the door and we told the people what we found."

"Were they scared?"

"Hell, yes! They thought somebody broke in and was inside their house. The whole time, they were waiting for somebody to jump up and ask where their silver was."

David laughed. "That's cool, Dad," he said. "Do you miss that?"

"What?"

"Being a policeman."

"Yeah," Dick said. He changed the subject. David went back to playing with the radio, pushing the buttons and turning the dial while he searched for a top-forty station. Outside, the temperature had dropped to twenty degrees. They had to keep the motor running to provide heat. Inside the car, their breath made mist on the windshield. Lights from the car dealers' lot shone through the car windows, creating an orange-yellow effect in the dark. David found his radio station and turned up the volume, moving his body in time to the beat.

"God, that's loud!" Dick told him. "Doesn't that hurt your ears?"

"What?"

"The music. Won't it damage your hearing?"

"No, Dad. That's how kids listen to music." Dick shook his head. They had had that conversation before. He knew there was no point in telling David that popular music wasn't worth listening to at any volume, that the heyday of rock and roll had gone with the Platters and the Diamonds and Buddy Holly and Bill Haley. He didn't try. He put his hand over his right ear to muffle the sound, and looked at his watch. Five o'clock in the morning. This was the dead of winter; they still had a while to wait before the sun came up.

Not long after David's fourteenth birthday in December, Carroll County had a snowfall that was not predicted. It began one Saturday evening while Dick was on his job, where he was scheduled to work until midnight. At first the snow was pretty; David and Shirley watched it through the window as they made hot chocolate and played a game of checkers inside. But as the snow continued to fall, David became worried about his father.

There was no way he would be able to get up the gravel driveway tonight, even with front wheel drive. Late at night, when the snow finally stopped falling and the ground was covered with about eight inches, David had an idea.

"I bet I could shovel a path, Mom," he said excitedly. "Not down the driveway, it's too far. But maybe I could shovel a little path straight down the hill. If Dad can get down Gillis Road, he can leave his car there and walk up my path."

Shirley was skeptical. "I don't know, David," she said. "It's a long way down that hill."

"Can I try?" he insisted.

"I guess so," Shirley said. "But come back in if you get too tired or too cold."

Outside with his snow shovel, David surveyed the scene. The shortest distance between himself and Gillis Road, he decided, was a route through the pine trees, straight down the big hill and alongside Aunt Ollie's house. He would not go near the gravel driveway, which would be a much less direct route. It would still be a tremendous job, David realized. The only reason it might be possible was that the nearly-full moon illuminated the entire hillside.

He set to work with his shovel. Fortunately, the snow was dry and not too heavy. But it was deep. David shoveled a path about two feet wide. He got halfway down the hill before he stopped to rest. Then he climbed the hill to the house. Because the hill was steep, he had to scrape the snow from the ground — otherwise, his father would slip and slide on the path. Inside the house, he let his mother fix him a cup of hot chocolate. He changed his socks and warmed his hands. Now Shirley was becoming anxious. It was well after midnight, and she had no way of knowing whether Dick would be able to drive even as far as Gillis Road, which certainly had not been ploughed. David was undaunted.

"He'll get here, Mom," he insisted. "I'm going back out and finish up."

He did. Towards the end, he got sloppier and the path got narrower, but it went all the way to the road. David stood at the foot of the path, leaning on his shovel, resting. He was tired but elated. Now he needed only for his father to arrive. As he rested, he could hear the sound of a car in the distance. It had to be his father. At last he saw Dick's car coming around the curve in the road. It moved at an excruciating pace through the deep snow, less than twenty miles an hour, David guessed. He waved his arms.

"Dad! Dad! Look!"

Dick, exhausted from having driven miles in the snow, wondering all the time how he could possibly get up the hill even if he got this far, suddenly saw David standing by the side of the road, holding a shovel and waving. Dick's first thought was that something must be wrong. What was David doing down here in the middle of the night, in this weather? Dick pulled his car to the side of the road as far as he could without putting it in a ditch, and stopped. David, now directly in front of his car, came around to the driver's side as Dick rolled down the window.

"David?" Dick said anxiously.

"Dad! Dad! I shoveled a path for you, do you see it?" He pointed to the path. Dick looked at it, incredulous. He burst out laughing. It was twenty minutes later when they reached the house and fell inside, cold and tired, collapsing into chairs and laughing with relief as Shirley brought them hot drinks.

They slept until noon the next day. When they awoke, David was stiff and sore from shoveling, and so was Dick, from climbing the hill. Shirley cooked eggs and sausage and English muffins. After breakfast, as he drank a diet soda, Dick announced that he was tired of his job with the car dealers. The hours were wrong, he said, and the job was boring. He would watch the *Carroll County Times* for other job openings. The newspaper did not publish on Sundays, but that week Dick studied the classified advertisements. About the time the snow melted, he began working for Londontown Corporation, manufacturers of London Fog rainwear, as a security guard in the distribution and office center in Eldersburg. The job was close to home, and he had normal daytime hours.

David continued to play football in a local league throughout middle school, and on the last day of eighth grade, his class was visited by Coach Ken Parker of South Carroll High School, where David expected to enter ninth grade in the fall. Coach Parker talked to the boys about the football program at his high school, and urged anyone who was interested to sign up for the freshman team.

"You don't have to be a jock," he told the students. "It doesn't matter if you never played before, either. Just sign up, we'll teach you whatever you need to know."

David filled out the form and turned it in. That was the last thing he did in middle school. At the end of the day, he and Chris rode the bus home to the Langhages' house. They were met at the back door by Amy, now a happy toddler, who reached out her arms to David.

"Hey, Amy!" David scooped her up and put her on his shoulders. He had grown so tall that Amy's head almost touched the ceiling. David galloped carefully through the Langhages' house as Amy screamed with pleasure, hugging David's head with her tiny hands. He deposited her on the sofa as Joyce Langhage came in with a plate of cookies.

"Anybody hungry on the last day of school?"

"Thanks!" David said. He took three cookies. "Mrs. Langhage, did you ever think me and Chris would make it through middle school?"

Joyce smiled benignly. "Of course I did," she said. "All you have to do now is make it through four years of high school."

David and Chris groaned. "Not today," Chris told her. "We're on vacation!"

Each of the boys took one more cookie as they went outside to play ball.

CHAPTER 8

Growing Up

Shirley stood on top of the hill and took a good look at the one-story cinder block house that she and Dick had occupied for thirteen years.

"This house is getting on my nerves," she announced.

Dick shrugged his shoulders. "Call a builder, then," he told her.

Shirley asked around for the name of a contractor. One Saturday afternoon in the fall of 1980, the man drove his truck up the hill and looked at the Heideckers' property. He took measurements and came back the next weekend with prices. On a piece of white lined paper, he drew a diagram with two large bedrooms, a bathroom, and a completely rebuilt kitchen. Dick and Shirley told him to prepare a contract.

Although they had enough money to get started, the addition would cost more than they had on hand. Shirley looked around for a second job. A modest restaurant in Mount Airy, called the Half Shell, had an opening for a cook. Shirley had never been paid to cook, but she had years of experience. She got the job. She began to work at the restaurant on Saturdays and Sundays from five o'clock until two in the morning, and sometimes one or two evenings during the week, in addition to her regular job at Webster's. Shirley, who had never needed a lot of sleep, enjoyed the new job. She liked meeting a new group of people, and thought the bustle of the kitchen was fun. She also earned a reputation as the best cook the restaurant had ever had.

That fall, David entered ninth grade at South Carroll High School. He chose to enter the academic program. The school was a modern, functional building which had opened in 1967, the same year that Dick and Shirley moved to the country. Sitting directly on Liberty Road, the school had over a thousand students, including many of the kids David had known from his elementary and middle schools and from little league, and an ambitious sports program.

Gillis Road, Carroll County. *Ann Turnbull*

South Carroll High School. *Ann Turnbull*

The freshman football program was open to all boys in the ninth grade. Anyone who signed up and who came to the practices was eligible to participate: the coaches simply created enough teams to accommodate whatever number of students wanted to play that year. No one was cut from the program, but the best players made the first string. In 1980, David Heidecker played guard on the first string freshman football team. They played against the freshmen teams of six other schools, and won half the games. David, with natural athletic ability and a background in league football, was among the most enthusiastic of the players. He was tall and lean — not broad-shouldered, but strong and fit.

Although Shirley, working two jobs, had less free time than ever, Dick had more. He now worked for London Fog from 6 a.m. until 12:30 p.m., and so was at home in the afternoons. He liked to go up to the school and watch David at football practice. Then they drove home together. David would be sixteen in December — too late to get his driver's license for this year's football season — but Dick promised him he could get it in time for next year.

In ninth grade, David met a classmate named Patrick Kenney. The boys had known each other before, but had not been friends. Patrick's first memory of David Heidecker was of David's picking up a chair and throwing it in the direction of a teacher in elementary school, after which Patrick had seen two teachers dragging and pulling David down the hall. Patrick had always been slightly in awe of David as a result of that incident. Now they were in the same ninth grade gym class. They met in the locker room, where they appeared to have been assigned to the same locker.

"This one's mine," Patrick said, as David tried to open it.

David looked at the number on the locker. "I thought they gave me this one," he said.

Patrick checked his assignment. "Yeah," he said sheepishly. "Mine's the next one over."

David shrugged his shoulders cheerfully. "That's okay," he said. He looked down at Patrick, who was several inches shorter than he was. "Is your name Patrick?"

"Yeah, Patrick Kenney. You're David, right?"

It was the beginning of an enduring friendship. Like many of David's classmates, Patrick was two years younger than David. He was also substantially smaller, with red hair and freckles. Patrick lived a mile or so from the Heideckers', within walking distance if you cut through woods and fields. Although David and Patrick rode different buses to school, they established the habit of taking the same bus home, with Patrick frequently going to David's house after school. Patrick had a difficult home life and seldom took anyone to his house; he enjoyed being away from home himself as much as possible. The Heideckers began to find Patrick a ubiquitous guest at their house. In the beginning, both Dick and Shirley had some reservations about Patrick as a friend for David. They saw him as a confused and lonely boy, somewhat unstable and perhaps with emotional problems. Shirley observed that he also had a very smart mouth, but Dick said he didn't care about that — his own mouth was a lot louder than Patrick's. As Dick and Shirley saw the closeness of the friendship developing between David and Patrick, they put aside their reservations. Patrick came to feel and behave like a member of the Heidecker family.

Patrick often slept at the Heideckers'. On cold nights they stayed inside, eating and watching television half the night before falling asleep on the sofa or in David's room. Sometimes Chris Langhage joined them. On warmer nights they pitched a tent outside and used their sleeping bags. Once they took a bottle of Dick's whiskey into the tent and got drunk. Dick figured out what had happened when all three boys threw up in the night and came inside, although Patrick tried to convince him they suffered from food poisoning. Dick didn't mind that David had experimented with alcohol, which he considered a normal rite of passage, but he worried a little about the Langhages' reaction if they were to learn of it. In the morning, he sat the three boys down on the living room sofa and stood in front of them.

"Fellows," he told them, rubbing his stomach, "what you were drinking is 86 proof."

Patrick interrupted. "We weren't drinking, Mr. Heidecker," he insisted. "It must have been something we ate."

Dick glared at him. "Don't insult me, Patrick," he said. "After sixteen years of being a cop, I'm not too stupid to know the difference between being drunk and being sick." Patrick lowered his eyes. "Look, guys," Dick continued. "There's other things you can drink that'll give you a lift without making you sick."

Patrick interrupted again. "Mr. Heidecker?"

"What is it now?"

"Can I go to the bathroom? I think I'm gonna be sick again."

Dick said, "Go ahead."

They listened to the sounds of Patrick throwing up as Dick waited for Patrick to return.

"Next time you want to try something, ask me for a beer. I don't know if I'll give it to you or not, but I promise you I won't make you sick."

The boys looked at him weakly, their faces pale and their heads wobbly. Dick turned to Chris. "You might want to keep this between you and me," he suggested. "I'll take the responsibility."

Chris nodded miserably. "Thanks, Mr. Heidecker," he said.

"David's mother can make some coffee for you all," Dick said. "Try some, it'll make you feel better."

David and Patrick found plenty of things to get into besides the liquor. The possibilities were endless, because David had a creative, energetic mind and Patrick was a perfect follower. The boys rebuilt their bicycles and made a ramp with cinderblocks and plywood which they used as a launch pad, Evil Knevil style. Both eventually wrecked their bikes and Patrick hurt his arm. Dick bought David a .22 rifle and taught him how to use it. He took it away after David and Patrick got tired of hitting soda cans and shot the outside lightbulbs around the house. Sometimes Dick and Shirley got mad about these exploits, but never for long. Patrick witnessed scenes in which Dick would yell at David, David would yell back, Dick would tell him how it was going to be, David would storm off by himself, and five minutes later everything was forgotten. From Patrick's perspective, David's relationship with his parents was fantastic. Sometimes he felt as if Dick and Shirley were David's brother and sister — "That's how well they get along," Patrick said.

In the spring, Dick and Shirley bought David a new Honda motorcycle for about $900. Shirley mentioned to Dick that they were supposed to be saving their money towards the new addition to their house, but really she had no objection to using some of it to buy things for David. David loved the motorcycle. Dick told him to keep off the roads with it, because he did not yet have his driver's license, and to ride it on their own property or Aunt Ollie's. David started out in good faith to follow the instructions, but soon began to ride his motorcycle with abandon. There were trails through the woods and in fields where he rode, usually with Patrick on the back, but they also enjoyed speeding up Gillis Road. David would ease the Honda down the gravel driveway and then sit at the foot of the hill, revving up the motor and listening to the sound get louder, finally cutting a wide left onto the road and advancing to maximum speed as he drove the cycle near the center of the road, leaning forward into the wind as it whipped his hair and Patrick's, riding helmetless through the countryside. Once in a while Patrick would get nervous and tug on David's shirt to make him slow down, but David never did.

"Man, look at this!" he would shout, barely able to make himself heard over the sound of the bike, and Patrick would close his eyes sometimes, and hold on more tightly, not wanting to let David know he was afraid.

More than once, they escaped the police by leaving the road and disappearing on a trail in the woods where a police car could not follow. One time a state trooper stopped by the house and told Dick Heidecker he was pretty sure he had seen Dick's boy speeding up the road on a motorcycle with another kid on the back. That time, David was grounded for three days; afterwards, he rode with slightly more discretion. The whole adventure came to an end when David, riding in the rain, crashed into a telephone pole, cracked his kneecap, and totaled the bike. It had about four hundred and fifty miles on it.

Dick told David that he and Shirley were not going to pay for a new motorcycle.

"You can save up your money and get this one repaired for around $500," Dick told him, "or pay for a new one yourself. Your mother and I are not going to pay for it this time."

David understood. He put his ruined motorcycle in the shed that used to house his little Shetland pony and waited to get his driver's license.

Ninth grade was the year that David discovered girls. Because he was so tall, perhaps, girls seemed to notice him, sometimes to pursue him. David began to look around in his classes to see who the pretty girls were. Sometimes he waited for a girl after class, or hurried to catch up with one on the way to lunch. He developed the habit of asking girls for their telephone numbers, and memorizing the numbers. Sometimes he and Patrick called a girl after school and talked to her for an hour or more. Once in a while they arranged to meet two girls at the Carrolltowne Mall on Liberty Road, or up in Westminster. There they went to the movies or had a milkshake before going their separate ways. Sometimes they included Chris Langhage and a third girl. David persuaded Patrick and Chris that they should practice talking to girls.

"I'll be me, and you be Kathy," he told Patrick.

"I don't want to be Kathy," Patrick protested. "How do I know the way girls talk?"

David sighed. "Be a sport," he said. "How are we gonna get the hang of this?"

Patrick was resigned. "Okay, I'm Kathy," he said. "Go ahead."

David cleared his throat. "Uh, hello," he said self-consciously. "I'm David Heidecker. Have we met?"

Patrick fluttered his eyelashes dramatically. "I'm afraid not," he replied in a falsetto voice.

David punched him in the shoulder, "Okay, forget it!" he said. "I'll practice in the mirror!"

He did. Soon he had developed the ability to approach a girl, smile engagingly at her, introduce himself, and ask her name, all with what he thought was an air of smoothness. He tried it out in the lunch room at South Carroll, and concluded he had it made. The girl said her name was Sandy, and she gave him her telephone number. That weekend, David met her at the roller rink in Westminster. He held her hand while they skated, and later he kissed her before Shirley drove up to get him. At home, he told his parents all about it.

"Dad, it was easy!" he said enthusiastically. "She acted like she really liked me!"

Dick chuckled. "Sure it's easy, son," he answered. "You should have seen your mother on our first date. She couldn't get enough of me."

Shirley glared at him. "That isn't true," she said. "Besides, we were a lot older than David."

David's interest in girls continued to grow. Often, if he met a girl he liked, he asked her to bring a friend for Patrick. Patrick liked girls, too, but he was less confident than David. He tended to watch David and try to emulate him. Once in a while, a girl that David liked preferred Patrick. Then David insisted that they both drop the girl, and start over.

"There's always another girl in the world, Pat," he said. "There's no reason to take any abuse."

"What abuse?" Patrick demanded. "You think it's abuse if a girl doesn't fall in love with you in the first ten minutes."

David thought about that. "Yup," he agreed cheerfully.

As ninth grade came to an end, Dick taught David to drive. They practiced in Shirley's white Plymouth station wagon. The paint was dull, not flashy, but David didn't mind. He learned to drive easily. Dick could see that he had excellent reflexes and good control.

"I'm not worried about whether he can drive," Dick told Shirley. "I'm worried about how fast he'll drive."

As they practiced, Dick told David stories, drawn upon his experience as a policeman, about automobile accidents, usually caused by speeding, in which people had been killed or seriously injured.

"One kid took the curve down on Liberty Road, past Randallstown, doing 70," he told David. "He couldn't come out of the curve, and the car went down the bank. It burst into flames and killed everybody in the car."

David shook his head. "I wouldn't go that fast around there."

"Then another time, I had to investigate an accident in the city," Dick continued. "A guy came across Fayette Street at high speed and couldn't stop for a red light. He hit a lady driving through the intersection and killed them both."

David shrugged. "I could always stop for a red light."

Dick became irritated. He sensed that although David was listening, he was not impressed. Dick tried to recollect his own adolescence to understand why. Suddenly he knew: because kids think they are immortal. Dick tried a different approach.

"If you drive too fast, you might not have an accident," he conceded. "You might live to brag about it. But if *I* hear about it, I'll take the car away from you."

David nodded earnestly. "I'll be careful, Dad," he answered. "I really will. Don't worry."

He got his driver's license in June. Dick and Shirley gave him the white Plymouth. David was ecstatic.

"My own car!" he shouted. "Now I can date and everything!"

Dick reminded David to keep his eye on the gas gauge and to carry a spare tire. David frequently forgot both. If Patrick pointed out that the gas was on Empty, David always said, "We can make it." Sometimes they didn't. Dick and Shirley became accustomed to late night telephone calls from various points in Carroll County.

"Dad, I'm outta gas!" David would say. "I'm really sorry, I was sure I had enough this time!"

Dick and Shirley would come out in the middle of the night to rescue David, carrying a gas can.

After he changed his first flat tire, David never replaced the spare. He always meant to, he said, but he forgot. Once he called Shirley from a pay phone at a gas station that was closed.

"Mom?" he said. "I have a flat and I can't find my spare. Can you come?"

Shirley drove there and brought him home. "Your father can bring you back tomorrow with a spare," she told David.

David said, "I'm awful sorry, Mom. Thanks a lot for getting me."

David thought of that summer as the high point of his life so far. He liked to get into the white Plymouth, carefully guide it down the unpaved driveway, and swing out onto Gillis Road and take off. At first, he often stopped in front of the Langhages' house and honked his horn for Chris to come out. One day, Chris's father came out instead. He opened the door of the car and got in next to David.

"I'm here for Chris, Mr. Langhage," David said.

"David, I want us to have a little talk," Bob answered.

"Okay." David turned off the ignition and waited.

"David, you're sixteen years old," Bob Langhage said. "Sixteen and a half. You're driving a car. Chris is fourteen. He won't be old enough to drive for another year and a half."

David sensed what was coming. "Mr. Langhage —"

Bob put his hand up. "Let me finish," he said. "David, you know how much we like you. You're almost part of our family. But I've been see-ing you drive this car up and down Gillis Road. You're driving too fast."

"But —"

"You think it's okay to drive fast because you're a kid, and you're strong, and your reflexes are better than they'll ever be again. But a lot of things can happen on the road that you don't know anything about yet. And if something gets in your way, you're not always going to be able to stop."

"Nothing's going to happen to me," David insisted.

"I hope it doesn't," Bob continued. "But I can't control that. The only thing I can do is tell Chris that he can't ride with you. That way, I can insure that nothing will happen to *him*."

"Mr. Langhage, I'm a very good driver," David protested. "My father taught me. I'm very careful."

Bob shook his head. "I'm sorry," he said. "You know you're welcome at our house any time. We hope Chris will continue to go to your house and that you'll stay good friends. But I've made up my mind. No driving with you yet."

David looked straight ahead. "Okay," he said curtly. He turned on the ignition and waited for Bob Langhage to get out. Then he made his tires squeal as he took off at high speed. He drove around the county angrily. Eventually he stopped at Patrick's house and blew the horn for Patrick to come out. He told Patrick what had happened.

"Don't you think that stinks?" David asked.

Patrick shrugged. "I don't know," he said. "They just don't want Chris to be in an accident."

"I'm not going to have any accident," David protested.

"But they don't know that," Patrick pointed out.

David looked at Patrick. "Yeah," he said. He laughed. "Guess what I did, Pat."

"What?"

"I laid rubber when I pulled away from Chris's house. With his dad standing there watching me."

"Are you serious?"

"Yeah." David paused. "Maybe that wasn't so brilliant, huh? When I'm trying to prove to him what a good driver I am?"

Patrick chuckled. "I guess not," he agreed.

"Listen, maybe I should stop by their house. Will you come with me?"

Patrick said, "Sure, why not?"

David pulled up carefully in front of Chris's house. He and Patrick got out together. David knocked on the front door instead of walking in the back door unannounced, as he usually did. Bob Langhage opened the door.

"Come in, boys," he said.

David had a habit of yawning when he got nervous. He found himself yawning now as he shifted his weight self-consciously. "Mr. Langhage, I came by to apologize," he said. "I shouldn't have driven off the way I did. I'm sorry."

Bob looked at him. "It's okay, David," he said cheerfully. "I know you were upset."

"Yeah, I was," David agreed. "But I shouldn't have acted like an idiot anyway."

Bob said, "I accept your apology."

Patrick took a step forward. "Mr. Langhage," he said, "I can vouch for David's driving. I mean, I've been in the car with him quite a few times, and he really drives well. We haven't had any accidents or anything."

Bob looked at Patrick. He said, "Patrick, I've already had that conversation with David. The subject is closed."

Patrick said, "Yeah, but —"

David swung around and grabbed Patrick's shoulders. "Cut it out," he ordered. "Did you hear Chris's father?"

Patrick shrugged. "Just trying to help," he muttered.

David turned back to Bob Langhage. "We have to go now," he said. "Tell Chris I'll give him a call later."

"Fine," Bob said. He shook hands with David.

David and Patrick spent the rest of the summer "cruising," as David called it. "That's an old-fashioned word that means driving around looking for girls," he explained to Patrick. Sometimes they hung around the arcades up at Westminster. Other times they went swimming at a place known locally as the "salt box," which was really a swimming hole formed by water from the Gillis Falls, in later years the center of a public park. Still other times they went roller skating, either at a rink down on Liberty Road, towards Baltimore, or up in Westminster. They went everywhere in David's Plymouth, and wherever they went, they looked for girls. They often attracted girls at the roller rink because David, who was a first-rate skater, liked to show off in the middle of the rink with fancy spins and turns. He and Patrick often left the roller rink with two new phone numbers.

Early in August, they met Christy and Karen, two sisters who liked to hang around the roller rink. The girls lived out in the country, between Woodbine and Westminster. David and Patrick drove them to their house from the roller rink. No one was home there. David and Patrick waited downstairs while the girls changed their clothes. Then they all went to a fast-food restaurant for dinner, and to the movies. Afterwards, David parked his Plymouth in a lover's lane that was well-known to Carroll County teenagers. He and Christy, and Patrick and Karen, talked and made out for hours. Christy told David that both of their parents worked all the time and were practically never home. When they were home, she said, they slept or watched TV and paid no attention to the girls. She and her sister had to take care of themselves as well as the house, she said. She was going into ninth grade in the fall, but her sister was a year younger, still in middle school. They could hardly wait to grow up and get out of their house, Christy said.

David, who was now almost six feet tall, was physically a man. He had been looking at girls for over a year, dating them in groups for almost that long, and chasing them frantically ever since he got his driver's license. He had not yet made love to a girl, but he had thought about it more or less incessantly since the summer began. When he and Patrick took Christy and Karen home that first night, the farmhouse was dark. The girls invited them to come in.

David hesitated. As much as he had looked forward to what he knew could happen if he stepped inside, he was ambivalent now that opportunity looked him in the face.

"We have to get home tonight," he said. "Thanks anyway."

Patrick stared at David in disbelief. Finally he said, "Let's make a date for tomorrow then."

David nodded. "Sure, okay," he said, yawning. "Do you girls want to go out tomorrow?"

Christy shrugged. "Sure," she said. "Come by at six?"

They agreed and the boys left. Patrick berated David all the way home. "We had it made!" Patrick shouted. "What did you say no for?"

"I don't know," David said.

At home, he awakened his mother to talk. He and Shirley sat in the living room, in the dark, sharing a soda. David said:

"Pat and I met a couple of girls."

Shirley looked at him. "Do you like these girls?"

David shrugged. "Not really," he said. "I mean, they're okay. We're not in love with them or anything like that."

Shirley waited. "Are they good-looking?" she asked, finally.

David nodded. "Yeah. Well, more like sexy looking, you know? The one I like is named Christy. She's not that pretty, I guess, but she's sexy. So's her sister."

"Patrick likes her sister?"

"Yeah, Karen. Their names are Christy and Karen. They live out in the country. It seems like their folks are never home."

"You haven't met their parents?"

"No. Well, actually, we've only been out with them one time. That was tonight. Their folks weren't home when we picked them up or when we took them home, either."

"I see."

"Mom, do you think it's all right to make love to a girl you just met?"

Shirley asked, "Did you do that tonight?"

David shook his head. "No," he said. "I wanted to, but I got nervous." He yawned. "We have another date with them tomorrow."

Shirley hesitated. "This is something you'll have to decide for yourself," she said. "Nobody can tell you what to do about that."

David jumped up. "Will you tuck me in bed?" he asked.

Shirley smiled. David was more than half a foot taller than she was, but once in a while he asked her to tuck him into bed. She always did, whenever he asked.

The next evening, David and Patrick picked up Christy and Karen and drove to a shopping mall. They had hamburgers and wandered around. Eventually, they went back to David's car and drove out to the girls' home. Again, the house was dark. This time, David accepted Christy's invitation to come in. The four of them sat on the living room floor, watching TV and making out, and at some point Patrick and Karen disappeared. That night, on a shag rug in a farmhouse, in the flickering shadow of a silent TV, David lost his virginity. Afterwards he asked Christy if it was the first time for her and she said yes, but David didn't believe her. On the way home, he and Patrick were quiet.

David and Patrick saw the girls every day for the next three days. On the third night, as David and Christy lay on the living room rug, David heard the sound of a car outside. He jumped up and began to pull his clothes on frantically, calling out to Patrick as he did so. When the front door opened, David and Patrick, carrying their shirts, made a beeline for the door. They rushed past the burly middle-aged man who stood there, leaped into David's car and took off. Afterwards, Patrick always swore he heard the sounds of gunfire. David drove like a maniac, as Patrick later described it to Chris, yelling, "For Christ's sake, is anybody chasing us?" Patrick, who was watching out the back window, told him no. David refused to let up on the accelerator anyway. He turned up the gravel driveway to his house and took the car to the top of the hill. There he stopped, breathed a sigh of relief, and turned to Patrick for the first time.

"Jesus," he said quietly. "That was close."

Patrick started to laugh. "Did you see the look on that guy's face?" he asked.

"See the look on his face? Hell, no! I ran past him so fast he was like a blur!"

Patrick said, "Did you ever tell Christy your last name?"

David thought. "I don't know," he said. "I don't think so. If I did, she wouldn't know how to spell it. Christ, what are you thinking?"

"Who knows?" Patrick said. "Maybe her old man would try to track us down?"

David looked at him. "I don't think so. From what the girls said, he won't care that much."

Patrick said, "I don't know about you, but I think we ought to find a couple of new girlfriends."

David laughed. "You bet your ass!" he said. "I'm not going within a mile of those two again!"

They went inside and fell asleep.

Later, they told David's father what had happened. Patrick was still worried that Karen's old man was out looking for them with a shotgun. Dick said not to worry, that if anybody came up the hill looking for the boys, he had a gun, too. He said it with a grin, knowing that the boys were overreacting, but Patrick felt better.

The boys took a break from meeting girls for the next couple of days. David said he thought they should find some girls from nicer homes anyway. A few days later, down at the salt box where a bunch of kids were swimming, they met Tina and Mary Ann, who were not sisters. David and Patrick asked the girls for a date. They said yes, but they both had to be home by eleven.

"My parents are very strict," Tina announced.

"Mine, too," Mary Ann told them. "The last time I got home five minutes late, I was grounded for the whole week."

David and Patrick looked at each other. "Sounds fine to me," David said. "We'll pick you up tonight."

They played away the rest of the summer, enjoying their freedom and leisure as the days grew shorter. By August, the addition to the Heideckers' house remained unfinished, although nearly a year had passed since construction began. The builder had completed the shell, but after that the Heideckers' money ran out, and he stopped work. Shirley still had her job at the Half Shell, but all the money seemed to go for other things. There were David's cars and insurance, his clothes, his spending money. No one in the family seemed to care a great deal about the addition, least of all David, who told his parents it had been the best summer of his life.

David's vacation came to an abrupt end in mid-August with the beginning of football practice — an intensive three-week program that required the presence of the students from nine until five, five days a week, while the rest of the kids were still on vacation. As an incoming tenth grader, David was eligible for the junior varsity team, but for large portions of the program, the varsity and junior varsity players were grouped together. On the first day, all of them had to sign a pledge agreeing to abide by certain rules, such as no smoking or drinking. Each player received a booklet, prepared by the head coach, containing pages of information: rules for body building and weight training, how to behave in the locker room, bus procedure. Every day, the kids spent some time in the classroom, several hours on the field, and the rest of the time working on individual skill areas. They worked out, trained, learned, listened and got in shape — all before Labor Day.

South Carroll's football program was the creation of its middle-aged head coach, a character named Ken Parker who had grown up in West Virginia, where he had been the Most Valuable Player on his high school team. As a young man, Parker had a football scholarship to the University of North Carolina, but he lost that when a hunting accident put him in the hospital for eight weeks during the summer. Without funds, he went to a two-year college in his home town and then to Marshall University in Huntington. There, knowing that he was not big enough or good enough to be a professional football player, he decided to spend his career as a football coach. One of

The Heideckers' house. The left-hand portion of the structure is the unfinished addition. *Ann Turnbull*

Aunt Ollie Houghton's house. *Ann Turnbull*

his early coaching jobs took him to MacArthur High in West Hollywood, Florida, where he met Nancy, a pretty English teacher. They were married four months later. Afterwards, they moved to Norfolk, Virginia, where Ken coached football and Nancy taught English. In 1967, the Parkers heard about an opening in Carroll County, Maryland, at a brand new school that would be only the second in the county to have a football team. Ken was interviewed and hired. He became the school's first football coach, and Nancy became an English teacher and cheerleading coach at South Carroll. Ken, then in his thirties, told Nancy this was their last move: he wanted to stay at South Carroll for the rest of his career. They bought a house a mile and a half from the school.

Over the years, Ken Parker became a legend at South Carroll. He created and shaped the Cavaliers, which eventually became the name given to all athletic teams at South Carroll — varsity or junior varsity, male or female, whatever sport. A dedicated and disciplined coach, he became known for caring more about his players than about winning. In fact, there were not many outstanding years in terms of wins and losses. There had been a couple of low points: in 1968, Parker's second year at the school, South Carroll lost to Frederick 66-7, and in 1981, the year that David Heidecker played on the junior varsity, the varsity was to win only two games, one of them by forfeit. But Parker was known to be an authority on football — if he heard that Ohio State had a new idea, he'd get on the telephone and find out what it was. He was also close to the players. He and Nancy never had any children; their home was open to the students. For kids without fathers, the coach filled in. Every August, the players who were going off to college came by the Parkers' house to say good-bye.

All football coaches at South Carroll were involved in the practice that began in August. Except for Ken Parker, whose time was fully occupied with the football and physical education programs, the other coaches all taught academic classes as well. The coach who worked closely with the J.V. was Jerry Ellis, one of the few black faculty members at South Carroll. Coach Ellis was a recent graduate of the University of Maryland, in his second year at South Carroll.

For David Heidecker, football practice was a whole new adventure. He had always loved team sports, including football, but he had never been in a program which required this much time, work, or discipline before. Neither Patrick nor Chris had gone out for football, and so David was without the support of either of his two close friends. He knew a lot of the boys in the football program, but he would not have called them friends. A lot of them seemed to belong to cliques, sometimes making David feel excluded.

As football practice progressed, the players with first string potential became obvious. Coach Ellis began the process, mentally, of dividing the boys onto different teams and assigning players to positions. He already had his eye on David, who was not the best player in the program, or the most consistent, but who was among the most enthusiastic. David was a funny kid, the coach thought. He reminded the coach of somebody who was standing on the outside looking in. Here was a kid, the coach thought, who wanted more than anything to be liked, to be accepted as part of the crowd, but who wasn't willing, or perhaps able, to do all the things that entailed. The other boys didn't dislike David, the coach thought, but he wasn't quite one of them, either. Partly it was because David did weird things, the coach reflected; he was loud and uninhibited, and did not seem to notice or care what everybody else was doing. And David was stubborn. If he got it into his head that he didn't want to do something just then, he could be hard to budge. But, boy did he love football! Coach Ellis had seen him out on the field, yelling at the top of his lungs for everybody to keep trying, just when the other kids were ready to break for the day. He had seen him get angry, too, if he couldn't do something, or if somebody else quit trying. But David was moody, the coach noticed; if he didn't feel like doing a certain play at the moment, you couldn't make him.

When Coach Ellis named the first string junior varsity, David was on the list as right guard. The first string players had to work extra hard. David didn't mind. He liked to be in the middle of things, yelling at everybody else to come on. Sometimes the other kids listened to him, Coach Ellis noticed; sometimes they didn't.

Dick Heidecker came to some of the practices after work. All the coaches had come to know him the year before, when David played on the freshman football team, because Dick had spent a lot of time hanging around the field, watching the practices and the games. In addition, Dick had offered to help out by hauling equipment for the games, things like that. The coaches took him up on it. They could always use some extra help.

The first game for the J.V. that year was against Martinsburg, in West Virginia. The Cavaliers lost. David was depressed for hours afterwards, even when the other players' spirits had revived. His father told him not to worry about it, that they had played a good game.

"Their guys were bigger than you, that's all," Dick told him. "You'll win the next one."

The custom was for the J.V. coach to pick two team captains after the first game. Jerry Ellis picked David as one of the captains. He thought long and hard about this. David was not the most popular boy on the team, nor was he the most mature. But his enthusiasm and willingness to play were unequalled, and he had excellent skills. Coach Ellis knew nothing about David's background. He believed that David had enough basic respect from the other players to be able to act in a position of leadership. Whatever respect he lacked, he would have to earn. Being captain would help him do that, the coach figured.

David's selection as co-captain was an occasion of great pride for his father. Dick asked Shirley to cook a special dinner, and invited Aunt Ollie to come up and join them. He would have offered David a beer, he told him, but drinking was against the rules for football players.

"Have a Coke," he said, instead.

After dinner, he made a speech, of sorts. "I always wanted to play football in high school," he announced, "but I couldn't put up with all those rules." He chuckled. "Besides, I quit school the end of tenth grade."

"David won't," Shirley said.

"That's right," Dick went on. He raised his glass of diet soda in an informal toast. "To my future Baltimore Colt."

David, who was seldom embarrassed by his parents' enthusiasm, grinned. Shirley served him a piece of cake and gave him a hug. Aunt Ollie said that Uncle Harold would have been proud.

It was two days later when David got in trouble with Coach Ellis. The team was on the field, on a cool autumn day under an overcast sky. The coach demonstrated a fundamental blocking skill. Some of the team members, including David, paid no attention.

Ellis said, "Heidecker, this is for your benefit too, you know. You're supposed to be setting an example."

David said, "We already know how to do that. It's boring."

"Well, not everybody on the team has your superior talents, Heidecker. Why don't you get up here and show us all how to do it?"

One of the players laughed loudly. "Yeah, Heidecker doesn't have to learn anything. He thinks he knows it all."

David turned around and yelled at the other player. "Go to hell!" he shouted. "Who asked you?"

"David, knock it off!" Ellis ordered. "Get up here and demonstrate the skill!"

"No!" David hollered. "You demonstrate it yourself!"

Coach Ellis had a disciplinary technique that he referred to as "ups and downs," also called grass drills. A player who was told to do ups and downs had to run in place until the coach told him to hit the ground, then bounce up and do it again. The coach told David to do it. David looked around casually. The whole junior varsity team was watching him. A couple of the players were snickering. David did a few baby chops with his feet.

"Not that way, David," the coach told him. "Do it right."

David kept fooling around. Finally, Jerry Ellis got mad. "Ups and downs!" he yelled. "Do it now!"

David stopped doing his baby chops and stood still. "I'm not gonna do this!" he shouted at the coach.

"You'll do it if you want to play football!" the coach shouted back. "You do it now or you're off the team!"

"The hell I will!"

"Heidecker, you do it now or get out — now!"

"Fuck you!"

David started walking. A few yards away, he turned around and took a last look at the coach. Then he ran all the way to the parking lot.

The rest of the players stood quietly, watching David's lanky figure get smaller in the distance. Suddenly, Coach Ellis shouted at the team.

"Okay!" he yelled. "Back to work! Let's go!"

He went through the motions of a little more practice, but he dismissed the players early. He went off to find Coach Parker. They met on the edge of the field, where Parker was on his way back from his own practice with the varsity team. Leaning against a tree under a sunless sky, Parker listened to Ellis's story.

"I'm not sure David Heidecker was the best choice to be captain," he said finally.

"Me either," Ellis said ruefully.

Ken Parker thought a minute. "Would you consider giving him another chance?" he asked.

Ellis shook his head. "I can't," he said. "It's not as if it was just me and David out there alone. The whole team watched him refuse to do what I said, watched him refuse to do his ups and downs, and heard him yell 'Fuck you' at me. If he gets another chance after that, what rules do we have?"

"Okay," Ken Parker said. "It's your call." He looked at Ellis. "David's father will want to talk to you," he added. "You might as well get ready for that."

The telephone call came that evening, to Ellis's home.

"Coach Ellis? This is Dick Heidecker calling. I'm David's father."

Jerry Ellis had just finished dinner with his family. He shuffled his kids out of the room, pulled up a chair and sat down. "Yes, sir," he said.

"Coach, I wonder if you could tell me what happened today."

"Okay. Well, we were having a football practice on the field. I was trying to show David a skill. I guess you know we had picked David as one of the captains."

"I know that," Dick answered. "I was very proud of that."

"Yes, sir. Well, what happened was, David refused to do what I was showing him. He said he already knew how to do it. Then one of the other players made some kind of a comment, which I didn't hear, and David yelled at him. So I told David to forget about the other kid, just pay attention to me. David wouldn't do that. So then I told him to do ups and downs, which is grass drills, something I do for discipline." Ellis hesitated. "Some coaches use push-ups, some use other things. It doesn't much matter what, you have to have something to maintain discipline and assert your authority."

"I understand," Dick said.

"Anyway, I told David to do ups and downs. He wouldn't do it. He pretended to at first, but he was just goofing off. He knew what I meant, but he was being stubborn. Finally, I guess I got mad. I yelled at him to do it now. That's when he cussed me."

"What did he say?"

"He said, 'Fuck you.' "

"I see."

"So, I really didn't have a lot of choice. I mean, the whole team was there watching this. I told David to shape up or ship out. He shipped out."

Dick Heidecker paused. Finally he said, "Coach, I wonder if you know anything about David's background."

"No, I don't," Ellis said.

"If you have a minute, can I tell you some things about David?"

Ellis was wary. "Yes, if you want," he said. "But I'm afraid I won't be able to change my mind."

Dick went ahead anyway. He told the coach about David's infancy and childhood, about his life in the foster homes and in an institution.

"He was in a place for emotionally disturbed children," he continued. "No wonder. To this day he has scars on his back from a beating in a foster home."

"I'm sorry," Ellis said sincerely.

"When we got him, he couldn't read. He couldn't tie his shoes. He wet his bed sometimes. My wife and I thought he needed a home and family and love, and that's what we gave him. He straightened out, started to go to regular classes. He got interested in sports, and as you might have noticed, he looks like a natural athlete."

"Definitely," the coach concurred.

"But see, sometimes he loses his temper on account of everything that happened to him. I'm not saying it's right, but it's what happens. Sometimes it's like he gets overcome with everything that happened to him before."

Ellis said, "Mr. Heidecker, I'm really sorry."

Dick coughed. "What I'm wondering is, do you think it's possible you could give him another chance? I mean, I know he owes you an apology. He knows that himself. But to put him off the team — well, that's rough. That seems kinda extreme, you know?"

Ellis swallowed hard. "Mr. Heidecker, I hear what you're saying," he told him. "I feel bad about what happened. I was the one who picked David to be captain, and I feel worse than anybody that it didn't work out." He hesitated. "But you see, if this had happened in private, just me and David, I could consider taking him back. I know he just got carried away, he didn't really mean anything malicious. But it didn't happen in private. It happened in front of the whole team, and all the other kids were watching to see what I was going to do. You see?''

Dick spoke softly. "Yeah," he said.

"I wish I could give him another chance. I like David. But I can't. I'm sorry.''

Dick Heidecker had never begged anyone for anything in his entire adult life. This was the closest he had ever come. "Okay," he said. "Goodbye.''

He called to David, who had gone into his bedroom. "David, come on out here.''

David came into the living room. "Yeah, Dad?''

"I talked to the coach. He said he's sorry, he can't let you back on the team.''

David looked at his father. "Okay," he said.

Dick walked over and put his arm around David's shoulders. "We'll just have to make the best of it," he said. "Next year you'll be eligible for varsity.''

David nodded. "It's all right, Dad," he said.

But David was extremely upset. He wasn't angry at the coach; he was mad at himself. He knew he had done a dumb thing. That Friday, when the J.V. Cavaliers had their next game, he skipped school. He persuaded Patrick to join him, which was not difficult. They took two six-packs of beer from the Kenney house and drove around in David's car, drinking and playing the radio. In the evening, David decided they should visit the Block, an area in downtown Baltimore that he had heard about but never seen. He told Patrick about it.

"They have naked women and stuff. They do stripteases for the audience.''

Patrick was wide-eyed. "Is it legal?" he asked.

"Yeah, I guess so. My dad told me it's right near the police building, so it must be legal.''

They set out, with David driving somewhat shakily but more carefully than usual. A heavy rain drenched the streets as they drove. David knew he had had too much to drink. He told Patrick to watch for cops and radar. David knew his way to the downtown area of the city, but he did not know how to find The Block. They asked directions at several street corners, and eventually found their way. They left David's car in a "No Parking" zone and got out.

David and Patrick stood in the rain on the corner of East Baltimore and Holliday Streets, taking in the sights. Neon signs flashing the names of clubs lit up both sides of Baltimore Street. Doors and windows were decorated with multicolored descriptions of the goods or services inside: Three Shows Nitely; Girls Noon to 2; Videos 25 Cents; We Change Every Day; Swedish Erotica; Sexual Aids; No Cover Here; Come Right In; Super Chicks. Outside many of the clubs was a disheveled "barker" whose job was to invite passers-by to enter the club. Discordant sounds criss-crossed the wet street: shouts of the barkers, honking horns directed at heedless pedestrians, raucous laughter and drunken arguments, hard rock music. The sidewalks on both sides of the street were crowded with pedestrians, including young girls apparently employed as strippers at one or another of the clubs, men in suits who might have come from the office buildings nearby, assorted customers and curiosity-seekers, uniformed police officers, and a variety of beggars and street people. One sad thin man approached David and Patrick and asked them for money. David looked at Patrick, unsure what they should do; then he reached into his pocket and handed the man a dime. They watched him walk away unsteadily, approaching others with the same request.

The Block, which originally occupied three or four blocks along East Baltimore Street, had been the glittering home of vaudeville and burlesque in the 1920's and before. Its cornerstone, the Gayety Theater, had housed performances by Sally Rand, Gypsy Rose Lee, Eddie Cantor, and Abbott and Costello. In later years, The Block contained club after club of live shows which eventually deteriorated to stripteases, pornographic bookstores, and erotic peep shows. The sleazy side of The Block, which had always been there, outweighed and eventually destroyed the flashy, fun side. In the mid-sixties, the city took a large chunk of The Block and razed it to build the new police headquarters, a shiny high-rise with a helipad on the roof. Later, another group of clubs was torn down to make way for a multimillion dollar retail mall. By then, as Harborplace became the lustrous new focus of downtown Baltimore, attracting large numbers of tourists and conventions to the city for the first time, city officials ceased to defend The Block as a tourist attraction; they considered it an embarrassment. By 1981, The Block had truly shrunk to a block. The part that still stood was surrounded by high-rise buildings and swarming with drugs, prostitution, and bums.

David and Patrick looked around for a club to enter. They selected one at random. The barker at the front door, an unshaven character wearing a dirty T-shirt under a leather jacket, leered at them.

"Hey, man, go right on in, this is the place," he announced monotonously. "Beautiful women, we got shows all night, make yourself happy."

The boys went inside to what turned out to be a large room filled with smoke. Its focus was a small stage rimmed with lights, around which was placed a circular bar. The rest of the room contained small black tables with chairs. As David and Patrick stood inside the door, they heard loud music that might have been a hybrid of punk rock and burlesque. A woman in her forties was on stage, wearing black lace panties and two turquoise stars on her nipples. David and Patrick watched as she undulated to music and grinned vacuously at people in the audience, some of whom engaged in cat-calls and whistles and the rest of whom ignored her. The boys took seats on two adjacent stools at the bar which had just been vacated. Now they were so close to the woman on stage they could have reached out and touched her. She looked old and fat to David and Patrick. They watched her kneel down before an older man who was two barstools away from them. She let her breast touch his cheek before dancing away. David, who still felt the effects of the beer, thought he might be sick. Her flabby thighs and posterior and her heavy breasts, practically in his face, nauseated him. He wondered if he could get a glass of water in here.

A scantily-clad waitress who was chewing gum came over to David and Patrick.

"What'll it be, fellows?" she asked, without interest.

"Coke," David said.

"One for me, too," Patrick said.

The waitress took a good look at them for the first time. "How old are you guys?" she asked accusingly.

David stared at the woman, who was also middle-aged and overweight. He felt too sick to lie. "Seventeen," he told her. That was only a tiny lie; he would be seventeen in December. The waitress shook her head, snapping her gum emphatically. "I can't serve you," she said. "You ain't even supposed to be in here."

"Couldn't we have a Coke?" Patrick asked.

"No, honey," she told him. "Cokes are $2 here. And you ain't allowed to be here anyway." She stared at them sympathetically. "Listen, why don't you go down to one of them video places, where they don't have the live shows? They don't care about your age down there."

"What do they have there?" Patrick asked.

"Videos. You put in a quarter and see a dirty show."

"Where are they?" David asked.

"They're all over The Block, hon. Just walk outside and you'll see them."

David and Patrick left, trying to appear nonchalant as they passed the barker on the way out. They saw that now he was doing a little dance on the sidewalk, his back and shoulders soaked from the rain. They crossed the street and went into a place that advertised videos for twenty-five cents. A muscular moon-faced man who looked like an aging wrestler stood behind a counter, looking bored. The boys glanced around. They discovered that the videos were arranged by subject matter.

Patrick whispered to David, "What's bondage?"

David shrugged; he had no idea. Finally, he told the moon-faced man that they wanted to see a regular video. The man led them to the adjacent viewing booths and told them, without interest, to put in their quarters. David's booth had writing on the walls. He thought it smelled like urine. He put in his money and watched the screen. A few minutes later, he and Patrick emerged from their booths. David still felt sick, but he laughed a little.

"Can't they even use good-looking people?" he demanded.

Patrick appeared to be in a state of shock. "Wow!" he said at last.

David turned to the moon-faced man. "My friend has no taste," he explained. "He thinks this is the greatest thing he ever saw."

The moon-faced man asked, without expression, "You want to see some more?"

"Yeah!" Patrick said.

David shook his head. "No, thanks."

"Then move on," the man told him. "There's no loitering in here."

David said, "What do you mean, loitering?"

"Loitering, hanging around. You want to stay in here, you pay another quarter, you watch another couple of minutes. If not, move along."

"We paid to be in here," David said. "We don't have to leave if we don't want to."

"Get out."

David stood up straight. He was at least three inches taller than the moon-faced man, although he was sure that the man was considerably stronger than he was. "Why should I get out of here?" he asked.

The moon-faced man looked up at David's face. "Because I don't like you, kid," he answered. "Now get your ass out of here before I throw you and your little buddy out in the street."

David leaned forward. "Yeah?" he said. "Do you want to try?"

A uniformed policeman came into the store at that moment. Wiping water from his sleeves, swinging his nightstick, he spoke jovially to the moon-faced man.

"Hey, Joe, how's it going tonight?"

"Going okay," the man said expressionlessly. "These kids were just leaving. It's past their bedtime."

David glared at the man, hesitated, and turned around. "Come on, Pat," he said. Patrick followed him outside.

On the sidewalk, Patrick waited for David to rant and rave about their mistreatment. David did. "Son of a bitch!" he yelled. "I should have punched his face in!"

"No way," Patrick said. "Did you check out his muscles?"

"Aw, so what," David said. "I just didn't want to get us arrested, that's all."

Patrick laughed nervously. "Good thing you didn't," he said. "I don't think your father wants to get out of bed and drive down to Baltimore to bail us out in the middle of the night."

David stepped under an overhanging roof for shelter from the downpour that continued. "You know what?" he said. "I want to call my dad. He might be worried about me."

They walked east on Baltimore Street, searching for a pay phone. Despite the rain and the late hour, there was still a considerable amount of activity along The Block. Barkers continued to holler; customers still went in and out of the clubs. David and Patrick passed a bag lady sitting on the sidewalk next to a trash can, surrounded by her meager possessions clustered by the wall of a building for protection from the rain. They heard her talking to herself, speaking nonsense. Across the street they saw two gay men embracing in the rain. David and Patrick walked a block before they found a pay phone on the corner. The boys squeezed in together and forced the door closed.

"Phew!" Patrick said. "This smells like an outhouse!" The booth was filthy. Trash lay on the floor; black marking ink covered the walls. David didn't care. He deposited four nickels and dialed his home number. Dick answered the phone.

"Dad?"

"David? Is that you?"

"Yeah, it's me, Dad. Guess where I am!"

"Are you okay?" Dick asked. He sounded drowsy.

"I'm fine, Dad. Were you asleep?"

"Yeah, I guess I was," Dick said.

"Sorry, Dad. I was afraid you'd be worrying about me."

"Are you out of gas?" Dick asked. "Do you have a flat or anything?"

"No, no, nothing like that. Everything's fine. Listen, Dad, you have to guess where I am."

"Where?"

David opened the door of the telephone booth and looked out at the street signs. "Dad, I'm at the corner of Baltimore Street and Gay Street."

Dick hesitated. "Baltimore and Gay," he said. "My God, you're down at The Block. Either that or you're at police headquarters."

"Right the first time!" David announced enthusiastically. "Pat and I are on The Block!"

"Well, are you having a good time?"

"Dad, we've had a great time!" David said. "We've done everything. We went into a club and saw a strip show. Then we saw some of those videos, you know, movies with people making love. We've seen everything!"

Dick chuckled. "Yeah?" he said. "Did you like it?"

"Yes, it's great! We had a ball!"

"Are you ready to come home now?" Dick asked.

"Yeah, I think so," David said. "We're kinda tired. Besides, we've done it all."

Dick asked, "Is it still raining?"

"Yes, it's pouring. It's been pouring the whole time."

"Well, drive slowly, then. Do you have enough gas in the car?"

"Yup. We're all set."

"I'm glad you called," Dick told him.

"Yeah, I didn't want you to be worrying."

"Okay."

"I love you, Dad."

"I love you, too, son."

"Good-bye."

David opened the door to the phone booth and stepped out. He looked around, trying to focus on where he had left the car. He remembered suddenly that he had parked illegally.

"Come on, Pat!" he yelled. "Maybe the car's been towed away!"

They took off running in the rain, past the store fronts with the flashing neon, through the milling customers, around the bums and beggars who straggled aimlessly. They ran and ran, coming finally to David's car and seeing with relief that the car was still there and did not even have a parking ticket. Laughing, they jumped inside and sat for a minute, breathing hard, shaking the water from their hair. David turned on the ignition and looked at the gas gauge. They had nearly half a tank of gas. He looked over at Patrick.

"You ready to go?" he asked.

Patrick nodded. "Yeah, I'm beat."

"I'm not even drunk anymore," David said. "I feel good."

He pulled out of his parking space carefully and headed for Carroll County.

David went back to school the next week without incident. When he passed Coach Ellis in the hall or outside, he always spoke in a friendly manner: "Hi, Coach, how's it going?" he would ask. Once, he even sought out Ellis's advice on a problem he was having with another teacher. The two of them never did discuss what had happened on the football field that day. David completed tenth grade with the best report card he had ever had. He got A's in physical education and biology; B's in English and history; and C's in German and algebra. Shirley smiled when she saw it.

"Remember when David was little and they said he was below average?" she asked Aunt Ollie. "They told us his intelligence was limited, remember?"

Aunt Ollie chuckled. "They told us he was short, too," she said.

That summer, David worked part-time at a hardware store. The rest of the time he loafed and swam and chased girls and hung around with Patrick. It was another good summer, the way summers ought to be — long, slow, lazy. Before Labor Day, David and Dick and Shirley drove to King's Dominion, a large amusement park in Virginia, for the day. David took a turn on every scary ride they had, dragging Dick along with him whenever he could. They left shortly before the park closed and drove a hundred and fifty miles home.

David did not go out for football in eleventh grade. Academically, he was coasting now. His hardest course was chemistry, but he was optimistic, having received an A in biology the year before. David did not study hard, but he did his work. He had learned to manage his time, to do what he had to do efficiently so that he had time left over for fun.

David's school records showed that he was absent twenty-nine days in eleventh grade, which added up to almost six weeks of school. On many of those days, he played hooky, sometimes with Patrick and sometimes with other friends. Aunt Ollie usually knew what he was doing, because she saw David or other kids driving up and down the gravel road. Once in a while she mentioned it to Dick and Shirley, who were philosophical about it. After all, Dick said, he wasn't in school at all when he was David's age, having dropped out at sixteen. Shirley said that if David could skip school and still get good grades, that was his choice.

By now David's white Plymouth station wagon had died; he drove a green Dodge that was passed down to him by his father. David went out with a lot of girls that year. He liked to date one girl at a time, and often gave her the rush in the beginning, but as soon as she started to get serious, he dropped her. He told his mother that everybody he met wanted to go steady. The telephone rang frequently at the Heideckers' house. Dick and Shirley joked that it always seemed to be another girl calling David. Dick thought it was funny to ask, "Is this Mary?" even though David didn't know anyone named Mary. David thought it was funny, too.

"Might as well keep 'em guessing," he told his father.

The addition to the Heideckers' house remained uncompleted — untouched, by now, for almost two years. Dick and Shirley tried giving David a regular allowance, and sometimes he earned money doing odd jobs for other people, but in the end they always gave him what he asked for. He seldom asked for anything they thought was unreasonable, and frequently he offered to earn the money on his own, but they never wanted to deny him anything. And so the unfinished addition sat, untouched. David never expressed any dissatisfaction with their home, and eventually, Dick and Shirley reached an unspoken agreement to spend the money on other things for now.

Eleventh grade was the year David tried pot. It started at an impromptu gathering of teenagers in another boy's back yard in the spring. There was food and soda and a little beer, with loud rock music coming from an oversized portable cassette player on the grass. David had come there almost accidentally: his date with a girl named Stacy fell through because she was grounded for having stayed out too late with him the night before. David wound up at the party instead and spent most of the time throwing a basketball through a hoop on the garage. He had just sat down on the grass when a boy whose name he didn't know handed him a joint. David looked at it. He had never tried it before. He took a puff. He waited, and took some more puffs. When he looked up, he saw that Patrick was sitting on a lawn chair smoking marijuana, too.

That spring, there were other parties at which people had pot. Sometimes a group of kids at the salt box had some, and once in a while it showed up in somebody's club cellar. David noticed that the same kids always seemed to have it. He didn't know where they got it, and never asked because he didn't care. If somebody handed him a joint, he puffed on it, but he really preferred beer. He also smoked ordinary cigarettes, which came naturally because both Dick and Shirley were chain smokers.

One day after school, David and Patrick stood in the Heideckers' kitchen, getting a snack, when Patrick took out a joint. David stared at it.

"Where'd you get that?" he asked.

Patrick grinned. "I got a source," he told David. "I can get it any time I want."

David looked disgusted. "So what?" he said.

Patrick said, "I've seen you smoke it, David."

"Sure I've smoked it. But I don't go out and *buy* it. I don't bring it into my own home."

"What's wrong with that?"

"What's wrong with it?" David's voice got louder. "This is my house. My father could walk in here any second." He took the joint out of Patrick's hand and snapped it in half. "Give me that thing," he said. "I don't want it in here."

Now Patrick was angry. "You don't have the right to do that!" he protested. "I paid money for that!"

"Then you shouldn't have brought it in my house!" David yelled. "My dad would bust my ass if he thought I brought pot in this house. And you'd never be in here again!"

"Shit on you, David!" Patrick hollered. He ran out of the house and down the gravel driveway, where he passed Dick Heidecker driving home. A few minutes later, Dick came into the house.

"Where was Patrick going?" he asked. "Looked like he was going to a fire."

David shrugged. "I don't know," he said. He turned to his father. "Dad, I want to go out for a while."

Dick said, "Okay."

David drove his car slowly to the Kenneys' house, looking for Patrick along the way. When he didn't see him, he realized that Patrick must have headed for home through the woods and fields. David got to the Kenneys' ahead of him and sat in his car in front of the house. After a while, he saw Patrick coming.

Patrick walked up to David's car and slammed his fist into the roof. "Get off my property!" he yelled.

"Pat, let me talk to you," David said.

"What about?"

"Get in the car with me, let's talk."

Patrick glared at David, then walked around to the other side of the car and got in. "What is it?" he asked.

David said, "Pat, look. I'm no goody-goody, you know that. I'm no angel, either."

"You can say that again," Patrick muttered.

"Okay, so I'm not. But just about everything I do, I talk to my parents about it. You know that. I've never lied to them about anything. And I can't tell my mom and dad that I smoke pot."

"How do you know?" Patrick asked.

"I just know," David said. "They wouldn't understand, and they wouldn't like it."

Patrick thought about that. "I guess they wouldn't," he admitted.

"And I don't even like pot, really," David said. "I don't want to do it any more." He reached into his pocket. "How much did you have to pay for that joint I tore up?" he asked.

Patrick shrugged. "Forget it," he said. "I think I'll give it up, too."

They drove over to Chris Langhage's house and invited themselves to some of Joyce's homemade doughnuts.

That summer, David got a job at Black & Decker. He was eighteen, with only one more year of school ahead of him. Working wasn't as much fun as just hanging around, but he wanted to earn some money so that he wouldn't have to ask his parents for anything during his senior year. Besides, most of his friends had summer jobs by now. There wouldn't be anyone to hang around with if he didn't. There was free time at night and on the weekends, anyway. David went out with a lot of girls that summer. He had something else on his mind, too. He had decided to go out for varsity football in his senior year.

CHAPTER 9

The Cavaliers

On a July evening in 1983, David wandered over to the gym at South Carroll High School to attend weight training. Coach Parker's football program offered weight training twice a week throughout the summer. The first time David went, no one said anything to him about his plans. The second time, Coach Parker came over and shook his hand.

"Hi, David," the coach said. "What's up?"

"Nothing much, Coach," David told him. "I just came by for weight training."

"I see. Did you come the other day, too?"

"Yeah, I did."

"Are you thinking about coming out for football?"

David yawned. "Yeah, I'm thinking about it," he said casually.

Ken Parker put his hand on David's shoulder. "Good," he said enthusiastically.

David continued to attend the sessions, which were held every Tuesday and Thursday from six until eight p.m. The sessions were rigorous and demanding. Everybody had to jog two laps around the track, do stretching exercises, and then lift weights in a series of exercises known to Parker as the "Big Five": parallel squats, bench press, shoulder press, dead lift, and bicep curls. The purpose of the program was to increase muscular strength, endurance, and speed. It was not a program for the timid, or for the casual athlete.

Coach Parker approached David again after one of the sessions. They were in the gym in late July, when the heat was extreme, even in the central section of Maryland not far from the foothills of the Appalachian Mountains. Little windows, high off the ground, provided the only natural ventilation, lamely assisted by a couple of large fans set up in makeshift fashion.

Boys rushed to the soda machine and the showers in a hurry to escape the heat and the workout itself, anxious to rejoin the lazy world of kids in summer. Parker intercepted David en route.

"David? I see you're still coming by."

David wiped his face with a towel. "Yes, sir," he said.

"Are you going to sign up for football?"

"I don't know."

"Practice starts the middle of August."

"Yeah, I know."

The coach looked directly at David. "I'd really like to have you on my team this year," he said. "I need to know if you plan to sign up."

David glanced around. He shrugged his shoulders. "Yeah, I'd like to sign up," he said.

Parker smiled. "Good, we've gotten that far," he said. "Now there's a couple of things I want to say to you. Number one, I'm real glad to have you in the program. I think it's great that you want to do it, and I don't believe you'll ever regret it. Number two, if you want to be in the program, you have to conform. You have to come to the practices, you have to abide by the rules." He paused. "Number three, you have to do what you're told."

David grinned. "I know," he said.

The coach punched him lightly in the shoulder. "Okay," he said. "Now come on in the office so I can sign you up and give you some of the material you'll need."

David left the gym with an armload of literature, all of which had been written and rewritten by Ken Parker over the past sixteen years. First and foremost was the Pride Book, which explained the physical training that was required and listed the schedule of football games for the season. There was also a Senior Leadership Guide, which explained what leadership is and which began: "Leadership is measured by this yardstick: Do your men perform well and willingly for you, the leader?" A twelve-page Football Pledge, which had to be signed by the player and his parents, contained rules, regulations, and guidelines for general conduct. The Pledge pointed out, "Smoking, drinking, and using chemical substances are out. Since peer pressure is great, this can be your most difficult challenge. Be a *MAN*."

When David showed the Pledge to his father, Dick Heidecker groaned. "I don't have to read all this, do I?" he asked.

"You're supposed to sign your name that you read it, Dad," David said.

"Could you summarize it for me?"

"Dad, it has all kinds of rules. It has training rules, locker room procedures, game conduct, stuff like that."

"Locker room procedures? They write that stuff down and hand it out?"

"Come on Dad. This is serious."

"Okay."

Dick struggled through it, making comments as he went. "This says curfew is 10:30 on all school nights, Sundays and nights before games. Players should not have dates or attend dances on the night before a game. Are you willing to do that?"

"Sure."

"This says any player involved with alcohol, drugs, controlled paraphernalia or tobacco products is out."

"Yup."

"This says, there will be no horseplay in the training room. Are they kidding?"

"Just sign your name, Dad."

Football practice began in earnest in the middle of August. The practices lasted all day, Monday through Friday. The boys came in the morning, worked out, practiced on the field, had classroom instruction, practiced on the field some more. In his mind, Coach Parker began to select his first string players. David Heidecker, now at six feet five inches, was the tallest member of the program. He was not the broadest or the strongest player on the team, but he was one of the fastest. The coach liked to watch his frenetic energy, his unbridled enthusiasm that kept his body in perpetual motion, even as his body itself had become hard, muscular and powerful from weeks of disciplined training. Fast, agile, fearless, aggressive — Parker could see that David had the ability to be an outstanding blocker. He and David agreed that offensive right guard was the position for David.

David attended football practice more faithfully than he had ever attended school. Dick came over and watched sometimes. He had already volunteered his services to Coach Parker, who told Dick they could use his help when the games began. The coaches always needed people to haul equipment and help out. During the practices, Dick liked to sit in the stands, smoking cigarettes as he watched David in action. Near the end of August, they had several scrimmages with other schools. By now there was no doubt in Parker's mind. David Heidecker would play first string varsity.

The Monday before Labor Day, Ken and Nancy Parker hosted Parents' Night for the football players and their families. Held in the South Carroll cafeteria, with cheerleaders present to set up refreshments, this event became a gigantic pep rally. Dick and Shirley attended with David and listened to Coach Parker explain the football program, discuss some of his expectations, and introduce the other coaches. Nancy Parker, who was the cheerleading coach as well as an English teacher, led some of the cutest girls in the school in cheers.

Right after Labor Day, David began his senior year at South Carroll. He found that after the time he had spent at the school in football practice, opening day was anti-climactic. As other kids shouted noisy greetings to one another and exchanged stories of their summer exploits, as they searched for lockers, received their schedules, and groaned at their class assignments, David felt as if he had already been there for a long time. Still, he was happy to discover that he had a class or two with Patrick Kenney, and also with Chris Langhage. Football had taken so much of his time that he had seen little of either of them for weeks.

"Did you join a monastery?" Patrick grumbled.

"No, I've just had a lot to do for football," David said.

"I hope you're not gonna turn into one of those jock snobs," Patrick told him.

"I can still go out every Saturday night. What do you say we find a couple of dates for this weekend?"

"Okay," Patrick said, slightly mollified.

South Carroll was a member of the Tri-State League where, because of its size, it was designated a Class A school. The year before, the Cavaliers had won five games and lost five, but this year they had twenty-three returning players in a varsity roster of thirty-nine. Coach Parker told the *Carroll County Times*, which assiduously covered high school sports in the county, "There's no 'superstars' on the squad this year, just a group of hard-working young men shooting for a successful season. The league gets tougher and tougher every year and we hope to be in the championship picture. I would like to have more size on the squad, but I'm satisfied. I am really pleased with the attitude of this ball club."

People who knew Parker were accustomed to his understated comments to the press. He was not known to announce that he had the best team in the county, that they were going to run over the other schools, that they would take the championship. Like all football coaches, Parker liked to win, but unlike some others, he didn't have to win. More important to the coach was his belief that his football program built character in his students, that it changed them as people and added a dimension to their lives. "You never know how you touch somebody," he liked to say. He had been deeply moved by one student, whom he had not known well, who came back years later to tell Parker that it was his influence on the football field that enabled the man to jump out of an airplane in Vietnam. Now in his seventeenth year of coaching at South Carroll, Parker was not about to change his style.

South Carroll played all of its football games on Friday nights. On September 9, 1983, the season opened with a home game against the Damascus Hornets. As always, the game inspired a large turn-out among the students, and also from the community where, as in all rural areas, there were fewer diversions. Dick and Shirley took their seats in the stands, both of them quietly thrilled at the scene unfolding before their eyes. David was allowed to start as right guard. The Cavaliers scored first, but the game was tied at the half.

Coach Parker.   *Courtesy The Carroll County Times*

The cheerleaders came out to stir up the crowd. When they took a break, Dick Heidecker stood up in front of the bleachers where he and Shirley sat. Putting his arms in the air, swinging his large stomach from side to side, he shouted, "Gimme a C!"

"C!" the crowd yelled.

"Gimme an A!"

"A!"

Shirley looked off into the distance, hoping nobody knew who they were, knowing at the same time that David wouldn't mind if people did.

"Gimme a V!"

"V!"

The third quarter was scoreless, but in the last quarter Damascus broke the deadlock on a 77-yard touchdown drive and kicked the extra point to bring the score to 15-7; then they scored again. The Cavaliers made a touchdown with 18 seconds remaining in the game, and lost it 23-13. Coach Parker told the *Carroll County Times*, "The kids were still trying, and we scored. We worked our two minute offense, and I thought it worked pretty well. The number one thing that they had over us was speed. They had a couple of fast receivers.''

David was dejected. He went home with his parents and rehashed the game, shouting criticisms at various failures on the part of the Cavaliers. Dick's and Shirley's efforts to console him were only partly successful; finally, they found a late night horror movie on television and watched it together.

Every Monday night after football practice, Coach Parker showed movies of the previous game. He required the team to watch, and they all critiqued the game. The movies did nothing to restore David's confidence.

"Jesus, what a play!" he called out. "We look like monkeys out there."

"Come on, David," somebody grumbled.

"Look at that!" David yelled. "The whole offense sucks!"

"Cool it, Heidecker," another player shouted.

Parker switched off the movie. "Fellows," he said, "we're watching ourselves to try to locate specific problems we can work on. That's the point of these movies. General derogatory comments don't help."

"Shit," David muttered audibly.

The coach ran the movie again. Afterwards, as the players filed out, David was startled to find that Parker somehow had maneuvered the crowd so that the two of them were alone together, as if the coach had created a complicated play that got everybody but David through the door. The coach stood directly in front of him.

"David," Parker said quietly, "don't be a wise ass."

"What do you mean?" David asked innocently.

"You know what I mean," Parker said evenly. "I mean, get your attitude in gear and get it there now."

David glared defiantly at the coach for a moment. Parker stared back with all the authority of a high school football coach in his seventeenth year in charge. David dropped his eyes.

"Okay," he said.

Parker punched David's arm. "That's the way," he said.

The Cavaliers played their second game against Centennial and won it 21-6. It was a sweet victory, not only because it was the Cavaliers' first for the season, but because it was the first time they had ever defeated Centennial. This time, David was ecstatic. He drove up to the Langhages' on Saturday morning, the next day, and picked up Chris. They went over to get Patrick and spent the afternoon "cruising," as David put it. They stopped by the roller rink in Westminster, where they encountered a group of girls they knew; before leaving, they all had dates for Saturday night. That evening, David and Chris and Patrick and three girls went to the Carrolltowne Mall for a hamburger, saw a movie there, and made out in David's car. It was, as David said, a great way to celebrate.

But the next Friday night, the Cavaliers were humiliated by a 6-0 shut-out by Liberty in front of twenty-two hundred spectators. It was a defensive game start to finish, with the Cavaliers managing only 97 yards against Liberty. South Carroll almost scored in the third quarter when the tailback broke through the right side of Liberty's defense untouched and raced 53 yards for an apparent touchdown, but Ken Parker shook his head as he saw the flag go up for a holding penalty that nullified the points. It was the Cavaliers' last opportunity to score.

Afterwards, in the locker room, Parker had few words for the players. It was not his style to castigate the team, even when the game they played was mediocre or worse. In his seventeenth year at South Carroll, there was not much that could happen on a high school football field that Parker had not seen before. He looked around at a very dejected group of varsity players.

"Guys," he said, "we play Martinsburg next week. They're a tough team — a lot tougher than Liberty. What do you think we're gonna work on this week?"

Somebody groaned. "Not getting penalized."

"Wrong," Parker said. "We're gonna work on everything! We weren't up for this game — we were coasting after Centennial. And we can't ever afford to do that. We're gonna run, we'll work on blocking, we'll practice the plays. We'll get our attitude up, and next week we'll win. I need everybody's help."

Outside, as was her custom, Nancy waited for him. They drove home together. Their house was a gathering place for football players, almost a second home for some of the boys, but tonight it was empty. As they pulled into the driveway, Nancy asked, "What did you say to the team?"

Ken sighed. "I'd like to take 'em all to the woodshed," he said ruefully.

After more than twenty years of marriage to Ken Parker, Nancy was pretty sure she knew what Ken would and would not say to his players after a losing game like this one. "You didn't say that, did you?" she asked skeptically.

Ken grinned. "Course not," he said. "I told 'em to get cracking, we have to beat Martinsburg next Friday."

"Can they?"

"Maybe," Ken said. "They're a good team, really. They haven't even started to show me what they can do."

"You're not getting soft in your old age, are you?"

"Nope. Wait 'til you see what I'm gonna make them do next week at practice."

"What?"

"Get psyched. That's what they need."

Nancy opened her car door. The crisp night air of an autumn evening in Carroll County made her want to hurry inside. "Come on," she called back.

Ken followed her out of the car. "You know, Nance," he said, "they really are a good bunch of kids."

"I know," she told him. They always were.

That week, Parker worked the players mercilessly. Their daily practices stretched out until darkness made them quit. The coach yelled encouragement at tired players as they ran through the plays over and over — "Go! Go! That's it!" At the end of each day, he gave another pep talk and told them to go to bed early. A lot of them did, exhausted.

David told his parents, "The coach has gone crazy. He thinks we played a lousy game against Liberty."

"You did," Dick told him.

"Yeah, I know."

"Did the coach say that to you, that you played a lousy game?"

"Nope. He didn't have to. He just said he wants us to beat Martinsburg on Friday."

"Can you?" Dick asked.

"Hell yes!" David shouted. "We are gonna beat their asses!"

They did. That Friday night, a jubilant Parker watched his team shut out the Martinsburg Bulldogs, in the rain, 10 to nothing. After the game, Parker told the sports reporter from the *Carroll County Times*, "Our kids came out ready to play tonight. This just goes to show that attitude is 90% of the game. I'm really proud of these kids." He added, "The big thing was that our offensive line was able to block well enough for us to move the wall. They executed the fundamentals, and we won. I thought we were well prepared for this game."

Dick Heidecker told David that the team was on the opening end of a winning streak. "You guys are going all the way," he said. "Now you're playing football."

Dick was right. The next week, they played the Frederick Cadets, a team who had not won a game since 1980 and who had lost nineteen straight games before this one. Parker told his players to put no stock in those statistics.

"Their record doesn't matter," he told the boys in the locker room. "Their defense is okay, and they have a new coach. Some of their losses were from sloppy playing, some games they were overpowered. Some were bad luck."

"Some they were dead," one player volunteered.

The team snickered. "No, they slept through the first quarter," one of them said.

"Their new coach put his mother in for the quarterback."

Parker got mad. "Hey!" he shouted. "Everybody listen up! If the team that Frederick gets to beat, after nineteen losses in a row, turns out to be the South Carroll Cavaliers, somebody's ass is in big trouble! Do you all read me?"

"Yes, Coach!"

"Okay! Get out there and play!"

The Cavaliers handed the Frederick Cadets their twentieth straight loss with a 22 to 0 shutout. Parker magnanimously told the sports reporter, "Frederick played well. It was a tough football game, we did not come in here and roll over them." He told the team, "Good going, I'm proud of you."

But he told Nancy, "This is likely to go to their heads. Two shutouts in a row, they'll think they're a professional team. I'll have to spend all week psyching them up again."

The next game, against South Hagerstown, was important to the Cavaliers. Not only was it the Homecoming game for South Carroll, which would bring hundreds of alumni to watch, but if they won it, they would be in first place in the Tri-State League. They did win it, with another shutout, 21 to 0. The victory also put South Carroll first in Class A, Region 1 in the race for the post-season play-offs. Afterwards, Ken Parker pointed out to a jubilant team that while they were defeating South Hagerstown, Frederick had finally ended its losing streak by winning over Martinsburg, whom the Cavaliers had shut out two weeks earlier.

"See what I mean?" he said. "Nobody loses forever. And nobody wins forever, either."

"We do!" David Heidecker called out.

The coach laughed. He was feeling good. The kids were playing well, and they were winning. The Region wasn't particularly important to Parker, but the League was. He was not about to let the boys relax. He spent the next week practicing the plays and psyching them up, and at the end of it they won their fourth game in a row. That Monday night, as they watched movies of the game, the coach did a running commentary.

"You see what happened in the second half?" he asked the kids. "We dominated the ball throughout the first half, and then the other team adjusted. You see how they did that?"

"They didn't do it good enough, did they?" one player asked.

"But look what I'm showing you," Parker said. "By adjusting, they made us work harder. And they might have stopped us if they hadn't made a big mistake on the kick-off which gave us the ball on their 47-yard line. You all see that?"

After the movies, David stayed to talk to Parker. He had something on his mind. "Coach, how come they never put my name in the paper when they write up the games?" he asked. "What does that mean?"

The coach chuckled. "It means zilch," he said, "Sportswriters do that. They talk about the quarterback, the fullback, the tailback. If you look at the sports section of any paper in the country, they all do that — not just in high school games, but college, pro, everything. The offensive line doesn't get in the paper. They're the guys doing the work, you won't win a game without 'em, but they don't get their names in the paper. It's always been that way, always will be, I guess." He paused. "Why?"

David shrugged. "I don't know," he said. "I think my dad would like to see my name in the paper."

Parker said, "Your dad understands what I just told you, David. And he knows what a good player you are."

"Am I?"

"Absolutely. Definitely. Your speed, your energy — and most of the time, your attitude."

David smiled. He got along with Coach Parker a lot better than he had with Coach Ellis in tenth grade. David wasn't sure whether it was his age — after all, he was two years older now, or whether it was Coach Parker. Parker, like Ellis, had certain disciplinary techniques that he used when he had to, but he seldom had to. The authority that came from his years of experience asserted itself. Besides, Parker seemed to have a handle on David. Maybe it was because of what had happened in the tenth grade, maybe it wasn't; the coach seemed to know that if he had to confront David, he ought to do it in private.

The Cavaliers' four-game winning streak snapped when they lost to the North Hagerstown Hubs. The game began inauspiciously for the Cavaliers when the Hubs got a touchdown and kicked the extra point just 92 seconds into the game. Nobody scored again until the last quarter, when tailback Keith Spicer capped a 63-yard scoring march with a three-yard touchdown to pull the Cavaliers within one point in the last two minutes of the game. Ken Parker called timeout to set up the last play. He could have let quarterback Brian Nave kick the extra point for a tie, but he didn't want to. He told the boys they were going to try for the two-point conversion which, if successful, would give them their fifth straight win. Brian Nave overthrew and the Cavaliers lost the game 7-6. Afterwards, Parker justified his decision to the press: "We went for the win," he said simply. "We felt we could score. The play was something we put in new this week. We thought that play would work against them."

In the locker room, Parker encountered an atmosphere similar to that of a morgue. He looked at his dejected players. "Get your heads up!" he shouted. "You played well. If it wasn't for a punt return, we would have won the game. Sitting here pouting won't change the outcome."

The loss had done more than end the Cavaliers' winning streak, though; it had made a shambles of both the Tri-State League race and the Class A, Region 1 standings. Now South Carroll was tied with Liberty for first place in the League, with three other teams right behind the frontrunners. There were two games left in the season.

The Cavaliers had another chance to make the two-point conversion work in the next game, which they played at Thomas Johnson. The game was scoreless until Thomas Johnson made a touchdown in the fourth quarter. With the clock running out, the Cavaliers marched 67 yards in 10 plays to score with only 40 seconds left in the game. Now Parker found himself in exactly the same position he had been the week before with respect to his options, and he made the same decision. Brian Nave, who had directed the scoring drive — which the *Carroll County Times* called "magic" — argued with him:

"Let me kick the extra point, Coach. I can do it and we won't lose."

"No, Brian," Parker said. "We're going for the win. Don't pass it to Chris this time, that's what they expect. You're gonna pass to Mike Stoll."

"Okay," Brian said.

On the field, the Cavaliers watched the Thomas Johnson defense move over to cover the wrong player. Nave did a perfect throw to Stoll, and the game ended, 8 to 7. The win clinched a tie for the Cavaliers as Tri-State League Champions, and kept them in the running for the Region. Brian Nave told the *Carroll County Times* reporter who covered the game that he had really wanted to kick the extra point, to which Parker replied: "That's why he's the player and I'm the coach." Parker said, "There was no doubt we were going to go for the two, but going for it has worried me. I've been waking up at three or four in the morning thinking about that situation. If you don't have a passer, you shouldn't try it. But Brian can pass." He added, "I used to coach from fear. I used to worry what people would say. Now I don't worry what they say."

What they were saying was that South Carroll had pulled off a miracle. They had played a beautiful game against a strong team, had scored their only touchdown in the last minutes of the game, and had succeeded in a tricky play that had failed the week before. The team was ecstatic. The next night, Saturday, they all met at the Carrolltowne Mall to celebrate. The team took over a pizza parlor, where a noisy party ensued. The boys made toasts to the team, to the coach, to each other; they vowed to defeat Westminster in their last game of the season next Friday. They spread out through the mall in a loud, formless mass, wandering aimlessly from store to store. David Heidecker, feeling exuberant at first from the victory of the day and the season, began to feel as if he were on the outside of the group. The football team had always had its cliques; groups of jocks who hung around together, talked

David Heidecker in football uniform, 1983.

and joked with each other, dated the cheerleaders. The team had been friendly to David throughout the season, but he had never been part of that group. Tonight he felt excluded. Angrily, he left the others and went to a pay phone. He called Patrick, but Mrs. Kenney said Patrick had gone out. David called the Langhages. Mr. Langhage answered the phone; he said that Chris had a cold and was asleep. Feeling depressed, David left the mall and went home alone. His parents were in the living room, watching an old movie on TV.

"Come on in, son," Dick called. "This is great, you gotta see it."

David looked at the screen, which was black and white. "What is it?" he asked.

"It's a John Wayne movie," Shirley said. "It's called Dakota."

"Yeah? What's it about?"

"Same thing they're all about," Dick said. "Right and wrong."

"Is it good?" David asked.

"Sure. Get a soda and join us."

"Okay."

David opened the refrigerator and looked longingly at the cold beer, but he had no intention of breaking training. He took out a soda and sat down next to his mother. Shirley put her hand on his shoulder.

"Did you have fun tonight?" she asked.

David shrugged. "It was okay," he said. "I'd rather be here."

He settled into the warmth of his home, enjoying the company of his family as they all watched John Wayne in the saddle.

South Carroll was scheduled to play its last game of the season against the Westminster Owls on November 11. The *Carroll County Times* "football predictors" picked South Carroll over Westminster. The Owl coach told the *Times*, "South Carroll has a lot of experience. They have something like 23 kids back from last year, and we lost most of our people. We know we're going to have a tough time." Historically, though, Westminster had beaten South Carroll 12 times, and the Cavaliers had beaten the Owls only three times. The two schools, which were the first in Carroll County to have football teams, were arch rivals. For the Cavaliers, who were already tied for first place in the Tri-State League, the stakes were their chance to stay in the running for the Class A, Region 1 championship. For Parker, a victory would give him a 7 and 3 season.

The Cavaliers played the game at home, in a cold rain. The Owls had complete control throughout the first half of the game. They took the opening kickoff and marched 76 yards for their first score. South Carroll's fullback fumbled on the Cavaliers' first offensive play to set up the Owls' second touchdown. Westminster scored on all four of their first-half possessions, including touchdowns on the first three; after they failed to make any of their extra points, their fourth score of the half came on a 31-yard field goal. At halftime, the score was 21 - 0.

When Coach Parker came into the locker room, he didn't say a word about winning the game. "I want you to go back out and play with pride," he said. He looked around the locker room, making eye contact with each of the players. "We've had a wonderful season," he told them. "We're 6 and 3 now. Remember what we did to Thomas Johnson in the last minutes of play? We're going out there now and we're going to finish our season with our heads up, playing the best we know how."

The cold rain had turned to light snow when the players came out of the locker room. After receiving the kick to begin the second half, the Cavaliers suddenly came alive. Yelling and screaming encouragement to his teammates, David Heidecker led the offensive line to open holes in the Owls' defense. On the first play from scrimmage, after trapping his men at the line, David came crashing down the field, leading tailback Tim Stach to the Owls' one-yard line.

To Coach Parker, David always had been their best blocker, and tonight he proved it. The other teams consistently underestimated David — because he was lean, he looked as if you could run through him. But you couldn't. Tall, agile, energetic, he was also strong, a lot stronger than he looked, and he was fearless. Other players held back sometimes, momentarily lazy or worried about getting hurt in threatening situations, but David never did. Now he was flying down the field, blocking with all his might to let the tailback come through.

In the first minute of the third quarter, Cavalier quarterback Brian Nave ran the ball over from the one-yard line to bring the score 21 - 7. South Carroll maintained control of the ball throughout the rest of the third quarter and into the fourth, but they were unable to score. David Heidecker was undaunted.

"Come on!" he was yelling. "Go, go, go, go!"

Halfback Keith Spicer, behind the now inspired blocking of the offensive line, carried the ball five straight times, scoring a touchdown with six minutes left in the game to trim Westminster's lead to 21 - 14. After that, tailback Tim Stach ran eleven yards into the end zone with 4:41 left to make it 21 - 20. Once again, Ken Parker had to choose between kicking the extra point or going for the two-point conversion; once again, he chose the two-points, and this time it failed. But there was time on the clock, and the Cavaliers were wide awake. Ken Parker ran along the side of the field shouting encouragement as the fullback intercepted a pass by Westminster and returned it 36 yards to the Owl one-yard line.

"Block!" Ken Parker ordered. "You guys on the line, block so we can get the ball through."

Dick Heidecker, watching from the sidelines, had his hand cupped around his mouth, shouting. "Go, Cavaliers! Come on, David! Run!"

Shirley Heidecker was on her feet, cheering, as snowflakes fell on her face. "Don't stop, David! Go on! Go on!"

It worked. The Cavaliers made two more touchdowns in the snow, in the final 1:10, winning the game 33 to 21. They came off the field in a state of ecstasy, hugging each other and the coach and doing great circular leaps, like deer. The Westminster coach told the sports reporters, "This is the toughest loss I've had in my six years here. This one will take a long time to get over." Ken Parker, chivalrous as always, said simply, "We did not panic. The Good Lord must be looking down on us or something." Then he said, "There's no doubt about it, that's the most remarkable comeback in all my years of coaching. Of course, what makes it so special is the fact that it came against a respected team like Westminster." To his team, he said, "Thank you, guys."

Although the regular season was over, South Carroll was now in the play-offs for the Region. Their first opponent was McDonough, a high school in Charles County. Parker watched films of their playing.

"We've got big problems," he told Nancy. "This is gonna be the toughest team we've played yet. They run a wing-T offense and they have a quarterback that major colleges are competing for."

"Can we win?" Nancy asked.

Ken shook his head. "I don't know how much our kids can do against these guys," he said.

Nancy winked at him. "We'll be there cheering," she said.

But it took more than cheers. Just before Thanksgiving, the McDonough Rams rolled past the Cavaliers in a 26 - 7 defeat for South Carroll. The loss eliminated South Carroll from the Region play-offs and ended their season. Coach Parker packed a suitcase, put Nancy alongside him in the car, and headed south to Williamsburg for a few days. This had become an annual ritual for Parker, established some years ago when he found himself in a severe depression each winter as the football season ended. He had developed some ways of coping: first, a brief trip out of town, and then, back in Carroll County, a strict regimen of jogging and other forms of physical activity. It helped. This year he left town feeling good about the season; his team had played well, they had made a good record, and they had tied with North Hagerstown as champions of the Tri-State League. Parker headed south with no regrets. And there was always another football season to come.

For David Heidecker, too, the end of football season brought a let-down. The program had consumed his life for three months, taking virtually all of his free time, requiring his full attention and energy, and redirecting his daily habits in a way he would not have believed possible. For three months, he had forgone cigarettes and beer, had given up a social life except on Satur-days, had observed, more or less, the coach's curfew. The football program had consumed his parents' lives, too; they had attended every game, cheering faithfully from the sidelines, and Dick had assisted Coach Parker by hauling equipment and helping to set up the field. Shirley had supported David's efforts to abide by the training rules, preparing nutritious meals for him and reminding him to get extra sleep, which was against his nature.

After the post-season game against McDonough, Dick brought David into the kitchen and handed him a beer. "Here you are, son," he said. "I think you earned this."

That weekend, David got together with Patrick and told him it was time to resume a social life. "Are there any girls left?" he asked Patrick. "Seems like a year since I had a chance to notice one."

Patrick said, "Are you kidding? Let's hit the roller rink."

David reverted to his old habits; within days, the 10:30 curfew was in his distant past. He and Patrick spent their time out of school together — driving around, meeting girls, skating, going out. By now, Patrick had his learner's permit for his driver's license. He was seventeen years old, but family conflicts had delayed his learning to drive until now. David allowed him to drive his car for practice, and gave him the benefit of his superior experience.

"*Drive*, Pat!" he would yell. "Don't just *look* at the accelerator, *press* on it! What do you think it is, a decoration?"

"I am pressing on it, for God's sake!" Patrick said. "Do you want me to do 60 on this curve? Your brakes don't even feel right, you know that?"

"Brakes, so what? You don't have to have brakes. Throw it into first and turn the wheels into a little bank, you'll stop every time."

"Jesus, David!"

Patrick passed his driver's test the first time, and now both boys had their licenses. Patrick seldom had the use of a car, but once in a while he managed it. Sometimes the boys borrowed Patrick's father's motorcycle, too, but they had to unplug the odometer first and then remember to hook it back up. David said he really preferred to drive his car, anyway — it was more romantic. "Girls don't want to hang on a motorcycle in the winter," he told Patrick. They got in the habit of double dating again, usually with girls who were friends of each other's. David told Patrick it was good to be free of Coach Parker's rules.

In December, David realized that he had enough credits to complete high school that semester. If he wanted to, he could finish up at the end of January. He would not actually receive his diploma until June, but he would not have to attend any more classes. The school administration permitted this arrangement for students who had a good reason to leave early, usually for students who wanted to begin their jobs. David began to think about it. It was also time for him to give serious thought to his entire future.

South Carroll required all seniors to meet with the school's guidance counsellor. David left his meeting with a lot of information, but no decisions. The counsellor had indicated that David had three options for his future: college, military service, or a job. There had been times in David's life when he had seriously considered going to college; in fact, he had arranged his courses to give him that option. By his senior year, however, David had virtually abandoned that avenue. For one thing, there was the money. For three years, he had watched his mother work two jobs, ostensibly so they could complete the house addition that had stood untouched for a couple of years. David knew that the money from the second job was all spent, mainly on him. The counsellor had talked to him about scholarships, had even suggested that David discuss with Coach Parker the possibility of a football scholarship. He had mentioned student loans and part-time work. But money wasn't the only consideration. David was tired of school. He was proud of what he had accomplished since his inauspicious beginnings in elementary school, but he was tired of it. He knew this might not be a permanent condition, that he would want to return to school someday, maybe take courses at night, but right now he wanted a break from it.

That left military service or a job. A lot of boys from South Carroll always went into the Army. The counsellor gave David some literature about the military, and the name of an Army recruiter in Westminster. David went to see the recruiter. He began to think that the Army was his best option. He didn't want to get a full-time job right away, and the service would postpone that. Besides, David didn't know what he wanted to do eventually, and the Army would give him a chance to find out. Not only would he be exposed to a lot of skills in the service, but later there would be educational benefits. He might be able to get his college education paid for, which would solve both of his problems with going to college right away: the financial worries, and the fact that he needed a couple of years to do something else first.

David went over to Coach Parker's house one night to ask his advice. Parker was used to this; over the years, hundreds of football players had come by to seek his opinion on how they should spend their lives. Unless he was talking to a boy with professional football potential, which was rare indeed, Ken Parker tended to listen to the student and to be very sparing with advice. He had no illusions about limits of his knowledge outside the world of football.

"What do your folks say?" he asked David.

David shrugged. "Nothing yet," he said. "I want to get my thoughts straight first, and then talk about it with them."

He and Parker sat at a small round wooden table in the middle of the kitchen. A gentle fire in a large old-fashioned fireplace in the living room warmed the whole area; the house was constructed without a wall between the kitchen and the living room. For the Parkers, who were not inclined towards formal entertaining, but whose house often overflowed with hungry teenagers eating hotdogs and potato salad, the arrangement was perfect. Nancy brought Ken and David each a piece of homemade cake and a glass of milk.

"What do you think your parents want for you?" Parker asked.

"My parents have always wanted me to do what I want to be happy," David said. "If I told them I wanted to go to college, my mom would probably get a third job somewhere and my dad would go out and sell something to get the money."

"But you don't want to go to college?"

"Not really. Not now, anyway. I think I'll want to go later, when I'm a little older. But not right now."

"And you don't want to get a full-time job yet?"

"What could I do?" David asked. "I can get a job with minimum wage, but it won't have any future. I don't want to do that the rest of my life."

"What kind of job would you like to have someday?" Parker asked.

"I don't know, I've thought about maybe going into engineering."

"Are you good at math and science?"

"Yeah, pretty much. I think I could do that."

The coach said, "You'll need more education for that. You realize that?"

"Sure, I know. But maybe I could get some of it in the Army, and finish up afterwards."

Parker nodded. "You're thinking straight," he said. "Sounds to me like the Army makes sense for what you want right now."

David grinned. "Do you think basic training will be as hard as your training, Coach?"

"Huh!" Parker grunted. "You ain't seen nothing, kid. My training is a bed of roses compared to the Army."

"Think I can do it?"

"Absolutely," Parker said. "I have no doubt whatsoever. Nancy?"

Nancy poked her head into the kitchen. "Did you call me?"

"Yes," Parker said. "Could you bring us another piece of cake, please?"

Home on Gillis Road, David brought up the subject of his future. He made it clear at the outset that he did not want to go to college right away. Shirley had ambivalent feelings about that. Both she and Dick had come from families where college was not even a consideration — higher education meant high school. But that was a different generation, and Shirley felt that David was smart enough to consider college, if he wanted it. David convinced her that he didn't.

"Not now, Mom," he said. "It's either get a job or go in the service. Those are the things I'm looking at now."

Dick said, "You have an awful lot of years ahead of you to go to work. And once you start, you don't usually stop."

"I know," David said. "I'm thinking that, too. The Army is only two years."

"You might like it," Dick said. "A lot of physical stuff, different places to go. A good way to spend a couple of years before you have to settle down."

The three of them decided that David could finish high school in January, if he wanted to. He would enlist in the Army with a deferred entry to allow him to graduate with his class in June. After January, he would get a job to keep occupied and earn a little money for his future.

When David told the Langhages about his plans, they were amazed. Chris did not have enough credits to finish high school that semester, nor had he given serious thought to his future.

"David, I'm impressed," Joyce told him. "It sounds as if you have your act together."

"Thanks, Mrs. Langhage," David said cheerfully. "I think it's just good luck."

"No," Bob told David. "When you think ahead, and set things up to work out for yourself, you make your own good luck."

David said, "Could I have a doughnut?"

"Sure," Joyce said. "Amy helped me make a fresh batch this morning, didn't you, Amy?"

"Amy!" David yelled. He picked her up and swung her around the room, causing her to shout with joy. He helped himself to a doughnut and invited Chris to join him at a Christmas party some girls were throwing.

Right after Christmas, David enlisted in the Army. He received a deferred entry date of the following August, 1984. After that, he applied for a job at Black & Decker, and was hired to begin in February. It was a minimum wage job in the warehouse, but David didn't mind; he would be doing it only for a few months, and he could save most of the money. Dick and Shirley signed the required forms so that David could complete high school in January and the school granted permission. In February, David took Patrick to see his Army recruiter in Westminster, and told Patrick to give the idea some thought.

That spring Aunt Ollie moved out of her house on Gillis Road. She had lived alone there since Uncle Harold died about five years earlier, and she had managed all right. But she was growing older, and the house was getting to be too much, even though Shirley came by every day and Dick and David helped out. An opportunity arose for her to sell her house to the county, which was buying several hundred acres of land for the purpose of building the Gillis

Falls Reservoir to provide public water to southern Carroll County. Aunt Ollie's property — but not Dick and Shirley's — was in the area that the county needed. Dick and Shirley used to joke that if the county ever got around to building the project, which was years away, they would be sitting on waterfront property. The county rented Aunt Ollie's house to tenants, and she moved in with her married nephew a few miles away.

Just before she moved, Aunt Ollie had a gigantic sale of most of the furniture in her home, which included a few valuable antiques. The sale became a social event, with friends and neighbors gathered around, and Aunt Ollie serving as a gracious hostess. People were amazed that she could cheerfully part with possessions representing years of her life, but Aunt Ollie told them, "When I walk away from something I don't look back." On moving day, her nephew brought a U-Haul truck and some friends and relatives to help with the rest of Aunt Ollie's household goods. Dick and Shirley and David came down the hill to help, with David doing most of the heavy work.

"What about this, Aunt Ollie?" he would ask. "Does this go, or do we trash it?"

Aunt Ollie looked discerningly at the item. "Trash it," she said confidently. "I won't have much room where I'm going."

David wrapped glassware and filled cardboard cartons. He wanted to keep busy through this day, which filled him with sadness. Aunt Ollie was the only "grandmother" he had known, the most important person in his childhood, after Dick and Shirley, and he had always taken for granted that she would be there, at the bottom of the hill, for him to wave to on his way in or out of his home. When the house was empty, he offered to follow the U-Haul to her nephew's home so he could help at the other end. Aunt Ollie gratefully accepted, and then decided to ride with David, in his car, as she left her old home. Shirley, who was crying, hugged Aunt Ollie and promised to be over the next day to help her get settled. Aunt Ollie waved to Dick as David's car pulled away behind the U-Haul, carrying what was left of Aunt Ollie's tangible possessions.

That spring, Shirley spent a lot of time with Aunt Ollie, at her new home. Soon she was situated in a pleasant room with everything she needed. The two spoke by telephone every day, and Shirley visited her twice a week. Aunt Ollie liked Shirley to take her shopping. In May, she made plans to spend most of the summer with other relatives in Boston, to escape the Baltimore climate and have a change of scene.

As the end of the school year approached, David began to wonder if he had missed out on certain end-of-school activities.

"Is this stuff fun?" he asked Patrick. "Are any of these parties worth going to?"

Patrick shrugged with all the nonchalance of a student who has never been part of the in-group. "No, it's a drag," he said. "We ought to make our own plans, find something exciting to do to celebrate."

They spent Memorial Day weekend in Ocean City, Maryland, in an inexpensive motel with a case of beer and a variety of girls. By Sunday they were out of beer and out of money, with barely enough cash left to pay the toll on the Chesapeake Bay Bridge. There was one day remaining in the holiday weekend, but David and Patrick took off, heading west, and beat the crowd home. It had been, as they both boasted, the way every red-blooded American boy should spend the weekend before his high school graduation. Dick and Shirley were just glad to have David back in one piece.

Graduation was held outside at South Carroll, where three hundred kids received their diplomas. Awards had been announced at an earlier assembly in May; David had not received any, nor had Patrick, or Chris, but as Patrick pointed out, making it through the twelfth grade was its own reward. Dick and Shirley proudly sat through the ceremony, with Dick grinning broadly and Shirley catching her breath as David's name was announced and he received his diploma. Shirley thought fleetingly of the early social workers and teachers, people who had told her that David was limited. Dick remembered the principal at David's elementary school who had expelled David because at age nine or so he was uncontrollable. He reached over and squeezed Shirley's leg.

Afterwards, Dick asked David if he wanted anything special to celebrate. David laughed. "No, thanks, Dad," he said. "I think I did all the celebrating I can stand last weekend."

Patrick interjected, "Yeah! You just better hope he didn't catch anything."

Shirley asked tolerantly, "What if I cook you a special dinner?"

"Great!" said David. "With steamed shrimp?"

"Why not?"

"Can Patrick join us?"

"Sure."

They headed home with Patrick in tow, as they had done so many times before. The Heideckers were pleased that Patrick had followed David's example by deciding to enlist in the Army. Chris, too, was seriously considering the Air Force, and had been up to Westminster to talk to the recruiter. Dick told the boys they were keeping the world safe for democracy as he handed each of them a cold beer.

CHAPTER 10

David and Gidget

"Let's go to the fair," Shirley announced unexpectedly.

Dick stared at her. "What for?"

"For fun," Shirley said. "We can get dinner there."

Dick was skeptical. "What's there that I want to see?" he asked.

"Food, Dad!" David said. "You can eat and Mom can hear Conway Twitty or whoever they have. Come on, we'll have a good time."

Dick was sitting comfortably in front of the television, watching a ball game. "I don't know," he grumbled.

"Come on, Dad, Mom won't have to cook if we go."

"I like her cooking better than any carnival food," Dick retorted. But he was talking to himself now. David and Shirley were getting ready to leave.

The Winfield Community Volunteer Fire Department held a carnival every summer. The fire house stood on Liberty Road, immediately west of South Carroll High School. If the weather was right, the fair attracted hordes of students, as well as other members of the community. In 1984 the carnival began on Saturday, July 14.

The Heideckers decided that David should take his own car, since he wanted to pick up Patrick on the way. By the time David got to the Kenneys' house, Patrick had been drinking beer most of the day.

"Come on, man," David said. "You won't be able to walk."

"Just give me a minute to grab a six-pack," Patrick protested. He did, and they were off. By the time they got to the fire house, Patrick was too drunk to get out of the car. David looked at him with disgust and told him to sleep it off. Patrick crawled into the back seat.

David found his mother. Dick had gone off to get a Polish sausage and diet soda, Shirley said. She and David walked together. There were rides, all kinds of food, and live music set up on a bandstand — a typical country carnival on a pleasant summer night. For David, there were many of his classmates from South Carroll, some of whom he had not seen since leaving school in January. Periodically, he returned to his car to check on Patrick.

"What is Patrick doing?" Shirley wanted to know.

"He's loaded, Mom. It's okay."

"Oh," said Shirley.

A girl waved from across the field. "David, wait up!"

David recognized Gladys Nunn, a friendly, heavy-set brunette he knew from high school. She had another girl with her. He shouted, "Come on over, Gladys!"

The girls did. Gladys asked, "How are you doing, David?"

But David was looking at her friend, a cute, diminutive redhead with the kind of white skin and freckles that redheads tend to have. "Hi," he said. "You're Gidget, right?"

Gladys's friend smiled shyly and nodded. "Yup," she said. David noticed that her smile was slightly crooked, which he found appealing.

Gladys said, "Gidget, this is David Heidecker. This is Gidget Geisler."

David said, "This is my mother."

Everybody nodded hello. Nearby, the country music band warmed up. Shirley moved towards the bandstand and found two seats up front. She sat down in one and saved the other for Dick.

David took Gladys by one hand and Gidget by the other. "Come on, girls," he said. "Now I have two of you."

The three of them strolled around the fair, holding hands. A couple of times, David called out to people he knew, "Hey, check out my new style — two at a time." Gladys wore short shorts and a halter. David took the opportunity to tease and embarrass her.

"Look at this," he announced to a passer-by. "Do you see what's in this halter top?"

"David!" Gladys said.

Gidget laughed. She could see that David was having fun. They walked until they were tired, and then Gladys suggested they sit in David's car and talk.

"My car's here, but Patrick's in the back seat of it, wasted," David said.

"What?" Gidget asked.

"My friend, Patrick Kenney. He's loaded."

"We can go to my car," Gladys suggested.

They did. There on a warm summer night, with the car doors open and the radio playing softly, David Heidecker climbed behind the wheel of Gladys Nunn's car. His left leg was stretched out onto the ground, with Gidget Geisler next to him, squeezed between his six foot five frame and Gladys's full body to her right, all of them so close together that David's right leg pressed against Gidget.

"Do you have a job?" Gidget asked him.

"Nope. I'm going in the Army next month."

"Did you sign up already?"

"Yes, last winter. I got deferred entry, but my time's almost here."

Gidget reflected. "Why do you want to be in the Army?"

"Something to do," David said. "It beats working, right?"

"Maybe not," Gladys interjected. "Don't you have to go to basic training, and all that?"

"So?" said David. "Do you think it's any harder than football practice?"

"Now I know where I've seen you!" Gidget realized. "The football team." She thought a minute. "How did you know my name before?"

David shifted in the cramped front seat. "I saw you around," he said nonchalantly.

"Saw me around where?"

"Here and there. In the halls. In band. One time I saw you in the library at school."

"Well, why didn't you say anything to me?"

"I did," David told her. "One time, Patrick and I saw you in the library, and I said to Patrick, I want to talk to that girl."

"Why didn't you, then?"

"I did. I went over to the table where you were, and I said, excuse me, but do you have the time?"

Gidget looked at David. "What did I say?"

"You said, it's two fifteen."

Gidget waited. "What else?"

"Nothing, that was the whole conversation."

Gladys burst out laughing and Gidget joined in. David shifted his weight in the driver's seat. He said, "Well, I don't particularly want to sit here next to a couple of laughing hyenas."

The girls stopped laughing. "I think it's neat you're going in the Army," Gidget told him. "My dad was in the Army when I was born. He was in Germany. That's where he picked out my name. He said it means 'small things.'"

"Your name is cute," David said.

In the car with the doors and windows open, they were surrounded by sounds of the summer fair. A hot dog vendor called out the price of his goods; a T-shirt saleswoman hawked her wares. A man who claimed to be able to guess your weight announced his skill loudly and repetitively. Lost children wailed for their mothers, and lost parents shouted for their youngsters. One or two dogs on leashes barked intermittently. Friends called to each other.

A man at the roulette invited people to part with their money. The electric guitar player with the country music band did Jim Reeves classics, moving from Four Walls to Put Your Sweet Lips a Little Closer to the Phone. On the car radio, the top forty station in Westminster played Stevie Wonder's I Just Called to Say I Love You.

Gidget asked, "Are you glad about going?"

"Sure, I'm excited about it, but I'll miss my folks quite a bit," David said. "I don't know if homesick is the right word or not."

Gidget nodded thoughtfully. "I can understand that," she told him.

David and Gidget and Gladys talked for a long time. The girls, who were seventeen, had been best friends since eighth grade. They were a year behind David at South Carroll. Gladys, a fun-loving girl with a strong sense of purpose, had completed her credits and graduated at the end of eleventh grade, leaving Gidget to face her senior year alone, as Gidget put it. The girls remained inseparable, although Gladys would be starting a job soon. They told David about the time they auditioned together for band and chorus, with Gidget playing piano and Gladys singing "The Rose." David discovered that Gidget, like both of his parents, was born in May. He and Gidget found out that they lived about five miles apart.

Gladys suddenly reminded Gidget of the time.

"Oh, my gosh!" Gidget exclaimed. "My father will be on the warpath if I don't get out of here right now!"

"Well, can I have your phone number?" David asked.

They exchanged telephone numbers. Then Gidget said to David, "Hey, I have an idea. Gladys and I usually go to the movies every Sunday. What about coming with us tomorrow?"

Gladys stared at Gidget in disbelief. She had never known Gidget to be so forward with a boy. "Good idea!" she said. "Can you come?"

"Sure," David said. He looked at Gidget. "I've had a good time tonight."

"Me, too," Gidget said.

"See you!" David walked off towards his car. Some yards away, he turned back and waved.

Patrick had crawled into the grass and fallen asleep — mercifully, David thought, considering the mess his car would have been otherwise. David pulled Patrick to the car and stuffed him into the back seat. Then he thought a minute. He couldn't take Patrick to the Kenneys' house in that condition. David drove straight home. Patrick was able to stumble into the Heideckers' house, where Dick and Shirley were watching television. David put Patrick on the sofa and got him some cold soda to drink.

"I lost you at the fair," Shirley said. "Did you have fun?"

"Yup," David said, "I met a girl."

"So what else is new?" Dick snorted.

"This one might be special," David said.

Later, when Patrick was awake, David told him about meeting Gidget.

"I know who she is," said Patrick. "The girl in the library who told you what time it was." He started to chuckle.

"Not you, too!" David said disgustedly. "I don't know why you all think it's so funny."

The next day, David couldn't wait for the movies. He got into his car and followed the directions Gidget had given him to her house. She lived in a modern split level home in a development called Glenvue Acres. The Geislers' home on Bluebird Drive sat back from the road on an acre and a quarter wooded lot. David pulled into the driveway and knocked on the front door wearing jeans, a football shirt with "Cavaliers" on it, and no shoes. When Gidget opened the door, he said, "Hi, kid," with his friendliest smile.

"Oh, no, you're hours early!" Gidget wailed. She was wearing shorts and a T-shirt with sandals, and she hadn't even begun to work on her hair for the day. Her father wasn't home, the house was a mess, and here was David Heidecker, standing at her front door grinning at her.

"I'm not here for the movies, I just dropped by to say hello. Relax!"

"Okay," Gidget sighed, with a tentative smile. "Come in, then. This is my brother Johnny."

"Hi," said Johnny. He was sprawled in front of the TV in the living room, watching a sports event. Johnny Geisler, aged fifteen, had the same red hair and freckles that Gidget had, but he was strikingly taller and bigger, with broad shoulders and well-developed muscles. David joined him in front of the TV while Gidget got him a soda.

"I sure wasn't expecting you right now," she told him.

"I don't like to do what people expect all the time," David said. "In fact, the unexpected is my habit." He looked around. "This is a nice house. Your folks aren't home?"

"No."

They talked some, and then Gidget told him he'd have to leave. There was housework she had to do before they went to the movies. David left, but not long afterwards he telephoned and they talked for half an hour. Gidget hung up reluctantly, thinking this was silly, she'd be seeing him soon.

The girls planned to meet David at the Carrolltowne Mall. Gladys came over to the Geisler house to help Gidget get ready. Gidget was fuming about her hair, but she finally got it to a state she approved of. It was then she discovered that Gladys had to do an errand for her mother before she could go to the movies.

"Gladys, you're always late!" Gidget moped. "I don't want to keep David waiting. You'll just have to drop me at the movies and catch up with us later."

They drove to the Carrolltowne Mall on Liberty Road, ten miles east of South Carroll High School, in the direction of Baltimore. They found David sitting on a bench in front of the cinema. Gidget sat down next to him and explained that Gladys had an errand and would join them in a little while. David and Gidget remained on the bench until it was time for the movie to begin.

"I wonder what's taking Gladys so long?" David asked nervously.

"She'll be here," Gidget assured him. "We better go in." She reached up and kissed David on the cheek. They walked into the movie theater holding hands.

The movie was The Last Starfighter, about an alien who takes a bored teenager off to another planet to fight against rebel invaders. David and Gidget didn't think the movie was very good, but David enjoyed laughing at it. In between wisecracks, he asked, "What's keeping Gladys?"

Gladys finally arrived halfway through the movie.

"It's about time!" David told her. "What did you do? Walk here?"

"How's the movie?" Gladys asked.

"Not great," said Gidget. "Did you bring us any popcorn?"

"No," Gladys said, "I don't have any money."

After the movie, the three of them went to a pizza place in the mall. David ordered a pepperoni pizza. While they waited, David regaled Gladys with his description of the first part of the movie.

"There was this monster from outer space who was really a sex symbol in disguise," he told her. "Kind of like the prince that got turned into a frog, only this guy was too ugly to be kissed, and so he could never be turned back."

"Who was the guy that had a face like a fish?" Gladys asked.

"That was fish face," David told her.

Gidget giggled. "Come on, David. The movie wasn't that bad."

When the pizza came, the girls said they were not hungry.

"What's the matter with you two?" David asked. "Are you on a diet?"

The girls exchanged knowing looks. Gidget had always been lean and trim, without a hint of fat or flab. Gladys, on the other hand, had a much fuller figure and a slight tendency towards overweight. The girls used to say that Gidget could eat anything without gaining a pound, while Gladys inhaled calories just by looking at food.

"You'll have to eat it, David," Gladys told him.

He did, at least most of it. David said loudly to Gladys, "I thought you said you were hungry. Or did you say *horny*?"

Gladys hid her face. Gidget was enjoying every minute. When they had finished all the pizza they wanted, they went out to the parking lot. David lifted Gidget onto the hood of his car and got up next to her. Gladys began to feel like a fifth wheel.

"I'm going for a walk," she announced. She went inside the mall, but it was Sunday night and the stores were closed. A lone security guard in a dark uniform walked along the cement. Gladys joined him silently. Soon she was telling him that she had come to the movies with her best girlfriend and a boy, that the girl and boy had just met each other the night before, but that it looked as if they were falling in love.

"I've never seen Gidget act this way with a boy before," she said. "Usually Gidget's pretty shy. And she never likes to act in a way that'll make a boy think she's chasing him. You know what I mean?"

The security guard nodded. "Yeah," he said.

"But here she was last night, just a couple of hours after they met, *inviting* him to come to the movies with us today. Can you believe it?"

"Yeah."

"It makes me wonder if I should have come today. I mean, maybe Gidget wanted to be alone with him, for God's sake. I sure don't want to horn in on them, or be where somebody doesn't want me, you know?"

"Yeah."

Gladys and the security guard paced the length of the mall and back, past dark store windows with iron grating in front, locked doors, empty tables and chairs, deserted benches, and fountains that had been turned off. There were shadows and noises, but they were vastly different from the sights and sounds of a busy shopping mall in the daytime. Back at the mall entrance at last, Gladys waved good-bye to the monosyllabic guard and stepped out into the summer night. David and Gidget were sitting in the front seat of David's car, making out. Gladys knocked on the roof.

"Hey, guys!" she called. "Gidget, your father, remember?"

"Oh, no, I'm late," Gidget wailed.

"Tell him you had car trouble," David offered optimistically.

He walked the girls to Gladys's car and gave Gidget a hug. "See you tomorrow," he said softly. It was no longer a question.

David turned and walked back to his own car. When he got there he called out, "Hey, Gladys! Thanks!"

Gladys rolled down her window. "Thanks for what?"

"Thanks for knowing Gidget!"

David followed the girls up Liberty Road to Route 27, where they turned right and he turned left. He took another left onto Gillis Road, and then a right into the gravel driveway. At the top of the hill, he turned off the motor and sat in the car for a while, looking out at the stars and thinking over the events of the weekend. He thought about the many, many girlfriends he had had before, most of them the teenage equivalent of the one-night stand. Some, he knew, had been pure physical conquests; others had presented a challenge which, when met, proved hollow. Now he had met a beautiful girl who was sweet and nice, and as smart as he was. She came from a nice family who cared about her, and in all probability she was a virgin. Could a girl like that be interested in him? Was he really six foot five and handsome, a football player and high school graduate, or was he just the little boy who had been shuffled from place to place because no one wanted him and who had gone to live in an institution because there was no family for him? David knew the story of how Dick Heidecker happened to be in Debbie Miller's house at three o'clock one morning in 1972, although it was not a topic of casual conversation in his home. He was haunted now and then by the thought that his adoption sprang from a random encounter, and not from any grand design for his life. Did he really deserve the love and happiness he had found with Dick and Shirley, or was that, too, an accident?

If he did deserve love and happiness, was he capable of making it work, David wondered. How would a girl like Gidget expect to be treated? You couldn't just hustle her into bed on the first or second date, that was for sure. She even had a father who demanded that she come home on time. That meant she was probably sheltered from a lot of problems. Did she like pretty things? Was this the kind of girl you were supposed to court with romantic gifts and words? "Courting" was not really an activity within David's experience. Was this something he could learn to do?

David had an idea. The next day, Monday, he drove over to Patrick's house.

"Pat, I need your help," he said. "Where do you go to get flowers?"

Patrick looked at him blankly. "What do you mean, flowers?"

"Flowers! Roses, carnations, stuff like that."

"What for?" Patrick asked.

"You know, flowers to give a girl."

Patrick suddenly caught on. "I get it!" he yelled. "You want to take flowers to Gidget!"

David shifted his weight. "Well," he said self-consciously, "so?"

"Okay! Geez! I don't know where to buy flowers. At a flower store, I guess. Are there stores that sell flowers?"

David thought a minute. "The yellow pages," he said suddenly. "We can find out in the yellow pages."

They did. There was no listing under "Flowers," but they stumbled onto one for "Florists." David picked out the one closest to their present location, out Liberty Road.

"We could call there," Patrick suggested. "Find out how much they are and all."

"What are you, crazy? Call there and make a fool of myself? We'll just go there. And act cool."

Once inside the store, however, David was confronted by a confusing array of flowers. He saw blooming plants, cut flower arrangements, hanging baskets and corsages; there were reds and pinks, lavenders and blues, whites, yellows. The aroma was close to overwhelming. In the midst of all the color was the proprietor, an overweight man of fifty-five with half glasses and a short-sleeved shirt and tie.

"Help you, son?" he asked with a friendly smile.

"Uh, well," said David. "I need flowers."

The man looked at him. "Okay," he said. "Any particular kind you have in mind?"

"Roses," David said confidently. "I need red roses."

"How many is that, son?"

"Well, a dozen, I guess."

"A dozen roses are thirty dollars, son," the man told him gently.

"Thirty dollars!" Patrick yelled.

David punched him with his elbow. "Can I buy just one rose, then?" he asked.

"Sure," the owner said. "That'll be two-fifty."

"Could you let me have some kind of a pretty box with it?" David asked tentatively.

"You bet," the man said. He selected a single red rose and placed it in a long thin box with colored tissue inside. "I'll put a little card in here in case you want to write a message. Would you like me to tie a ribbon around the box for you?"

"That'd be great!" David said enthusiastically. He paid for the rose. "Thanks a lot!"

He and Patrick headed east in David's car. On the way, David chain-smoked cigarettes and talked rapidly about the evening's plans. This was the day he was going to meet Gidget's father, he told Patrick. Gidget said her father was pretty abrupt with her boyfriends, that he asked a lot of personal questions. She said it made her nervous sometimes just having boys in the house when her father was home. What did Patrick think David ought to talk about to Mr. Geisler? Did he have any suggestions? Patrick did, but David was not amused. He changed the subject. Did Patrick know of a good movie to rent, since the Geislers had a VCR and that was part of the plan for the evening? Patrick said he and his brother had recently seen a horror film called The Evil Dead. It was great, Patrick said, really gory and horrible. David would love it. What about Gidget, David asked, would she like it? Certainly, Patrick announced, she wasn't a prude or anything like that, was she? David mulled over this suggestion for a minute. He lit another cigarette and turned on the car radio.

At home, David shaved and showered and bantered a little with his father. At four o'clock in the afternoon he set out for Bluebird Drive.

Johnny Geisler opened the door to David's knock. "Gidget, for you!" he yelled.

Gidget bounced to the door. "Hi."

"Hi, Gidge," David said, a little shyly. "Is your father here yet?"

"He's still at work," Gidget said. "He'll be along in a while."

"Do you want to go to the video store with me and rent a movie?" David asked.

"Sure. Wait right there!" She bounced back inside to give her hair one more quick brushing and pick up her purse. "Okay, I'm ready!"

In the front seat of the car, David picked up the long thin box with the ribbon around it. "I think this is for you," he said.

Gidget looked up at him. "Can I open it now?"

"Sure, why not?"

She lifted the solitary rose from its box. "David, this is beautiful," she said. She reached up and kissed his cheek. "I love it, thank you."

The card inside the box fluttered to the floor of the car. Gidget picked it up. "What's this?" she asked. She turned it over. David had written:

"I love two things,
you and the rose.
The rose for a day,
you forever.
Love,
David."

Gidget reread the card without saying anything. David started the car and put his arm around her.

At the video store, they examined a number of movie titles. Finally David said, "Patrick saw a horror movie called The Evil Dead. Do you want to try it?"

Gidget shrugged. "Why not?"

They took it to the counter.

"The Evil Dead, huh?" the man commented. "You like blood and gore, do you?"

"Blood and gore?" Gidget repeated warily.

"Yup, blood and gore!" The man leaned over the counter and lowered his voice. "I'll tell you when to look out. Where you want to watch out is when the woman sticks her pencil in this other girl's ankle. Watch out after that."

"Sticks her pencil in somebody's ankle?" Gidget repeated. "*In* their ankle?"

"Yup, right in there. Blood pouring out like crazy. It's a mess."

Gidget looked questioningly at David. "Come on, be a sport," David said.

She smiled. "Okay."

They checked out the movie.

Back at Bluebird Drive, John Geisler had arrived. Gidget's parents were divorced, and he had his fiancee, Kathy, with him. John Geisler stood up to shake David's hand and say hello. Afterwards, David always wondered how Mr. Geisler, at five feet nine inches tall, was able to look *up* at him in such a stern and disapproving manner. He did not know that John Geisler did not really disapprove. That was his standard look for Gidget's dates.

"Make yourself at home," he told David. "Kathy's fixing dinner now."

"Thank you, sir," David said. He sat down carefully on the couch. Fortunately, there was a rerun of an old situation comedy on TV which everybody seemed to be watching. David looked at it, too. At dinner, David sat next to Gidget, who was strangely quiet. John Geisler, who was a sheet metal mechanic and a supervisor at Westinghouse, engaged David in conversation about his high school background, football, his work history, his future in the Army, and his plans for his life's work.

"What are you actually doing now?" he wanted to know.

"Well, actually, I'm just sort of waiting right now," David told him. "I'm due to leave for Fort Benning, Georgia, on August 21, and that's only five weeks away. That's what I'm doing, I guess."

John Geisler gave him a long look. "I see," he said.

After dinner, John and Kathy retreated to allow Gidget and David and Johnny to take over the living room. "Wow!" David told Gidget. "I feel like I was under a magnifying glass."

"He does that to everybody I go out with," Gidget explained. "Don't pay any attention to that."

"Let's try out the movie," David suggested.

"What's it say on the box?" Johnny asked.

David read: " 'The Evil Dead is designed to pull scream after scream from the base of your spine and from the depths of your soul.' " He let out a phony scream. " 'It is a tale of the supernatural forces which occupy the darkest forests of man's domain. Ever-present, ever-listening, the evil dead lie and wait for the one ancient incantation that will give them license to possess the living.' " David looked ominously at Gidget and Johnny, and lowered his voice. " 'Five vacationing college students unwittingly resurrect these incredible demons from their ancient slumber. Now there is no escape. The guilty must be punished.' " David's voice rose as he continued with exaggerated expression: " 'One by one the students themselves are shockingly transformed into monsters whose own thirst for revenge becomes *insatiable*! There is only one way to stop them through the act of bodily *dismemberment*! To survive this grueling terror, former friends and lovers combat each other *until only one man remains*! He must now defend himself long enough to discover the horrible secret of the evil dead . . . or die trying!' "

"What's dismemberment?" Johnny asked.

"Cutting off people's arms and legs and things," David said. "Man, this sounds great!"

Gidget looked dubious. "I don't know," she said.

"Come on, Gidge, let's give it a try."

"Okay." They put the videotape inside the VCR and pushed the "play" button.

The Evil Dead, made in 1979, is ninety minutes of one of the goriest movies ever made. As the five college students find an old tape recorder in their mountain cabin, and play the tape that talks about demons, Gidget holds tightly to David's hand. Suddenly, one of the girls in the movie, Shelley, hears a noise outside and goes out in her bathrobe to investigate. She calls, "Is there anybody out there?" She walks into the woods, going farther and farther away from the cabin as strong winds blow, thunder is heard, and shadows pass across the moon.

"Yeah, right!" David yells. "Here they are in the middle of nowhere, and this broad leaves her friends and goes off into the woods with her bathrobe on!"

"David, I'm scared," Gidget says.

"How can you be scared when it's so silly?" David says. "This isn't scary, it's just fun."

By now he has both arms around Gidget.

Shelley, now deep in the woods, suddenly is surrounded by mist, eerie noises, and falling branches. Vines encircle her brutally and begin to choke her around the neck. The vines move as whips, ripping off her bathrobe and hurling her to the ground. The scene becomes violently erotic. Shelley is on the ground, writhing and thrusting her hips up and down as vines beat against her and branches assault her between her legs. Screaming, she somehow extricates herself and runs back to the cabin. Finding the door locked, she retrieves the key and unlocks it just one step ahead of the unseen monster. She screams to her friends that the woods are alive, that she wants to get out of here. They try to reassure her, but to no avail. Ashley, one of the boys, offers to drive her into town. They go off into the night. Ashley suddenly stops the car and gets out. Shelley follows him. The bridge is out. There is no way back to town. Shelley becomes hysterical as they head back to the cabin.

"I don't blame her!" Gidget says.

"Aw, you're as bad as she is," Johnny says. "Scared of your own shadow."

"Let's turn it off," Gidget suggests.

"Turn it off?" David says. "Gidget, there hasn't been even one drop of blood so far, not one drop!"

When Shelley and Ashley return to the cabin, Shelley is transformed into a hideous ghoul — evidently one of the evil dead. She picks up a pencil and stabs one of the other girls, Linda, in the ankle. Blood spurts out. Shelley now has superhuman strength. Her eyes are white and she is hideous. The other boy, Scotty, picks up an axe and attempts to fend her off. By now, Linda is turning into a monster, too.

It's too much for Gidget. She gets up and goes into the kitchen. "I'll make popcorn," she calls back. "Let me know when it's over!"

"Gidget, what's the matter?" David asks.

"It's a little too gory for me," she says. "You go ahead and watch. I'll be right here fixing something to eat."

The two girls in the movie, Shelley and Linda, attack the two boys. One of the girls gnaws off her own hand at the wrist and it falls to the floor. In one bloody scene, Ashley grabs the axe from Scotty's hands and cuts off Shelley's feet and other parts of her body. The pieces lie around on the floor, throbbing. The legs are pulsating. Unidentifiable internal organs move up and down. The boys determine they must bury Shelley. They put the body parts into a sheet which they carry outside and bury. They begin to talk about getting out of there.

"No shit!" David yells. "Wise up, fellows!"

"What's happening?" Gidget calls.

"You don't want to know," David tells her.

"Well, tell me when it's safe for me to come in with the popcorn."

"Okay."

Now Linda, Ashley's girlfriend, transforms back and forth from human to monster. Once she says, "Oh, Ashley, please help me." When he tries to, she turns into a ghoul again, this time singing a children's nursery rhyme. Ashley drags her across the floor and chains her to a wall. He gets a chainsaw and is about to dismember her when he notices her necklace he gave her earlier that evening during the only romantic interlude in the movie. Now he can't do it, and besides, she has changed back into a normal person. He leans over and caresses her.

"Gidget, the popcorn!" David calls.

"Is it safe?" she asks.

"Yup, come right now, it's fine."

Gidget comes in with popcorn and sodas and napkins. She looks at the TV. It seems calm; she sits next to David again.

In the movie, Ashley unchains Linda and carries her outside. Thinking she is dead, he intends to bury her with love and gentleness. As he digs her grave and carefully puts her in and covers her with dirt, everything is serene. Then he notices her necklace lying on top of the grave. As he reaches to pick it up, Linda bursts from the ground, once again a ghoulish monster. She attacks Ashley viciously. He picks up a heavy wood beam and hits her with it over and over, but without effect. In desperation, he grabs the shovel and swings it, accidently decapitating Linda. Her headless body now assaults him. They fall, with Linda on top. Blood pours out of her neck onto his face. Her head, some yards away, continues to laugh and shriek. Ashley finally extricates himself from the decapitated body of his girlfriend and heads back to the cabin, covered with blood.

"Oh, my God!" Gidget screams. "This is sick!" She runs back to the kitchen.

"I think I've seen enough, too," Johnny says.

Now David is alone in the living room. "Guys, what's wrong?" he calls. "Come on, it's almost over!"

"That's okay," Gidget says. "I'll wait in the kitchen for you."

Back in the cabin, Ashley still has to deal with the third girl and now with Scotty, who also has joined the evil dead. He tries to reach the book about demons which, he belatedly suspects, is responsible for all his problems. He manages to throw it into the fire as the girl is about to kill him with a poker. As the book burns, Scotty and the girl dismember spontaneously. The parts of their bodies fall off. There are gruesome special effects. Their insides fly out of their bodies onto Ashley. Their skulls disintegrate and are covered with insects. As Ashley walks into the daylight, a mysterious windlike force overcomes him, and the movie ends with Ashley screaming. The credits roll to the accompaniment of an upbeat ragtime score.

"Okay, you cowards, the movie's over," David called. "Come on back to the scene of the crime."

Gidget came in and sat on David's lap. "That was the worst movie I ever saw in my life," she told him. "I think it took away my appetite forever."

David laughed. "It was fun," he said. "That movie wasn't scary. It was too silly to be scary. It was just a little gross, that's all."

Gidget kissed him. "Want to go downstairs?" she asked. "There's nobody in the club cellar, and we have a stereo down there."

They went down the steps to the Geislers' club basement, which was one large room, partially paneled, with inexpensive furniture, a small TV, and a stereo. Because of its location, the room was naturally cool and insulated from the summer heat. The atmosphere changed abruptly as David and Gidget sat next to each other on the sofa, quietly holding hands. Gidget talked gently and seriously to David about her childhood.

"We used to live in Baltimore," she told him. "We moved here when I was in fifth grade because my mother wanted a bigger house."

"Were you glad?" David asked.

"Yes," Gidget said. "Our old house was okay, but it was a rowhouse with no yard. You could hear the neighbors' radios and stuff. This is a lot nicer."

"I like your house," David said.

"We almost didn't get to move in," Gidget told him. "The builder went bankrupt and we had to do a lot of the work ourselves. We used to come up every weekend and work. We even had to cut down some of the trees and haul the wood away."

David asked, "When did your folks split up?"

"Ninth grade," Gidget said. She put her head on David's shoulder. "It was awful. My mother went to live with her parents, near Baltimore. Johnny and I went with her at first. We hated it, though. The school was crowded and the kids there were tough. We came back in a few months and I just popped back into my classes at South Carroll."

"So where's your mom now?"

"In Baltimore. I see her every couple of weeks."

"Do you miss her?" David asked.

"Yes." Gidget ran her hand through her long red hair. "I'm better off here, though. My friends and all are here."

David nodded. He got up and walked around the club basement, touching the paneling here and there. He told Gidget that he was adopted by the Heideckers, that his original name was different. Gidget seemed surprised.

"I thought if you were adopted, you didn't know your real name or who your parents were," she said. "How come you do?"

David lit a cigarette and looked around for an ashtray. Not finding one, he located a cracked saucer. "That's if you're adopted right after you're born," David told her. "Then they lock up your birth certificate and everything, and you can't find out. But I was around eleven when I was adopted, so of course I was using my real name all along. There was no way they could keep it a secret."

Gidget was shocked. "Eleven years old! Where were you before that?"

"I came to live with my parents when I was eight," David said. "I stayed with them from then on. Before that I was in an institution for about a year."

"An institution! For what?" Gidget was holding David's hand.

David shrugged. "For being an orphan, I guess. I didn't have any other place to be." He laughed. "Maybe I was an ugly kid."

"But what happened to your real parents?" Gidget wanted to know.

"My father I don't know about," David said. "My mother couldn't take care of me, I guess."

Gidget was horrified. "That's sad," she said. "Do you hate her for that?"

David hesitated. He put out his cigarette in the cracked saucer. "No," he said finally. "I don't think so. But I would like to meet her and ask her why."

"Why what?"

"Why she gave me away. I'd really like to ask her that one question."

Gidget was thoughtful. "Do you think you ever will, though?"

David pulled her onto his lap. "I don't know," he said. "First I'd have to find her. She might not even be alive. Or she might have moved away."

"Did you ever try to find her?"

"Not really. I looked up her name in the phone book once, but it wasn't there. Maybe, if I did find her, I wouldn't even want to talk to her."

Gidget nodded. "Do you remember her at all?"

"No," David said. "She gave me away when I was a baby."

"To an institution?"

David kissed her lightly. "No, to some other people. Like a foster home. I lived in a bunch of foster homes before the institution."

Gidget was fascinated. "Really? Were they nice to you?"

"No, not usually," David said casually. "I guess some of them were, some of the time. But mostly they weren't."

"What did they do?"

"Hit me sometimes. Beat me. Scared me." David's face was just a few inches from Gidget's, and he gazed steadily into her eyes. "A lot of times they didn't pay any attention to me. They didn't teach me how to do things or take me anywhere. They weren't a father or mother to me. They weren't affectionate. One lady hit me up and down my back with the heel of her shoe. She put my hands in boiling water, too. And at this one place, they put me in the attic and then came up with sheets on to frighten me because I was afraid of the dark. Things like that. I can't even remember all the things, or who the people were. I don't want to. I shut it out of my mind."

Gidget was quiet for a minute. "Was it better at the institution?" she asked finally.

"In some ways it was. But I was lonely there. I wanted to live in a family that was nice to me."

Gidget ran her finger along his cheek. "How do you get along with your parents?" she asked.

"I get along with them terrific," David said. "I always have. The most important day of my life was the day I became David Heidecker."

"What day was that?" Gidget asked.

"The day they took me out of the institution for good," David told her. "I was eight years old." He put his arms around Gidget and kissed her. "You know what?" he whispered.

"What?"

"I never brought a flower to a girl before."

"Really?"

"Yup."

Gidget kissed him back. "Let's make out," she said.

Gidget had a part-time job at a plant and garden center. She had to work the next evening. At seven o'clock, David and Patrick arrived at the store unannounced. Dressed in jeans, T-shirts and old sneakers, with unruly haircuts, they did not look much like customers. Gidget's boss called her aside.

"Gidget, who are those boys? Are they customers?"

"Well, no," Gidget admitted. "The tall one is my boyfriend. They're on their way to bowling."

"Get them out of here."

Gidget did. But an hour later, David called her at the store.

"Where are you?" Gidget asked.

"We're at the bowling alley," David said.

"Well, how's it going?"

"Gidget," David said. "When I get out of the Army I want to marry you."

"What?"

"Because I love you."

Gidget said, "I love you, too, David."

Then Patrick was on the telephone. "Gidget, I don't know what you said to David just now, but he has one hell of a grin on his face."

Gidget hung up. Her boss was looking at her, and besides, she was speechless.

The next day, Wednesday, July 18, David told Gidget that he wasn't going to date anybody else, and he didn't want her to either. Gidget agreed. She offered her school ring to David and he took it. He put it on a chain and wore it around his neck.

"I wish I had a school ring to give you," he said wistfully. "I never got around to buying one."

In the four weeks that were left before David was to report to the Army, he spent part of every day with Gidget. They often skated at a roller rink, sometimes with Patrick, sometimes with a group, sometimes alone. They went to the movies, went swimming, drove around, walked, talked, laughed. They were kids in summertime, but the imminence of the Army kept David incessantly aware that this was the last summer of his childhood.

David discussed with Dick the possibility of changing his plans. "Dad, is it too late to stay out of the service?" he asked.

"Yup," Dick said. "You're in now."

"But I want to be with Gidget," David told him.

"I know. But you will be. You're not going to the end of the world, and it won't be forever, either."

"It feels like it," David grumbled.

The first time David took Gidget to his house, Dick and Shirley were not at home. David went there one afternoon on a whim. Driving east on Gillis Road, he suddenly made a sharp turn onto the steep, rutted road that was his driveway. He shifted into low gear and wound his way up with skill born of experience.

"Where are we?" Gidget asked.

"This is my house," David said. "Want to see it?"

"Sure," Gidget said. She leaned forward to get a look at the place where David lived. He conquered the hill, made a right turn alongside the house, and stopped.

"This is not Buckingham Palace," David announced seriously. "It's where I live. Like it or leave it."

Gidget looked at the small house with the unfinished addition attached to it. She took in the grassy hillside, the flowering bushes and shrubs all around, the American flag towering over the house, the trees in the distance. The road they had just left seemed far behind them now. The sounds were of nature, not of civilization.

"I like it," she told David. "I think it's cute."

David laughed. He wiped the back of his hand across his forehead. "Phew!" he said. "We're over that hurdle, then. Do you know that one girlfriend of mine broke up with me because she didn't approve of my house?"

"Are you serious?"

"Yup. She told me it was a shack, and she wasn't interested in people who live in shacks."

Gidget was indignant. "That's terrible!" she said. "You should have broken up with her for that!"

"Well, I would have," David explained. "I guess you could say it was mutual. She didn't dig my house, and I didn't dig her." He leaned down and kissed Gidget. "Want to come in?"

"Are your folks here?" Gidget asked.

"Nope. They're at work."

They went inside, and David showed Gidget his home.

"What are you building on there?"

"That's going to be the new addition." David laughed. "It's already old," he said. "We've been building it for about four years."

"Really?"

"Uh-huh. I guess it'll get finished someday."

They saw the living room, with pictures of David all around. David took Gidget's hand and walked her to the door of his bedroom. They looked in, but he made no effort to take her inside. They drank a soda and returned to David's car.

"You have to meet my folks," he said. "I want you to get to know each other."

That happened at a crab feast in July. The Heideckers and Gidget, like most Marylanders east of the Appalachian Mountains, were avid crab-eaters. Despite the mess, it was a perfect occasion for Gidget to meet David's parents because everybody was occupied. As crab shells and discarded claws piled up in the middle of the table spread with newspaper, Gidget observed that Dick and David were doing most of the talking, and that they were doing it to each other. Far from being offended, she felt relieved — she didn't have to worry about what to say. As the afternoon wore on, she realized that she didn't have to worry anyway. David was totally relaxed with his parents, who appeared to be wholly approving of David, whatever he said or did.

Dick pushed his huge pile of crab shells into a large trash can and sat back for a moment. He focused his eyes on Gidget. "So you like crabs," he said.

Gidget nodded self-consciously. "Yes," she said.

"Would you like a beer?"

Gidget was taken aback. She was seventeen years old and not accustomed to being offered beer by adults. "No, thank you, Mr. Heidecker," she said. "I don't drink."

Dick's eyes twinkled. "What do you mean, you don't drink? Are you in training?"

Gidget was puzzled. "In training?"

"Right. Last year when David was in training, he couldn't drink, either. Coach Parker made him sign a pledge that said so."

Gidget smiled. "Oh," she said.

"But you look kind of dainty for the football team," Dick went on. "I bet that long hair would get in your way, too."

Gidget said, "I did play on the softball team last spring."

"Did you have to sign a pledge?"

"No," she told him. "I just don't like to drink."

Shirley said, "Don't pay him any mind, Gidget. He's just a big tease."

Dick said, "Don't anybody tell her about Mary."

"Mary?" Gidget asked. "Who's Mary?"

"Mary was a girlfriend of David's," Dick said. "She couldn't take a joke."

"What happened?"

"We were fooling around up at the house one day, and Mary didn't have much of a sense of humor. She ran out of the house and got lost in the woods."

"Then what happened?"

David put his hand on Gidget's shoulder. "He's making this whole thing up," he told her. "I never even had a girlfriend named Mary."

Dick snorted. "If he didn't, that's the only name he never had."

David said, "Come on, Dad. You'll give Gidget the wrong idea."

"What wrong idea? She doesn't know what a playboy you are?"

Gidget said, "I know he's had some other girlfriends."

Dick lowered his voice. "I'll tell you one thing," he said to Gidget. "He never had one as pretty as you before. Or as nice, either."

Gidget giggled self-consciously. She liked David's parents. They made her feel comfortable, as if they approved of her because she was with David. They were the least pretentious people she had ever met, too; they didn't try to impress you, or be something they weren't. Gidget had no way of knowing whether or not David's father told each of David's dates that she was the prettiest and nicest, but later David assured her that he did not.

"I never heard my dad say that to anybody," he told Gidget. "Cross my heart."

Gidget believed him. He seemed as open and straightforward as his father.

On many occasions after the crab feast, David and Gidget spent evenings at home with Dick and Shirley. Among Shirley's skills was the ability to prepare wonderful meals without apparent effort — a talent acquired, Gidget supposed, from a combination of her job at the restaurant and years of waiting on Dick hand and foot. Gidget, too, was at home in the kitchen, and enjoyed helping Shirley. After dinner, they watched television together, or David and Gidget retreated to David's room for privacy. More often than not, Dick and Shirley fell asleep on the sofa in front of the TV. Whichever way the evening went, Gidget came to feel at home there and, surprisingly, not at all inhibited by the nearness of David's parents. She and David separately concluded, early on, that they were more comfortable at the Heideckers' house than at the Geislers' house.

"Your father makes me feel like I'm in a goddamn laboratory," David said once. "I feel like I can't relax there."

"He doesn't mean anything," Gidget said loyally. But she knew what David meant. Without any real discussion about it, they came to spend much more of their time at David's house than at Gidget's. It was hardly surprising, then, that David and Gidget were intimate for the first time at the Heideckers', in David's room, with Dick and Shirley some twenty feet away in the living room. It was August, 1984, and David had waited longer than he was accustomed to wait for that moment. For Gidget, who had waited all of her life, the circumstance that Dick and Shirley were in the house gave her momentary pause.

"David!" she whispered. "What about your parents?"

"It's okay, babe," David assured her. "They're probably asleep, and anyway, they're open-minded."

Both of them had crossed a threshold of sorts. Gidget was intensely in love for the first time. She had allowed herself to become intimate with this boy, who she knew was really a man, just a couple of weeks away from being a soldier in uniform. She sensed that she was passing into adulthood, with everything that implies; her days of living heedlessly, day by day, without direction, would soon be gone. For David, a different dilemma presented itself. Military service, which had once seemed the solution for his immediate future, including perhaps the gateway to higher education and a constructive career, now appeared as a giant obstacle to his time with Gidget. Why, damn it, hadn't he met Gidget before he allowed himself to sign up?

In the summer days that were left to them, David and Gidget spent some of their time with Patrick. But Patrick began to realize that his nights out with David were coming to an end. By now Patrick had graduated from South Carroll High School, and in August of 1984 he, too, enlisted in the Army, with his entry scheduled for November. Patrick had a job and his driver's license, and he was making the most of his freedom while it lasted. He continued to do things with David, but Gidget was almost always there.

They all enjoyed roller skating. Frequently David was the best skater in the rink. Besides enjoying the thrill of danger and close calls, he was skilled and graceful on the floor. He could entertain himself for hours with backward motions, spins, dodging in and around groups of skaters, and coming to sudden halts. He could skate rings around Patrick, who was cautious and not particularly coordinated. He was also a much better skater than Gidget, who was smooth and coordinated but not competitive or flashy. When they went together, Patrick observed, David would spend ten minutes showing off wildly for Gidget, and the next hour guiding her protectively around the rink with exaggerated chivalry.

It was at the roller rink that Gidget first saw the volatile side of David. One evening they were part of a group that became disorderly. David was in the middle of things, showing off, skating fast, talking loudly. At nine o'clock the manager singled out David and directed him to remove himself from the rink for rowdiness. David stormed outside; by the time Gidget followed him out, he was slamming his open hand against the outside of the building.

"Damn it!" he yelled.

He hit the building again and again. Gidget was frightened. "David?"

David turned and looked at her. "Those creeps!" he shouted. "Did you see that son of a bitch pick me out to harass? Did you see all those other guys being louder than me, causing more trouble, but nobody said a word to them?"

"David, he did speak to them," Gidget said. "He told everybody to calm down."

"Yeah? So what? How come I'm out here and they're still inside? Do you know it's always like that, always has been, all my life?"

Gidget couldn't think what to say. "Let's go home," she ventured at last.

"Go home?" David shouted in her face. "Go home while those other creeps are still skating around in there? You must be nuts!"

He opened the trunk of his car and took out a set of nunchakus.

"What's that?" Gidget asked.

"It's a weapon!" David shouted. He hurled them around in the air.

"David, what for?" Gidget persisted, her voice sharp with anxiety.

David looked at her. "It's not for anything," he said finally. "I just have 'em for fun. Don't worry about it." He put the nunchakus back in the trunk and locked it.

"You scared me," Gidget said. "Why did you get so angry about such a little thing?"

"It's not little to me to be picked on," David told her. "I don't mean to get angry like that, but sometimes I can't help it." He paused. "I was much worse when I was younger," he went on. "I used to smash anything I could get my hands on, including other people, if I thought somebody was crossing me. I guess it was because of not having a real family, and being mistreated so much."

"Oh," Gidget said.

David took her hand. "Let's go for a ride," he said. They got into his car. "But remember one thing — I'm never coming back to this dump again, never!"

Within twenty minutes they were in David's bedroom, where David made gentle love to Gidget. He seemed mollified, no longer disturbed by the incident at the roller rink. But Gidget had seen David's short fuse, and learned

Gidget

quickly that is was an integral part of his personality, not an isolated phenomenon. He blew up often, and suddenly, and sometimes he blew up at her. Once it happened when Gidget talked to another boy in line at a pizza place. Outside the shop, David leaned down and hollered in Gidget's face.

"You made me feel like two cents in there!" he shouted. "You were just totally ignoring me, you were so goddamned interested in that creep! What am I, a piece of shit?" He slammed the side of his fist against the top of his car.

Gidget started to cry. "David, that was a boy from my class in school," she sobbed. "How can I not speak to somebody like that?"

"Well, damn it, you were paying more attention to him than to me!" David yelled. "Just don't treat me like I'm nobody, that's all."

Gidget covered her face with her hands and turned away, her shoulders shaking. David suddenly put his arms around her. "Gidge, I'm sorry," he said. "I didn't mean to yell at you. Please don't cry. I love you."

Gidget cried against his chest.

"Please, please don't cry. I won't ever yell at you again, I promise."

But he did. There were several more arguments that summer, all of them over trivial matters. David would become angry, raise his voice, hit inanimate objects, calm down, be sorry. Gidget learned that he could be jealous, even though she gave him no reason to be. No one else interested her, but it didn't matter. David would yank the chain with Gidget's school ring on it from around his neck and thrust it at her.

"Here!" he would shout. "Take it back! Give it to somebody else. You sure don't want me to have it, do you?"

But she never took it back, and he always let her put it gently around his neck again.

"David, why are you so angry?" Gidget asked him once. "Why do you get jealous when I don't care about anybody else but you?"

"I just lose control, Gidge. It's from all those things that happened to me growing up." David said.

"That's an excuse," Gidget said. "You can't use your background as an excuse for acting dumb."

"Well, I'm in a good mood most of the time," David said cheerfully. "I've really gotten a lot better than I once was."

It was true. Gidget usually saw the other side of David — his upbeat, personable, happy-go-lucky, generous and giving nature, the part of him that had made her fall in love with him so quickly. She never observed him arguing with his parents, never even heard him complain about them. He didn't fight with Patrick. And he didn't fight with her very much, certainly not about anything important. She made up her mind that she would just have to put up with David's short fuse.

Gidget wanted to show David her old house in Baltimore, which she herself had not seen since fifth grade. Her father gave her directions. They drove to the western edge of Baltimore City and found the intersection of Frederick Road and Beechfield Avenue. Gidget pointed up Beechfield.

"Up there," she said. "That was our street."

They found the house. David parked in front of it and held Gidget's hand as they sat in the car. Both of them were struck by the contrast between the Geislers' old and new neighborhoods. This neighborhood was made up of steep, narrow streets lined with cracked sidewalks and lines and lines of red brick rowhouses. The sidewalks and front steps and little porches teemed with people on a warm evening. There was constant city noise from children playing, dogs barking, radios, stereos, traffic, sirens, buses. The sounds of domestic arguments could be heard between the walls, and bits of gossip floated from one porch to another. The Carroll County neighborhood had no sidewalks. The distance between homes was such that a person standing outside of one house would have had to shout at the top of his lungs to be heard by someone at the next house. Radios could be played at full volume without annoying anyone, and the only sound of traffic came from an occasional motorcycle in the country. The Geislers' street in Carroll County ended in a circle with no outlet. From their back door, which was made of sliding glass that went onto a wooden deck, they could see tall trees, birds, squirrels, and fields in the distance.

David drove the car up Beechfield Avenue. Gidget suddenly spotted her old school.

"That's my elementary school," she said. "My mom used to walk me there every day."

David looked at the school. The road ran past it, up a steep hill where it disappeared. He kept looking at it.

"What is it?" Gidget asked.

"That road," David said. "I want to see where it goes."

He drove past the school, up the winding hill. Six blocks past Gidget's old school, the road ended at the entrance to what looked like an academy. A large white sign at the entrance said: RICA. David stopped the car and took Gidget's hand.

"I thought the road looked familiar," he said. "Son of a bitch! This is the institution I lived at."

"Right here?"

"Well, it wasn't here when I lived in it," David explained. "But when I had to come back to the institute and ride the bus to school every day, this is where I came."

Gidget smiled. "I was right down the street."

David looked at her. "It must be destiny." He turned the car around. "Let's get out of here," he said. "Back to the country."

They spent some of their time with Gladys who, like Patrick, was coming to understand that their relationship threatened to change the nature of hers with Gidget forever. Gladys was happy for Gidget. In a certain inevitable way she was jealous, too. But she knew the kind of accommodation she needed to make in order to keep her place as Gidget's best friend. She accepted David as her good friend, too. The three of them still went to the movies at the Carrolltowne Mall on Sundays, still got pizza together, still drove around and talked and laughed.

Gidget told David that Gladys was boy crazy. "I always used to tell her, we can't go around picking up boys," she said.

"What did Gladys say to that?" David asked.

"She said, we're not picking up boys, we're introducing ourselves to boys. Then I said, how is that different, and Gladys said, don't be a wet blanket."

"Are you?"

"No. I always tell Gladys, you'll chase anything in pants, and she always tells me that I'll die of old age waiting for the perfect date."

David kissed her. "Not anymore," he said. "Your perfect date is here."

They also spent a lot of time with Dick and Shirley, who asked Gidget to call them by their first names.

"What am I, an old man?" Dick demanded. "I'm not your grandfather, you know. I'm your friend and you're my son's girl."

"He's right," Shirley said. "We want you to call us by our first names."

Gidget thought a minute. "I'll call you Richard," she told Dick. "It sounds more dignified."

Dick laughed. "Okay," he said. "What about Shirley?"

"I'll call her Shirley, if that's all right."

Gidget took David to meet her mother in Baltimore. Linda was a warm, youthful person, still in her thirties, who made David feel at ease. She didn't ask him anything about his work history or his future plans. Instead, she told him stories about Gidget's childhood, including a bout with pneumonia that Gidget suffered at the end of the fifth grade.

"Her doctor kept telling me just to wait, the fever was bound to break," Linda told David. "I ended up carrying Gidget into the emergency room in my arms. She spent eight days in an oxygen tent."

"Was she okay?" David asked.

"Eventually," Linda told him. "No thanks to her doctor, I might say."

"Did you ever call him again?"

Linda chuckled. "I'll say I called him. I called him every name in the book."

David liked Gidget's mother. She seemed friendly and accepting. David told her he hoped they would meet again soon.

As the date for David's departure approached, David and Gidget began to talk seriously about their future.

"I wish I weren't going," David told her. "If I had met you before I signed up, I'd have done things a little different."

"I wish it, too," Gidget said wistfully. "What am I going to do the rest of the summer? And what about next year, when I'm still in high school?"

David stood up and began to pace around the Geislers' club basement, rubbing his stomach. "You better not be planning to date anybody else!" he told her.

"David, of course not. I don't even want to be with anybody but you. I'm talking about how much I'm going to miss you!"

David sat down and took Gidget's hands. "Look," he said. "I'll be at Fort Benning for three months. I know my parents will come down there to visit me at least one time. There's no way they're going to go three months without seeing me. You can come along with them. So that's one time anyway that we'll be together. And I'm sure my dad will pay for me to call you once in a while. So we'll have that. And I'll write to you. Will you write back?"

"I'll write you all the time!" Gidget told him. "I'm great at that."

"Well, I don't know if I'm very good at it, but I'll do the best I can," David said. "Actually, I haven't written very many letters before."

Gidget looked at him. "What happens when your training at Fort Benning is over?" she asked.

David reflected, his hands on Gidget's shoulders. "I'm pretty sure I'll get some time off then. I'll be able to come home and we can be together. Then I'll be sent somewhere, one of the Army bases."

"What if it's very far away?"

"We'll work it out, babe. There's no way I'm going to stay very far away from you for too long. Trust me for that."

"I will," Gidget said. She climbed onto David's lap and let his long arms engulf her. Then she heard her father calling from the top of the steps.

"Gidge? Are you and David down there? It's getting late."

David lifted Gidget off his lap and stood up. He winked at her. "I'm on my way, Mr. Geisler," he called upstairs. He and Gidget walked up holding hands, and Gidget stepped outside to be with David for one more minute before they had to say goodnight.

CHAPTER 11

Fort Benning

Fort Benning, Georgia, the largest infantry training center in the Free World, bills itself as "the Home of the Infantry." The fort occupies nearly three hundred square miles of grass, sand, woods, roads, flat land and hills. Its architecture is varied and its low-rise buildings multi-colored, ranging from red brick to white aluminum siding. A three-thousand pound steel statue of an infantryman, known to the soldiers as "Iron Mike," stands twelve feet high in front of Infantry Hall. The fort sits alongside Columbus, Georgia, a southern city which almost touches Alabama and is the second largest city in the state of Georgia. It is a stone's throw from the house at Warm Springs where President Franklin Roosevelt died in 1945. The surrounding countryside, once slave territory, contains tobacco fields and pecan orchards. Fort Benning is almost seven hundred miles from Carroll County, Maryland.

On August 21, 1984, David Heidecker took his first airplane flight to become a part of Company E, 5th Battalion, 1st Infantry Training Brigade at Fort Benning. Like thousands of recruits before him, he spent his first few days at the reception station. His hair was cut and his body examined, prodded and poked. He was issued articles of clothing and two sets of dress greens. He took aptitude tests, had a classification interview, went to orientation meetings. His permanent file was created. He was assigned to barracks.

On August 23, he wrote:

Dear Gidget:

We have been apart 3 days as I am writing this letter and it feels like a lifetime. I know that I have told you I love you but I just realized how much. My parents, you and Patrick are all I have thought about. This Army life is pretty easy so far but we have only been here for 3 days. We start basic tomorrow. I have made some

The Geislers' house on Bluebird Drive. *Ann Turnbull*

friends. One of them is always falling asleep in class. Boy does he catch hell. We are wearing our uniforms and the boots are hell. All my hair is gone. It feels weird and looks weirder. We have gotten our dog tags and they are always messing up my name. Well, got to go.

> Love you 4-ever-n-longer,
> David

P.S. Are you going to marry me when I get out? If you want to know if I'm asking, I am. PLEASE SEND ME YOUR PICTURE.

A few days later, David wrote again:

Dear Gidget:

Hi, how is my sweetie? I miss you so very much but don't worry about me, I'm doing okay. I have to work on my marching. My friend Bobby is a lot worse than me. We started PT, that's Physical Training, and I enjoy it. It's hard but it really makes you feel good about yourself after you finish. Today we had 8 hours of class on the M-16 rifle and it is easy as hell. We had a guy get caught drinking coke and he has KP (kitchen patrol) for 3 days. Another platoon had 2 guys court martialled and thrown in jail for the rest of their military career. I guess the Army isn't going to take any shit. All they did was back talk the sergeant. I'm not going to do that!

I talked to my mom and dad today and they told me I could call you direct. I like that because I miss you very much. I try to tell you in so many different ways how much I do really love you. I want to spend the rest of my life with you. I figure if you want we could get married after you get out of school. I will be stationed in Kentucky after this. But it's all up to you! If I had my way I would be with you forever, I mean it!

> Love you 4-ever-n-longer,
> David

David's life had taken on a new dimension. All around him were young recruits from various parts of the country, many of them reacting to Army basic training in very different ways. Some failed miserably at it, others tolerated it, and some, like David, seemed to embrace it. As a tall, lean, muscular young man of nineteen who had played varsity football, David thrived on the Army's rigorous physical training. He was taught rifle marksmanship, land mine warfare, employment of hand grenades, anti-tank weapons, individual tactical training, armor tactics. He struggled with the confidence course and the obstacle course. He was told repeatedly that the Army's goal is to transform each recruit into an infantryman who is combat ready — physically, psychologically, and in terms of skills.

David found that soldiers in basic training have little time of their own, and almost none for the development of personal relationships with others. Nevertheless, he discovered that soldiers in basic training become "buddies" in the sense of sharing a common experience, or maybe, just being in the same boat. On a Sunday night he told his buddy Frank:

"I didn't expect to get homesick at my age."

Frank shook his head. "Me either," he admitted. "Where you from?"

"I'm from Maryland."

"Maryland. I'm from North Carolina, I'm really not that far from home, but I guess I feel just as homesick as you do. Were you ever away before?"

"No, this is my first time." David lit a cigarette and extended his pack to Frank. "Cigarette?"

Frank took one from David's pack. "Thanks," he said. "I miss my girlfriend, too. Her name's Gidget."

"Gidget, huh? Mine's Gail. G and G."

"Do you write her much?" David asked.

"Yeah. We're just a few hundred miles apart, but it may as well be the world."

"You know, the Army would be okay if you could have your girlfriend in your bunk with you," David said.

"Yeah, and your drill sergeant on the next continent."

They both laughed. Bitching and moaning was part of the game. Whether the recruits enjoyed the training or not, they wouldn't let on; instead they had to talk about their tired feet, their aching muscles, their thirst for a beer, and their hatred of the drill instructor. The Army brass might talk about leadership, courage and teamwork, but the recruits talked about s.o.b.'s, assholes, and mayhem to be committed against the sergeant. It was all part of being in the Army.

David had expected to miss Gidget and had prepared himself psychologically to deal with that. He had never had occasion to write letters before, and wasn't sure how he would do. It turned out that he didn't mind writing at all — he found it was a way of feeling closer to Gidget. What took him completely by surprise was the extent to which he missed his father and mother. It had not occurred to him before that except for a night here and there, maybe an occasional weekend, he had never been away from them since he was eight years old. He found that when things got him down at Fort Benning, the two people in the world that he really wanted to talk to were his parents.

One week after David's departure, just before school opened, Gidget accompanied her family on a spur of the moment vacation at the beach in Wildwood, New Jersey. Gidget was unwilling to leave before the mail came. She had not yet received her first letter from David, and was unable to write to him without his official address. There was grumbling from Johnny and Kathy, her father's fiancee, as they all waited for the mailman, but John Geisler said he understood. His patience was rewarded when the mailman did arrive with David's first letter. Gidget happily joined the others in the car, clutching the letter. In Wildwood, they stayed in an inexpensive motel with wall-to-wall cots in their room. Gidget spent most of the time alone, on the beach gazing out to sea, or on the boardwalk where she stopped frequently to look into store windows. Once, at an arcade, she put quarters into a photo machine and got a strip of black and white pictures of herself. She put another quarter into a machine that produced a metal coin on which was imprinted "7/18/84

DAVID AND GIDGET FOREVER''. She put a second quarter into the same machine and got an identical coin. She sent a letter to David, enclosing one of the coins and the strip of photographs. She wrote:

> Here is a special coin I made for you at the beach. The date is for when we started going steady. I have another coin just like it for me. I'm going to keep it with me all the time.

She bought a pretty postcard and sent that, too.

They came home from the beach on Labor Day and Gidget began her senior year at South Carroll High School. Three weeks after he had left Carroll County, David called. Johnny Geisler answered the telephone at Bluebird Drive.

"Person to person for Miss Gidget Geisler," the operator announced.

"Gidget, long distance!" Johnny yelled.

Gidget dove for the phone. "Hello?" she nearly whispered.

David was saying her name as the operator attempted to verify her identity. "Gidget? It's David."

"David, I'm so glad to hear from you!"

"Me, too! Have you been getting my letters?"

"Yes, two so far. Did you get mine?"

"Yup, I got two of them. Keep 'em coming, okay? It gets lonely here!"

Gidget stretched out on the sofa with the telephone receiver in her hand. "David, I miss you so much. Do you know that school has started and I'm a senior?"

"Yeah, I know. How is it?"

"Okay so far. I think it's going to be pretty easy. But it's terrible here without you, and I don't even have Gladys at school any more. It's not going to be really fun this year at all."

"You're not going out with anybody else, are you?"

"David, of course not!"

"Just joking, babe. Listen. I really miss you, too. You can't even imagine how lonely it is down here without you. You're all I think about day and night."

"Do you like the Army, though?"

"So far, anyway. It's a lot of work, especially physical, but it gives you a good feeling. Also we're learning a lot of neat stuff. We're having rifle marksmanship, we're going to have hand grenades, mine warfare, stuff like that. Just like the movies, only you get a lot grubbier than they do in Hollywood."

David and Gidget quickly passed the next ten minutes, each excitedly enjoying the conversation with the other. Finally, Gidget asked, "David, is this call expensive?"

"I guess so. My dad said I could call once a week and he'd pay. What about if I try to make it every Friday night, would that be a good time for you?"

"I guess you want to make sure I don't go out on Friday nights, right?"

David laughed. "No, I just want to talk to you. I wish I could call every day."

"Me too," Gidget said. "David?"

"Yeah, babe?"

"I sent you something. You probably didn't get it yet, did you?"

"I guess not. It'll probably come soon. What about some pictures of you, did you send any yet?"

"Yup. I hope you like them."

"I *know* I'll like them," David said. "I wish you could mail me yourself instead of just pictures. Listen, I talked to my parents, and they're going to come down here later this month. You'll come with them, won't you?"

"I sure want to! I have to ask my father, though."

"Why would he mind? I mean, my parents will be with us the whole time anyway."

"I know. It'll probably be all right. Your mom already mentioned it to me."

"Good. I really miss my parents, too. Even Patrick! You know, I figured out that this is the farthest I've been away."

"In your life?"

"Yes. Did I tell you that after I finish here I'm going to be stationed at a place in Kentucky? It's called Fort Campbell."

"How far away is that from here?" Gidget asked.

"I don't know exactly, but somebody said it's a little closer to home than Fort Benning is. Besides, once I'm finished with basic training I'll get a lot more leaves and time off and stuff. This is the longest stretch right now."

Gidget sighed. "I hope you're right, because it's too long for me," she told him.

"How's Johnny?"

"He's fine."

"I haven't heard anything from Patrick, but I wrote to him once."

"I hope he'll write you back."

"Well, babe, I guess we're going to have to end this conversation. I don't think my dad would appreciate it if we talked all night."

"David, I'm really glad you called. I miss you so much."

"Me, too, babe. You know how much I love you."

"I love you, too, David."

"Bye for now," David told her.

"Good-bye."

Gidget had always enjoyed school, but now she went with a sense of melancholy. She felt that many of the seniors had changed over the summer, as she had. Everybody seemed older, more jaded, less enthusiastic. They were no longer just kids in school; they were on the last leg of a journey that would take them to adulthood and the end of childish pleasures. For many of them, this would be their final year before they obtained full-time employment; a large number of them had just spent the last real summer vacation of their lives. Some were consumed with the rigors of college applications. All of them had to consider their future plans; they could no longer live one day at a time. There was considerable traffic in and out of the guidance department, where a Snoopy poster announced: "Everybody knows the world's coolest students go to South Carroll." Gidget signed up to be a Teacher's Aide and joined the staff of the school newspaper, but her heart was not in it. Her best friend was no longer at school and the boy she loved was seven hundred miles away.

Her father tried to talk to her. "Gidget, this is your last year of high school," he pointed out. "This should be a happy time for you. You ought to be going to parties, doing things with the other girls, and boys, too. You should be having fun. Do you think it makes sense to be going steady with a boy who's in Georgia?"

Gidget sighed and said she was going to do it anyway. She went into her room and wrote a letter to David:

Dear David,

I miss you. School is just a drag without you and Gladys. Everybody seems bored. I'm working on the school paper, but it's just for something to do. I'd like to write an article called 'Why I love David Heidecker.' But I don't think the teachers would let me.

What is ahead for us? Are we going to get engaged? When, if we are? We're already going steady but we're hundreds of miles apart. I looked at the map in my book to see where you are and could hardly believe we're that far apart. I sure hope I can come down there and visit you later this month.

I dream about you every night. Don't forget to call whenever you can. I love your letters, please keep writing. Count the days till we're together again.

Love you 4-ever-n-longer,
Gidget

David wrote back:

> Dear Gidget,
>
> Hi. What's up? Alot here. Friday was hell. We went to the gas range and got gassed about 6 times. They taught us how to use our mask. We all got put in the gas chamber and made us take our mask off and keep our eyes open and walk out. It really puts a burn into your skin. After all this we had to walk home with 50 pounds of stuff on our backs for 13 miles. My feet are sore but I feel good because all of this is a requirement for graduation.
>
> Enough Army talk. I got your letter Thursday. I cried when I read it. I didn't know if you knew how much I love you but I guess you do. You are the first girl I ever really loved and I'm glad we will spend the rest of our lives together. Your pictures were great. I love the coin. I have it with me all the time. Whenever I get depressed I take it out and think of you and it makes me feel good. I remember one time you said that after 5 years or so of marriage people just don't tell each other how much they love each other. I promise you every day of our lives I will tell you *I love you.*
>
> I've been thinking of your questions. Yes we are going to get engaged. As soon as possible. I figure after you get out of school we can get married. How many kids do you want? Is your father going to let you come down on the 29th? I hope so. I never thought I could feel this way. I picked the prettiest and best girl in the world. How is school going? I know it is difficult seeing others, I feel the same way when we go in the PX but we'll make it through and come out even better. Well, I have to go get my hair cut again. I LOVE YOU.
>
> Love you 4-ever-n-longer,
> David

Gidget began to spend time with Dick and Shirley. At first, she would call to say hello, read part of a letter from David, ask if David had written to them. They began to call her to share news from David. They invited her to come over. Gidget had her own car by now — a dark green Impala that had belonged to her father. She would go to their house in the late afternoon, wait for Shirley to come home from work, help her with dinner. She went bowling with Dick and shopping with Shirley. They told her to make their home her home, to bring her girlfriends over if she liked. Sometimes Gladys Nunn came, too. Gidget got used to speaking to Dick and Shirley every day, seeing them several times a week. Once she told Gladys:

"They're David's parents, but they're more like friends. You can tell them things, and they won't criticize you or anything. Whatever you want to do, it's okay."

Gladys agreed with her. The two girls liked to drop over, have dinner, hang around. A couple of times they spent the night there, in David's room.

Dick Heidecker asked Gidget what their plans were. Gidget hesitated. "Shouldn't you ask David?" she said.

"I'm asking you."

"Well, sometimes he talks about getting married, but we're not exactly engaged," Gidget said shyly.

"Why not?" Dick wanted to know. "I got married to Shirley when I was nineteen. David's almost twenty. He's not slow, is he?"

Gidget only smiled. She enjoyed talking to David's father. She couldn't talk to her own family yet about marriage. They would think she was too young, dismiss her feelings. John Geisler would want to know how David intended to support her. He would want proof of David's responsibility. Dick and Shirley, on the other hand, seemed to encourage the relationship. They didn't dampen the romance of it by talking practicalities. Besides, being with them was as close as Gidget could get to being with David.

They began to plan their trip to Fort Benning. David would have only one Saturday free to be with them. Because of the distance, Dick thought they should leave on Friday, spend Friday night in a motel near Fort Benning, and spend Saturday night there, too. They were willing to drive; all Gidget had to do was get in the back seat. She took this up with her father. John Geisler was wary at first, but Gidget persuaded him that she would never be out of the Heideckers' sight. He gave his permission.

They left Carroll County on Friday, September 27, driving south on Route 95 and then on Route 85. They passed Washington, Richmond, Durham, Spartanburg, Greenville, Atlanta. Gidget slept in the back seat while Dick and Shirley took turns driving. They stopped at McDonald's and Stuckey's. After Atlanta they began to see signs. "Columbus 55." "Fort Benning 30." "Columbus 20." Gidget woke up. She was cramped and restless. She started to work on her hair and make up. She knew they would not see David until the next day, but just getting close inspired her to fix herself up. Dick and Shirley were worn out. They stopped at a Days Inn near Fort Benning and got a room for two nights. They each took a rest and a shower and went to dinner in the restaurant. Later they watched TV and went to sleep.

On Saturday morning they made their way to Fort Benning and David's barracks. David was waiting for them. None of them had seen him for five and a half weeks. He looked lean, tough, and nearly bald. He grabbed Shirley and Gidget at the same time and hugged them both. He put his arms around Dick and hugged him, too.

Dick said, "You got a hair cut, huh?"

Shirley said, "How are you doing, son?"

Gidget said, "David, I've missed you!"

David was not permitted to leave the base. He proudly showed his visitors around, pointing out landmarks, showing them his barracks, introducing them to some of his buddies. As they walked, he told them about his latest accomplishment.

"I qualified for the M-16," he said. "I hit 34 out of 40 targets. That makes me a sharpshooter, just two away from 'expert'. I can't complain, though. One of my buddies, Jimmy, didn't qualify. He gets one more chance, and if he doesn't make it he gets recycled."

"What's that?" Gidget asked.

"Recycled means you get put in another company with more time to go until you finish." David squeezed Gidget's hand. "I can't get enough of you," he said. "Mom, was she this pretty before, or have I just forgotten?"

Gidget was happy just to hold his hand, look up at his face, and listen to him talk. David told them about his platoon's barely missing the award for the M-16. "One guy shot 11 out of 40, that's why we didn't win," he said. "Our drill sergeant was so mad, he went into our barracks and threw our beds and everything he could find all over the place. Then he gave us three hours to clean it up."

Gidget was horrified. "That's mean!" she said.

David and Dick laughed. "That's the Army," David explained. "It's not really mean, it's just how they do things. We also qualified in grenades. Qualify means you've passed a requirement for graduation. We got run over by a tank, but it's okay, you're in a cement hole, and then we jumped out of the hole and shot at the tank. It was great."

"You look muscular," Shirley told him.

"I ought to look muscular! We still have P.T. all the time. We're having land mine warfare, too. A lot of this stuff we're having is great. You have to qualify at a lot of different things in order to graduate. So far, I've qualified at everything the first time they gave the test."

"Do you get enough to eat?" Shirley wanted to know.

"It's not gourmet, Mom. They fill you up, that's about it."

Dick and Shirley gave him some time alone with Gidget. David held her on his lap on a bench under an oak tree. "I've missed you so much," he told her. "Thinking about you is the only thing that gets me through all the aggravation. That and your letters."

"Me too," Gidget said. "It's such a drag at home without you, David. I just go to school, do my work, you know. I feel like I'm just waiting."

"It seems like you really get along great with my parents," David said. "I do."

"I'm so glad about that. The three of you mean so much to me. You know what? My mom wrote to me before and said she really likes you. She said she knows I love you, and she knows you love me, too. I think she'd like to see us get married. Of course, so would I!"

"Me too," Gidget said. "What about telling people that we're going to get married? Can I do that?"

"Why not? As long as you're sure you want to marry me, you can tell anybody you want. Tell the Pope, even."

"I wouldn't mind telling the Pope, but it's too soon to tell my father," Gidget said.

"What's his problem?" David asked. "You even had to argue to get to come down here today, and look at us, sitting on a bench with our clothes on, in front of God and everybody, with no way to make love if we wanted to."

"Don't you want to?" Gidget asked.

"Are you kidding? It's taking all the will power I have in the world to keep from ripping your clothes off right here."

Gidget smiled. "I kind of wish you would," she said.

When they said good-bye to David that evening, they would have no opportunity to see him the next day. Dick and Shirley and Gidget spent another night in the Days Inn before setting out for Carroll County on Sunday. They had a quiet trip home; they all agreed that David was in good shape and great spirits. Gidget made a silent calculation. This was the last day of September, which really made it October. If everything went well, and David completed his basic training on schedule, he would finish up in November. The three of them could come back to see him graduate, and would drive him home to Carroll County. He would have a week or so before his next assignment. Gidget thought she could tolerate that.

She received her next letter from David a few days later. He wrote:

> Dear Gidget,
>
> Hi sexy. I love you, I love you. Sunday was a bitch. I missed you so much. I really felt like part of my heart left with you and part of yours was left with me. That part felt okay.
>
> Time is going fast, we only have 47 days left. We really only have three weeks of training. The rest is clean up.

I can't wait until we have time (real, lots) to spend together. I dream about it every night. I felt bad when you left, I was so upset I couldn't even tell you I love you, but November 20th I *will* show you how much I really do.

Well enough about me. How are you? I hope you are feeling good and carrying on with life. I want you to have fun (no, not in that way) and don't get so upset. Just think about how much fun (yes, that kind of fun) we will have when I get out of this place.

I got a letter from Mom and she said you ran into rain on the trip home. I hope the trip back was okay. Well, I got to go, I love you and miss you very much.

Love you 4-ever-n-longer,
David

David liked to picture Gidget in his mind, to study her long red hair, her white skin and freckles, and most of all, her crooked smile. She had told him about her smile. She was born with a pinched nerve on the left side of her face, she said. Her mother was positive it was caused by the use of forceps and other acts of negligence by the doctors, but they had told her she couldn't bring a lawsuit because the doctors and hospital were military. Once or twice, Linda had investigated the possibility of corrective surgery, but doctors advised against it. They would have to cut into Gidget's face, they told Linda, and there could be damage to other nerves. The Geislers decided just to live with the condition. As Gidget got older, she learned how to compensate so that it was barely noticeable. She told David that doctors now knew how to correct that condition at birth. David didn't care — he thought her smile was cute.

"It makes you special," he told her.

The time passed quickly for him. Despite missing Gidget and his parents, David continued to enjoy basic training. For each skill required for graduation, he qualified at the first opportunity. More amazing to David was the fact that he had learned how to get along in the Army without getting into trouble. Once in a while he thought about the nine-year-old David who had flung a chair at a teacher and had been in the midst of fistfights every week. He thought about his confrontation with Coach Ellis. Nowadays, he didn't even get excited when the drill sergeant hollered in his face, or made him do a senseless exercise over and over. He no longer worried about being "recycled," although the drill sergeant threatened them all incessantly. He knew he was going to make it.

He did. On November 20, he was one of 216 soldiers from Company E to graduate. Dick and Shirley and Gidget drove down again to watch an impressive ceremony which included the Army song ("The Army keeps rolling along!"), the infantryman's prayer ("Almighty God, whose will it is that we be leaders of men. . ."), and the Infantryman's Creed ("I am relentless. I am always there, now and forever. I am the infantry! Follow me!"). David received a blue "yearbook" containing his picture and numerous photographs of his company in various phases of basic training. He was ready to leave Fort Benning.

Two days before Thanksgiving, David Heidecker came home to Carroll County. This time, the trip home was anything but quiet as Dick and Shirley took turns driving while David and Gidget kissed and held hands in the back seat. The car was crowded with four people and David's belongings; they laughed and talked and joked as the car headed north. The little house on Gillis Road had never looked so inviting to David, its roof brushed with a light snow, the flag fluttering confidently in the wind, even though the hill was empty of flowers or trees in bloom, and the summer sounds of nature were absent. David took two long strides to the refrigerator and took out a can of beer.

David had one week's leave before he was to report to Fort Campbell, Kentucky, and the ambition to have all the things he now realized he had missed since August: cold beer, snacks from the kitchen, TV, his own clothes, free time, sleep, a car to drive, movies and roller skating, his own bed. And, of course, his parents and his girl.

David and Gidget spent a few wonderful hours together before reality began to erode their euphoria. Gidget, after all, had been in Carroll County the whole time. All she wanted now was a week with David, and as few interruptions as possible. What David wanted was to visit all his old friends and familiar places, in addition to spending time with Gidget and his parents. The night they got home, David told Gidget he wanted to see Patrick the next day.

"But, David, I just want to be with you," Gidget protested. "Don't you know how long I've waited for you?"

"Babe, I've been waiting just as long," David insisted. "I want to be with you, too. But I've been in, like, captivity. I need to get loose, hang around a little. I gotta see people and do things. There'll be time for everything. You'll see."

David called Patrick the next day.

"Man, it's really you!" Patrick yelled. "Do you know I only have one day of freedom left?"

"What do you mean?"

"The Army! Tomorrow I leave for Fort Leonard Wood, Missouri!"

"I'm on my way over," David told him.

David and Patrick hugged each other as Patrick bounded out of his house. "Man, your hair!" Patrick said.

David shrugged. "My hair's long compared to what it was," he said.

"Oh, no! Don't tell me that!"

"Come on, let's go for a ride."

They rode aimlessly, talking and joking. David drove to the salt box, but no one was there; it was winter. They continued to ride, heading nowhere in particular.

"So give me the low-down," Patrick urged. "Is it as bad as they say?"

"No, it's worse," David told him.

"Worse?"

"I'm kidding. You won't mind it. There's a lot of crap to it, but most of it is kind of fun. You get to play soldier, only with real guns and tanks and grenades and stuff."

"Tanks?"

"Sure. It's more fun than a motorcycle." David laughed. "Remember my old Honda, Pat?"

"Do I! Remember the time we rode up Gillis Road and a state trooper came up behind us?"

"Yeah, we took off in the woods. That was one frustrated cop, wasn't he?"

"And then you wrecked the bike on a tree," Pat said. "Remember?"

"Sure I do," David said. "It had less than 500 miles on it."

"Did it?"

"Yeah. That was a pretty stupid thing to do. And boy, was my dad pissed! I hope I've changed some."

They both laughed. "Where we going?" Patrick asked.

"I don't know. Maybe to McDonald's, what do you say? That Army food gets on your nerves after a while."

"Don't tell me that!"

"You'll never starve," David told him. "It just gets boring, is all."

He drove out to Liberty Road and pulled into a McDonald's. He and Patrick went inside. David ordered a whole meal and Patrick got a soda. They sat at a table.

"David, I'm a little scared," Patrick admitted. "This is a whole new thing for me."

"It's new for everybody at first," David said. "Look, you're gonna make it. Just let me give you one piece of advice, okay?"

"Sure."

David looked straight at Patrick. "Don't, do not, get in trouble," he said levelly. "When the drill sergeant hollers in your face, do what he says and don't talk back. Don't tell yourself that he's a creep, and why should you take his shit? Don't even begin to think like that. Take his shit, and let your mind wander someplace else. You have to because he's your boss, and if you fight him, you'll lose. You hear me?"

"Yup," Patrick said.

"And Pat? Remember when we were kids, and I used to backtalk the teachers all the time? Remember that?"

"Sure do," Patrick said.

"Remember how mad I used to get if anybody tried to push me around?"

"Yes."

"If I could take all that crap from the sergeants, and not get into any trouble, you can, too. You hear what I'm saying?"

"Okay," Patrick said solemnly. He reached over and took a handful of french fries. "Hey, are you still with Gidget?"

David grinned. "Sure am," he said. "You can't even imagine how much I missed her down there. And she was great — wrote to me all the time and everything."

"That's good," Patrick said. "I still don't have a steady girl like that. I kinda wish I did, except now I'd be leaving her, wouldn't I?"

"Yeah. You might be better off. I've never been happier in my life since I met Gidget, but it was terrible not being with her. I'm in love with her, Pat," David told him. "I'm hoping we're going to get married someday."

Patrick looked at him. "Married? Do you mean that?"

"Yeah, I do."

"God, I can't believe it! Married!"

"Well, not today," David said. "Listen, I want to stop by South Carroll and see everybody. Want to go now?"

Patrick laughed. "You want to go *to* South Carroll? Remember all the days we hooked?"

David finished his Big Mac. "How could I forget? Come on, it'll be fun."

"Yeah, why not? I haven't been there since May myself."

They drove down Liberty Road and turned into the school. Grinning at Patrick, David pulled into a parking space reserved for faculty only. "What're they gonna do, suspend me?" he asked. It was the day before Thanksgiving vacation at South Carroll. David and Patrick patrolled the halls, waving at various acquaintances and stopping to talk with others. A lot of the kids commented on David's hair: "Hey, what did they do, shave your head?" David explained good-naturedly that his hair was actually *long* now.

A girl asked him if he were an officer yet. Patrick told her, "Hell, yes, he's the general!" One of David's teachers came over to say hello. The boys looked through a classroom window and saw two dozen restless teenagers waiting to be released. A bell rang, and the two boys were caught up in a maelstrom of students rushing noisily for the door. Swept along with the tide, they emerged into the parking lot, where David tried unsuccessfully to find Gidget. He drove Patrick home and headed for Bluebird Drive.

Gidget opened the door. "Where were you?" David asked. "Patrick and I went up to South Carroll to see everybody, and I figured you'd be there."

Gidget was upset. "David, why did you do that without telling me? I stayed home from school today."

"Why?"

"To sleep, get ready to be with you. You should have told me."

David put his arms around her. "I'm sorry," he said. "I just thought you'd be there. Come on, want to go for a ride?"

They did, but Gidget was quiet. "What's wrong, babe?" David asked.

"Nothing," she said.

"Let's do something. Want to go roller skating?"

"Okay."

Many of their friends were at the roller rink. David was his most daring, skating fast and fearlessly in long loops, doing little rings around old acquaintances, waving at long-lost friends. Gidget skated delicately around the side, keeping a watchful eye on David. Once she saw him skating between two girls, holding their hands. She took off her skates and waited outside. David finally came out.

"Gidge, what's the matter?" he asked.

Gidget was crying. "David, you're not paying any attention to me. I came here with you and you're even skating with other girls."

"What?" David took a giant step backwards. "Gidget, come on! Those aren't girls, they're just people I haven't seen for a long time. What's with you, anyway?"

"I want to go home," Gidget sobbed.

David shrugged helplessly, not knowing what was wrong or what to do. Finally he said, "Okay, I'll take you home."

He drove silently to Bluebird Drive while Gidget leaned against the car door and wept quietly. When they got to the Geislers' house, Gidget's father was there. He looked suspiciously from Gidget to David.

"What's wrong?" he asked.

When Gidget said nothing, David volunteered, "Uh, Gidget is a little upset, Mr. Geisler. It's not anything, though."

"Yes it is!" Gidget cried. She ran upstairs and disappeared into her room.

John Geisler looked at David. "I guess you had better go," he said.

David said, "Okay, sir." He walked back to his car and drove around for a while. He finally went home, where he told his parents what had happened. Dick patted his shoulder.

"It'll work out, son," he told David. "Things like this happen."

But Gidget was still upset. Her father came into her room and demanded to know what had happened. When Gidget couldn't explain, he got angry.

"I don't want you to see David anymore," he said. "If he doesn't know how to treat you, he won't be coming around after this. You tell him that's what I said."

John Geisler could not understand why this announcement made Gidget cry even harder.

That night, Gidget drove over to David's house. David was out, but Dick and Shirley were at home. They brought her inside and gave her a soda. Gidget told them what had happened.

"Shirley, I love David," she said. "I waited for him all this time since he went away, and now I feel like he doesn't even want to see me."

Shirley said, "Gidget, he does want to see you. But he's young. He's been living in a barracks all this time and he has a few things he wants to do."

Dick chuckled. "He wants to see you, all right," he said. "But Shirley's right. He needs to get some things out of his system. Give him time."

"We don't *have* time, Richard," Gidget said. "He'll be leaving in five days."

"He'll come around," Dick told her. "Give him a little space, is my advice."

Gidget drank another soda and composed herself. She sat with Dick and Shirley and watched television. Around 10 o'clock, David came in. He saw Gidget and stopped in his tracks.

"Hi, David," Gidget said.

"Let's talk," David told her. He took her into his bedroom and closed the door. "What's going on?" he demanded. "What are you so upset about?"

Gidget looked down. "Nothing, I guess," she said. "I guess I just want you all the time."

"And what's with your father? He practically threw me out of your house today!"

Gidget began to cry again. "David, it's worse than that," she said. "He told me I can't see you anymore."

David looked at her. From around his neck he took the silver chain containing the coin from Wildwood, New Jersey. "Maybe you ought to have this back," he said. "Maybe you think it's dumb."

"Dumb?" Gidget said. "No dumber than you are, wearing it all the time like a fool. Don't you know it's just a cheap thing out a machine on the boardwalk?"

David looked at her tear-streaked face. "Would it be all right with you if I kept it?" he asked.

Gidget fell into his arms. "Oh, David! I love you so much! What are we fighting for?"

David held her tight. "I love you, babe," he said. "Now. You got us into this mess with your old man, you're gonna have to get us out."

Gidget smiled at him. "I will," she promised. "Just don't let's fight anymore."

They made love in David's room, and afterwards they lay in each other's arms and talked for an hour. Gidget felt at peace for the first time since David's return. David, too, felt totally fulfilled and happy. Eventually, he reminded Gidget that her family would be wondering where she was. They got dressed slowly, touching each other and talking softly. David walked Gidget outside to her car, his arm around her.

"Drive carefully," he told her. "I love you."

When John Geisler found out that Gidget had seen David, he made her hand him her driver's license and told her she couldn't drive the Impala for a week. He had fleeting second thoughts when Gidget shut herself in her room, but he had become increasingly unhappy about Gidget's relationship with David. As he told Kathy, he had nothing against David personally, it was just that things were looking too serious. Besides, David looked awfully *mature* for Gidget — six feet five inches tall and in perfect shape. What exactly were they doing downstairs in the club cellar, or, worse, in David's car? Gidget made up her mind that she didn't care what her father said about David. There were five more days before David had to leave, and she managed to be with him every day and evening. After all, her father went to work every day — it was impossible for him to keep tabs on her successfully. Gladys was happy to drive Gidget anywhere she wanted to go, including the Heideckers' house, and Gidget could always tell her father she was at Gladys's. The five days passed smoothly, almost blissfully, with Gidget becoming more and more integrated into the Heidecker family. Once David took her to meet Aunt Ollie. She served them lemonade and homebaked cookies, and told Gidget how lucky she was to have a young man like Davey.

The night before David left, they had a snowfall that closed the Heideckers' driveway to all but the hardy in fourwheel drive vehicles. Dick and Shirley and David and Gidget shoveled out the car, laughing and throwing snowballs and chasing one another. It was the last scene they all remembered after David departed for Kentucky.

CHAPTER 12

Fort Campbell

David's assignment to the 101st Airborne Division (Air Assault) was a random act, but nevertheless a source of pride to the Heideckers. The Division, which was known as the Screaming Eagles from its bald eagle emblem, had attained fame during World War II as the first on the beaches of Normandy during the D-Day invasion in 1944. From there, the 101st participated in glider operations to seize bridges behind German lines in Holland, and then in the campaign at Bastogne during the Battle of the Bulge. The Division received the Distinguished Unit Citation from General Eisenhower in 1945 before going on to capture Berchtesgaden, Hitler's vacation retreat in the Ruhr Valley. Much later, elements of the 101st Airborne went to Little Rock, Arkansas, to maintain order during the integration of Central High School. In 1965 the Screaming Eagles landed at Cam Ranh Bay in the Republic of Vietnam, where three years later they engaged in combat operations against the enemy's Tet Offensive. More recently they went to Granada. The Division had been at Fort Campbell since 1956.

David Heidecker was assigned to Alpha Company of the 3rd Battalion, 502d Infantry Regiment of the Division. David's company contained 113 soldiers, all of whom knew, by December, that they would go to Egypt the following summer as part of an international peace-keeping mission. David was assigned to an A Company barracks. Fort Campbell itself was a self-contained community. On the base were swimming pools, a golf course, theaters, a gym and sports arena, numerous chapels, a post office, the PX and commissary, banks, a military museum, mess halls, and countless housing, recreational and training facilities.

David's day soon became routine. After formation at 6:30 he had an hour of physical training, then breakfast followed by work formation at 9 o'clock. The rest of the day, he engaged in infantry training, practicing how to dig a fox hole, how to read a map, how to clean a rifle — any number of activities designed to build an infantryman, and some activities aimed at the future mission in Egypt. There was far more free time here, but for David, separated from his girl by several hundred miles, there was not a lot he wanted to do.

Early in December, David wrote Gidget that he hoped to get leave for Christmas. He continued:

> If I can get a few days, we'll be together again. I can't wait!
>
> I talked to Dad about us. I told him that I set up bank accounts and the credit union so when we get married we'll be pretty squared away.
>
> We also talked about my Army plans. If we get married after I get back from Egypt I'll have more rank and it will be easier for us. He said he was proud of me. That made me feel so damn good. He has said it before but this time he said it like I was a man. You know he loves me and you very much. He thinks I couldn't have picked a better girl to be with and I agreed with him!

But one Friday night in mid-December, David called to say that he might not make it home for Christmas after all. The Army was playing around with everybody's leave, he said, and some of the soldiers were going to get screwed. That's the way it worked in the service, he told Gidget, especially when you didn't have any rank; they told you what to do and there wasn't a lot you could do about it. But by the time he learned that his Christmas leave definitely had come through, David had another idea. He called his father.

"Dad, I've got a plan," he said excitedly. "You know I told Gidget I'd be coming home for Christmas, and later I didn't know if I'd get my leave, and I told her that."

"Did you get it?" Dick asked.

"Yeah, I did! I just found out I got it for sure."

"Great, son," Dick said. He was watching a football game on TV and drinking a diet soda.

"The thing is, Dad, Gidget doesn't know it's definite, and I'm thinking about making it a surprise for her."

Dick chuckled. "You mean, just show up at her front door?"

"Yeah, what do you think?"

"Sounds fine to me," Dick said. He got up and turned the TV down. "Do you have a way to get here?"

"Well, sort of," David said. "I'm getting a ride with a buddy named Tim. He lives in Hagerstown and that's how far he'll take me. Could you pick me up there?"

"Sure," Dick said. "No problem."

"And Dad?"

"Yes, son?"

"I want to buy an engagement ring for Gidget when I first get home. You know, as part of the surprise."

Dick was silent for a moment. "You want to buy an engagement ring for Gidget?"

"Right, that's what I said. Do you approve?"

"You know I do, David."

"That's great!" David said enthusiastically. "What about Mom?"

"Your mom's working at the restaurant now, but I know she'll approve, too," Dick said.

"Good. Would there be a store in Westminster that sells engagement rings, do you think?"

"Sure there would. A couple of stores."

"Would you or Mom come up with me, help me pick it out?"

Dick laughed. "Yup," he said. "I think your mother might have better taste."

"Okay," David said.

Shirley arrived home later to find Dick still staring at the television set with the sound turned down. "What are you doing?" she asked.

Dick said, "David called. He's coming home for Christmas and he has a ride as far as Hagerstown. I can pick him up there."

"Good," Shirley said.

"He also said he wants to buy an engagement ring for Gidget."

Shirley sat down. "Well, we were expecting that sooner or later, weren't we?"

"Sure," Dick said. He looked at Shirley. "David's young," he said.

"So were you," Shirley reminded him. She reached over and took his hand.

On Friday, December 21, Dick drove thirty miles to Hagerstown to meet David at the home of his Army friend. They got back home after the stores closed. Early Saturday morning, David and Shirley drove to Westminster. They had $350 in cash, $300 of which David had saved at Fort Benning, the balance being a gift from Dick and Shirley. At the jewelry counter of a discount department store, David examined dozens of rings. He looked at the price tags, held some of the rings in his hand, and asked Shirley's advice.

"Is this a real diamond, Mom?"

"Of course it is."

"Is it big enough?"

"Sure. Size isn't the most important thing."

"Do you like yellow gold best, or this white gold?"

"I like them both. White gold is nice."

Suddenly, David froze. "Mom!" he whispered loudly.

"What is it?"

"There's Gidget's father."

"Where?"

"Right over there. And that's Kathy with him. Oh, God, what if they see me?"

"Duck down," Shirley said.

David hunched awkwardly over the counter as John Geisler and Kathy stood at the next department, just a few yards away. Shirley had never met them; so it made no difference if they saw her. But David was supposedly in Kentucky, unable to get his Christmas leave. Shirley tried to think of a cover story in case they noticed David. Their puzzled saleswoman gaped at David as he huddled suspiciously over the glass top, pretending to study the jewelry inside. Shirley watched with relief as John and Kathy walked away. She nudged David.

"They're leaving," she said. "You can get up now."

David looked up warily. Finally, he stretched to his full height. "That was my girl's father," he explained to the salewoman. "They don't even know I'm in town, let alone picking out a diamond ring for their daughter."

The saleswoman smiled warmly. "I see," she said.

She showed him other rings, and at last David selected a white gold diamond solitaire. His hands were so much larger than Gidget's that he could not even slip it onto his little finger, but Shirley could. They decided it was perfect.

"My girl is very delicate looking," David told the saleswoman confidently. "She needs dainty things like this."

The woman took their cash and placed the ring in velvet inside a little black jewelry box. She handed David his receipt, and he put the box in his pocket. He and Shirley headed home, with David talking excitedly all the way.

"Mom, I can't wait to see the look on Gidget's face when she sees me. Do you think she'll really be surprised? What do you think she'll do when she sees the ring? I sure hope she likes it. We've talked an awful lot about getting married, expecially in our letters, but it's not like I actually said to her, will you marry me, or I actually *asked* her if she would. I mean, we definitely want to get married, but you know what I mean? What about her father, do you think? Will I have to go over and talk to him and all, or don't people do that anymore? He's kind of strict, and I don't think he really likes me that much. Do you think that will be a problem? Boy, I can't *wait* to see her."

Outside at Bluebird Drive, David could see the Geislers' Christmas tree through the picture window in the living room. There were lights and small wooden carvings and mistletoe, Santas and angels and reindeer. Snow lay on the ground where David stood, but it was not new snow; it spread over the hard ground in soiled clumps where the plough had been. David kicked his shoes on the side of the door so as not to track dirty snow inside. Then he rang the doorbell and hoped that Gidget would answer it. She did; in an instant they were in each other's arms.

They spent Christmas Eve at the Heideckers' house. Dick and Shirley had a tree, too, and lights and decorations to create a festive atmosphere in the little house. As usual, things proceeded there more or less spontaneously, without any real schedule or sense of urgency. There were presents all around, mostly for David, which they opened after dinner that Shirley and Gidget cooked together. Gidget had bought a new wallet for David, and had made some cards covered with hearts and poetic comments. When it appeared that everything had been opened, David went into his bedroom and came out with the little black jewelry box in his hand. He looked at Gidget self-consciously.

"Stand up," he told her.

Gidget looked at Dick and Shirley. She stood up. David said, "I want to ask you to be my wife." He opened the little box and carefully took out the diamond ring. He looked at Gidget.

Gidget said breathlessly, "Yes." David took Gidget's left hand and slipped the ring on her finger. He kissed her hand. He sat down and pulled her onto his lap. They hugged in silence for a few minutes. Then they walked outside in the cold together. Both of them were thinking that David would have to leave for Kentucky the next day.

Gidget spent that night at her mother's house in Baltimore. Linda, who had met David only once, seemed pleased about the engagement. The next day was Christmas. David telephoned Aunt Ollie and then made a quick visit to the Langhages'. He gave Amy, who was now in elementary school, a stuffed kitten he had brought back from Fort Campbell. She gave David a huge hug before he had to extricate himself and explain that he had to go back to the Army. Then Dick and Shirley and Gidget drove David to Hagerstown to get his ride to Fort Campbell.

It was Christmas afternoon when Gidget arrived home. John Geisler and Kathy were in the living room. Gidget sat down with them. She extended her left hand.

"Look what David gave me for Christmas," she said.

Kathy reached out for the ring. "Can I see it?" she asked.

"Don't take it off," Gidget cautioned.

"Why not?"

"Because," John Geisler said. "It's her engagement ring."

Kathy was shocked. *"Engagement* ring?"

Gidget was smiling at her father. "Uh-huh," she said.

Kathy shook her head. "Good heavens, you're engaged, I can't believe it. When did this happen?"

"Last night," Gidget said. "At the Heideckers' house."

"Do David's parents approve?" John wanted to know.

Gidget nodded. "We won't be getting married for a long time, Dad," she said. "Of course, I still have to finish school and everything. And David will be going overseas next summer."

John looked at her. "I guess I'm going to have to get to know David Heidecker a little better," he said.

The last day of December, 1984, fell on a Monday. Gidget Geisler, seventeen years old, with a diamond ring on her finger and a fiance six hundred miles away, was confronted with the question of what to do on New Year's Eve. Everybody she knew, including Gladys, had a date. John and Kathy had plans. Even her brother Johnny was going to a party. Dick and Shirley planned to spend the evening at the Half Shell, where Shirley was scheduled to work. They invited Gidget to join them and she accepted.

"It's not Times Square," she told Gladys, "but it's something to do."

The Half Shell was having a party, with a band and hors d'oeuvres. There was a cover charge, but Gidget and Dick got in free because of Shirley's job. They occupied a table in the corner where Shirley joined them from time to time. A boy in Gidget's class was there, too, and he danced with her a few times. Dick drank a lot of beer and danced a couple of dances with Shirley, and some with Gidget. Gidget hoped for a phone call from David, who knew where they would be, but none came; at midnight she kissed Dick on the cheek and lapsed into silence. At 1:30, the restaurant served breakfast, and afterwards Dick and Shirley argued about who would drive home, with Shirley accusing Dick of having had too much to drink, and Dick denying it.

"Is this fair?" he asked Gidget. "I was sitting at a table in full view of everybody while Shirley was hiding in the kitchen where nobody could see how much she drank. Maybe she drank twice as much as me, who knows?"

Gidget took Shirley's side, but without enthusiasm; she was too depressed to care. She spent the night at the Heideckers' house, in David's room. Early in the afternoon on New Year's Day, 1985, she got up and went home. Her father told her, "David called you last night."

Gidget was stunned. "What!"

"David called. It was a little after midnight, because we just got home when he called."

"Damn," Gidget shouted. "He knew I was going to the restaurant. He was supposed to call there."

John Geisler said, "Watch your mouth, now."

Gidget went into her room and slammed the door.

David had returned to a bleak Fort Campbell, where he was confronted with slow days and empty nights. His assignments were mostly tedious and unchallenging, in contrast to the tasks he had had at Fort Benning. There was more leisure time and considerably more personal freedom, but less physical training and far less sense of accomplishment. David wrote to Gidget that "basic training" was misnamed — it should be called "only training." There was the opportunity to make friends, and David did, but everybody he got to know was just passing through, as he was. There were Army buddies — drinking companions, men to go to the movies with and to join in forays off the base, where one might meet girls, but David, at age twenty, was engaged to Gidget and considered himself ineligible. He knew that he would not have another leave before May, which made this the longest period of separation for him and Gidget so far.

"Five months to go, with nothing but letters and long distance phone calls," he wrote his mother. "I'm getting tired of all this. I wish I could be back home in Carroll County."

The time passed just as slowly for Gidget. She was in the middle of her senior year in high school, with months and months to go before she could expect to see David again. She saw Gladys frequently; they still went to the movies on Sundays and roller skated from time to time. And they talked: now Gladys was frantically searching for her own fiance, without success. "Gidget, I'm jealous!" she would say. "I want to get married too." But Gidget's wedding seemed so far away, so distant, that Gidget could hardly get excited.

"I just miss David," she would say wistfully.

Gidget approached Shirley about getting a job at the Half Shell. It would be nice to put a little money away for when she got married, but mainly she needed something to do. Shirley asked her employer, and Gidget was hired part-time as a waitress. She worked from 4 until 9:45 three nights a week, usually including Friday or Saturday night; that solved part of the problem of how to spend her weekends. It also gave her more proximity to Shirley. The job itself, waiting on tables, was something new to Gidget. For years she had helped out at home, even assuming full responsibility for housekeeping and cooking during some periods, but this was not the same. Here there were customers who couldn't decide what they wanted to order, who asked her advice and then disregarded it — or blamed her if the meal turned out wrong; people who were rude or impatient, who expected more than they were entitled to; people who forgot to leave tips, or maybe didn't intend to; customers who whistled and made vulgar remarks, men who wanted to touch her long red hair. There were good customers, too: polite, friendly people who thanked her profusely for everything, who complimented her on her service, who left nice tips. Shirley told her that a restaurant is a reflection of the world, that she could expect to meet all kinds of people there, good, bad, and in between, and that the best approach was to stay calm and roll with the punches. Gidget tried. Once, three men who had had too much to drink refused to let her leave their table to wait on others; in desperation, Gidget fled to the kitchen and told Shirley. Shirley Heidecker strode through the kitchen door directly to the rowdy table, where she inquired loudly, "Do you gentlemen have a problem?" The men paid their bill and left. Gidget smiled at Shirley; she was learning a few things.

The next time David called, she asked him, "Have you ever heard of a thing called assertiveness training?"

David said, "Is that one of those women's lib things?"

"Not exactly," Gidget told him. "It's about learning to stand up for yourself. Guess who's teaching me?"

"Who?"

"Your mother." They laughed together.

Easter came and went, and winter gave way to spring, in Kentucky as well as in Maryland. David spent as much time as he could outside, especially in physical or athletic endeavors. Gidget tried out for a softball team at South Carroll, and made it. She wrote to David:

> I am so spastic you can't believe it. I can't figure out how I made the team, except I guess everybody else is even more uncoordinated. Anyway, I am getting pretty good at hitting the ball, and every once in a while I pull off a miracle of fielding, too. It's just something to do until we can be together.

David had requested leave for May. He knew that Gidget's birthday was May 9, and the senior prom at South Carroll would be held on May 11. Early in April, he wrote to Gidget:

> Dear Gidget,
>
> Hi, honey, how's everything going? I was so relieved when I found out I got my leave. I can't wait to see you again, especially all dressed up. I can't believe that on the 18th it will be our 9 month anniversary. That seems like a long time but actually it isn't when you think we are going to be sharing the rest of our lives together.
>
> I'm counting down the days, right now it's 36 days and by the time you get this letter it will probably be 30 days. I think about coming home all the time. I miss you.

Well, I got to get some sleep, it's 11:35 here, 12:35
there where my heart and mind are.
I love you very much.

Love you 4-ever-n-longer,
David

He talked to his parents about the logistics of his May leave, and they eventually decided that Dick and Shirley would drive to Fort Campbell to bring David home. On the morning of May 8, David went to company headquarters to tell Alan O'Sullivan, the company clerk, where he could be found when his parents arrived. O'Sullivan, a twenty-two year old Nebraskan with service in Korea, had been at Fort Campbell only since March, but had become acquainted with David soon after his arrival. Alan was as tall as David, but heavier; with a friendly, open face and an easy manner, he reminded one of a youthful Andy Griffith. Some hours after David had alerted him, Alan looked up from his desk and deduced that the two people who had just walked into company headquarters were David's parents.

"You must be Mr. and Mrs. Heidecker," Alan said enthusiastically.

"That's right," Dick told him.

Alan stood up and extended his hand. "I'm Alan O'Sullivan, company clerk," he announced. "Nice to meet you. I know David's expecting you. I'll send somebody to get him."

"Thank you," Shirley said. She and Dick sat down in two straight chairs. They had left Carroll County before dawn, driving through Virginia and Tennessee in intermittent rain to reach Fort Campbell. Gidget, who was taking her final examinations of her senior year, could not join them this time. Alan asked Dick and Shirley if they had accommodations for that night. Dick said they didn't, but there were several motels in Clarksville, Tennessee — the closest city to Fort Campbell — and they would find one there after they got a chance to see David. David suddenly bounded into the room and hugged both of his parents. The first thing Dick and Shirley noticed was that David's hair was a little longer. The three of them thanked Alan and left company headquarters.

"Have a good time," Alan called after them.

Army regulations did not permit David to leave the base until after midnight, and so Dick and Shirley slept in a motel in Clarksville. Early the next morning, they picked up David at Fort Campbell and headed northeast. With three of them taking turns at the wheel, they made the trip home by early evening with almost no stops. It was May 9, Gidget's eighteenth birthday.

David stopped by his house long enough to shower, eat, and change his clothes. At 7:30 in the evening he was knocking on Gidget's door. A minute later he was lifting Gidget off the ground, shouting with joy and hugging her.

He had brought her a necklace and some perfume for her birthday. He spent some time at her house, with Johnny and Kathy and John Geisler, and later he and Gidget went out for a ride. It was Thursday night and Gidget was still in school; they had to make it short.

"We'll have four days together," David reminded Gidget as they said good night at her door. "We have lots of time."

Gidget put her head against his chest and nodded resignedly.

Dick and Shirley had arranged to take Friday off from work, in addition to the two days they had already taken for the trip. Spring had come to Carroll County, and David, who had left home in the snow, delighted in the sight and smell of the blooming hillside on which his home stood. He walked the fields with Shirley, his arm around her waist, telling her of Army life in Kentucky and hearing the latest news of home. "What about Aunt Ollie?" he wanted to know. "Is she okay? Do you think I'll have a chance to see her soon?" He and Dick drove the back roads, watching out for rabbits and squirrels and even deer, trading Army stories and stopping for a beer now and then. In the little house, Shirley cooked and the three ate and laughed and talked.

Saturday night was Gidget's senior prom at South Carroll. David showered and shaved, singing and clowning with his father as he transformed himself from a grubby unkempt lad to a suave gentleman. "Look, Ma, I even brushed my teeth twice today," he shouted across the house. Shirley smiled up at him. "I wish I could be your date," she said. David leaned down and kissed her cheek. He called good-bye to Dick, then nearly leaped out the door, carrying a corsage of red rosebuds that he and Dick had bought that afternoon. In the Geislers' living room, he was momentarily speechless at the sight of Gidget in a lovely new dress, her red hair falling softly over her shoulders and her left hand delicately sporting her engagement ring. "Wow," he whispered softly, before regaining his composure and resuming the comic side of his personality. "Come on, babe, my pumpkin's outside."

The high school gym was elaborately decorated, filled with sounds of music and laughter as young people in nice clothes milled about. Gidget found out that David was reluctant to dance to the fast numbers unless he had had some beer, which he was not having that night; she had to wait for the slow dances. She also found him to be aggravatingly sociable, spending too much of his time talking to old friends and girlfriends. But after the prom they went off together and spent some hours in David's bedroom. Gidget's father, who seemed somewhat more relaxed since Gidget had acquired her engagement ring, had at last agreed that she could stay out all night on this very special occasion.

"Of course, he thinks I'm at my girlfriend's house," she giggled.

They talked about their future. "I want to be with you forever," David told her. "When can we get married?" He lay on his left side, his head propped up on his left hand, his right hand caressing Gidget's long hair.

"I want to get married this summer, after I graduate, but I know my parents couldn't tolerate that." Gidget had her right hand on David's bare chest.

"Why?"

"Oh, you know. They need more time to get adjusted. I guess they don't understand that I'm growing up." Gidget smiled.

"Do you know what?"

"What?"

"I love your crooked smile."

Gidget's hand went automatically to her face. "You know I don't like it," she reminded him.

"I don't care, I love it," David insisted. "It's cute. It sets you apart from the rest of the people in the world." Gidget took her hand away from her face. "Anyway, how long do you think we'll have to wait?" David went on. "I'll be leaving for Egypt in July, and I won't be able to come back at all until my time over there is over."

"When will that be?" Gidget asked.

"December, I think. So if we can't get married before July, we'll have to wait until December."

"What about New Year's Eve?" Gidget suggested.

"Sure, that'd be neat," David said. "Only it's too damn far away."

"For me, too," Gidget told him. "But I can't help it."

"Maybe if we try talking to your folks," David offered optimistically. "Maybe they'll come around."

He put his arms around Gidget and moved closer to her in the bed. They kissed each other longingly and began again to make love. "I love you, Gidge," David whispered. He kissed her again and again, making love to her once more until finally they were exhausted and fell into sleep in each other's arms.

They decided the next day to talk to Gidget's father about their plans. David, becoming uncharacteristically nervous, tried to persuade his parents to come along, but they explained this was something he had to do by himself. He and Gidget sat primly on the sofa in the Geislers' living room while John and Kathy sat across the room in separate chairs. John Geisler looked directly at David.

"Tell me how you could handle things if you and Gidget were to get married in June, David," he said.

David looked at John Geisler. "Handle things?" he repeated.

"Right," John said. "Tell me what living arrangements you would have down there in Kentucky."

David shifted in his seat. "Well, actually, I'm not sure," he said. "I guess we would find a place to live off the base. That'd probably be nicer for Gidget, don't you think, Gidge?" He looked at her for encouragement.

"I don't see how Gidget could have an opinion, since she's never been there," John pointed out. "How much does housing cost off the base in that area?"

"Actually, sir, I don't know," David admitted. "I never really had any occasion to get that information."

"Could you afford to support my daughter on what the Army pays you?"

"Oh, yeah, absolutely, I'm very sure of that," David said confidently. "No problem about that at all."

John leaned forward in his chair. "How much do they pay you?" he asked.

David told him.

"But you don't know what your rent would be?"

David fidgeted. "Well, uh, I don't know an exact amount. I mean, I never had to think about it quite like that."

"But now you do," John pointed out.

"Yeah, I see," David said. "Well, I don't know an exact number, but I could find that out pretty easily, I know that."

"Are utilities included, or is that extra?"

David shook his head. "I don't know."

John sat back in his chair. "What do you have in the way of insurance?"

"Insurance?" David looked blankly at John.

"Yes, insurance. Life insurance."

"I'm pretty sure the Army gives you that," David told him.

"How much do they give you?"

David yawned. "I don't know, really," he said. "But I could find that out, too."

John stood up to pour himself a soda. "Anybody else want soda?" he inquired. Nobody did. He resumed his seat. "David," he said finally, "I don't feel like I'm getting very much information here. You say you don't know how much apartments cost. You don't know what's included. But you're sure you and Gidget could afford to live. My next question is, *how* do you know that?"

David was silent. He looked over at Kathy, who, like John, was looking directly at him. She said, "David, try to understand what we're saying. We're not against you and Gidget getting married. We just need to know whether you've thought this through and if you can handle the practical side of it. Getting married isn't a fairy tale, you know. People don't just live happily ever after. They pay the bills. They go to work. There's a lot to think about."

David moved a little closer to Gidget. "I know that," he said. "I've thought about all those things."

Kathy went on. "We're saying you shouldn't get married this summer. Change our minds, if you can. We're listening."

David yawned again. He thought for a minute. "You're right, I should have more information," he said finally. "What makes me think it can work is that I haven't had any money problems so far. And also, my parents are always willing to help me out if they need to."

John Geisler stood up. "David," he said, "if you get married, you'll have to stand on your own two feet, not rely on your parents. If you have to rely on your parents, then you are not old enough to marry my daughter." He finished his soda. "Do you know," he continued, "that when I was in the Army in Germany, before Gidget was born, I had to pay for my own telephone calls to Linda — I did *not* charge those calls to anybody — and it used to take twenty quarters for me to call her? Twenty quarters is five dollars, and this was in 1967. Do you realize that?"

David did, because he had heard it before. He realized also that he had said the wrong thing. He was beginning to believe that this conversation was futile, that nobody was listening to him, and that he was making a fool of himself. He looked over at John and made one last effort. "I love Gidget," he said.

John softened just a little. "I know that, David," he said. "I appreciate that. And don't think I don't like you, or that I'm not in favor of you and Gidget getting married. I just want to make sure you know what you're doing."

"I know that, Mr. Geisler," David said. He was holding Gidget's hand tightly.

"You'll understand better when you have your own daughter," John said.

"Yes, sir," David said politely.

Outside, David exploded. "Shit!" he hollered. "I might as well have been talking to the wall of your house. What is your father's problem, anyway? I know goddamn well we can find a place to live and pay our bills. So what if I don't have *every single detail*? What does he think I am, a goddamn computer, with every fact at my fingertips? Doesn't he know that all kinds of people get married and live fine without all that shit? I can't believe it. I wish my dad had been here. He would've explained everything so easy."

Gidget held his hand. "It's okay," she said quietly.

"And what the hell does he mean that I have to 'stand on my own two feet' after we're married? What does he think I'm standing on now, my head? Just because I have parents who are willing to help me out when I need it, why does he make that sound like a crime? Do you know how many fucking times I've had to hear that stupid story about his twenty quarters in the pay phone in Germany? So what? What is he trying to prove?"

Gidget was starting to cry softly. "I'm sorry," she said.

David stopped yelling and put his arm around her. "Hey, it isn't your fault," he said. "I'm not mad at you."

"I know, but you're mad at my father, and we can't get married for months," Gidget sobbed.

"Oh, baby, come on. I'll stop being mad at your father. Really I will. Look, I know he means all right. He's just stubborn, that's all."

"So are you," Gidget said.

"Look, honey, let's not get all bent out of shape. We'll get married in December if we can't change his mind, and we won't stop trying to change his mind."

"How?"

"I think you ought to work on him. We have a whole lot better chance of bringing him around if you talk to him than if I do."

"You mean now?"

"No, no, no. After I'm safely back at Fort Campbell."

"You coward."

"It's not that. It's that me talking to him won't do any good, but you talking to him might."

Gidget nodded seriously. "You're right," she said. "I'll do it."

In the end, she wore John and Kathy down. There were never-ending phone calls to and from Fort Campbell, Gidget's incessant pleas, her tears and arguments, and most of all, perhaps, John Geisler's unspoken fear, common to parents since time began, that if he did not permit this wedding soon, something worse might happen to his daughter. The weekend after David returned to Fort Campbell, Kathy and Gidget went to Pizza Hut for lunch. Kathy said, "Gidget, your dad and I have been thinking. If it's really important to you and David to get married this summer, we think you're old enough and mature enough to make that decision. Is that what you would like to do?"

Gidget dropped a pepperoni onto the table and stared at Kathy. "Are you serious?" she whispered.

"Really," Kathy said. "Your dad made up his mind last night. Pick out a date."

"I can pick out a date in one second," Gidget told her. "Let's see, my graduation is June 6, and that's a Thursday. The first Saturday after that is June 8. That's the date, June 8."

Kathy looked aghast. "That's three weeks from today!" she exclaimed. "Do you mean that you want us to put your wedding together in exactly three weeks?"

Gidget smiled broadly. "Exactly!" she said.

CHAPTER 13

The Wedding

Gidget and Kathy flew into action. Their first charge was to secure a church for the ceremony. The Geislers belonged to Taylorsville United Methodist, a picturesque country church on Route 27 near Liberty Road. That church, they found, was already taken for June 8. But the Heideckers' church, Ebenezer United Methodist, was available. Shirley arranged for the wedding to take place there, at Ebenezer, with Gidget's minister from Taylorsville to perform the ceremony.

Gidget sought David's approval for this the next time he called from Fort Campbell. "Is it okay with you to get married in your church but with my minister?" she asked.

David was standing at a pay phone on the base with three soldiers waiting to use it. "Baby, it's okay with me to get married in a field if you want, or a parking lot or a cathedral or maybe on the median strip in a major highway," he told her. "All I care about is being with you. Go ahead and make any arrangements you want."

"David, I love you," Gidget said.

She started out by making a list; the list itself was nearly overwhelming. After "Get church" she wrote: invitations, photographer, flowers, rings, wedding cake, food for reception, bridesmaid, my gown. Occasionally she felt on the verge of hysterics.

"Gladys, I can't stand it!" she cried as they addressed invitations to some seventy people from a list compiled by her family and the Heideckers. "Kathy wants to get a three-tiered cake, and Dad says that's too much, and I don't even care! My mom says I have to carry a big bouquet of summer flowers, and I just want a rose. What am I going to *do*?"

Gladys, calm as usual, continued to write addresses as she intoned, "You'll do exactly what you want to do, Gidge. This is your wedding, not theirs."

"But, Gladys, it's all so complicated! Will you help me pick out a gown?"

"Sure," said Gladys. "I'll help you do everything."

"What would I do without you?" Gidget sighed.

Gladys chuckled. "You know, Gidge, things could be a whole lot worse," she pointed out. "What if your mom wanted to run this wedding instead of leaving it to your father and Kathy? What if Dick and Shirley wanted to push their way into the act? Suppose David had a lot of ideas about how this wedding should be? If you just stay cool, Kathy will do all the work and you and I can make all the decisions."

Gidget giggled. Gladys was right. Her mother was willing to leave the wedding to John, who was happy to defer to Kathy. Dick and Shirley were glad to help but had no interest in running the show, and David didn't care how they got married, just as long as they did. Gidget picked up her list and began to make decisions. She made up her mind to carry a single rose down the aisle, representing the first flower David had ever brought her, as well as the song that had meaning for her and Gladys. There was going to be one bridal attendant, who would be Gladys, and a best man, who would be Patrick Kenney: by sheer dumb luck, Patrick had been sent back to Carroll County for a few weeks to work in the Army recruiting office. Johnny Geisler would usher. They would have the traditional wedding march. Kathy found a photographer. Gidget and Gladys picked out matching wedding bands for Gidget and David. They arranged for food to be served at a reception in the parish hall after the wedding. They called a hairdresser who agreed to come to the Geislers' house on the day of the wedding to do Gidget's hair. Gidget found an old-fashioned wedding gown with lace in a size 3. Gladys selected a lovely lime green bridesmaid's outfit.

Three days before the wedding, just in time to watch Gidget graduate from South Carroll High School, David Heidecker came home. On June 6, 1985, he went up to his old school with John and Kathy and Johnny to watch about two hundred seventy-five seniors receive their diplomas. For David, who had done the same thing a year before, the occasion was nostalgic. For Gidget, two days before her wedding, it was anti-climactic. There was no graduation celebration for her, only a few minutes of sharing her yearbook with David. On page 208, under "Messages From the Heart," appeared: "David — I treasure our moments together — I live for the ones yet to come. Love you 4-ever-n-longer. Gidget." They spent the evening with Gidget's family reviewing the details of the wedding.

David was amazed at what had transpired in his absence. He told his mother, "It's like I closed my eyes and somebody planned my life."

Shirley asked, "Are you having any second thoughts?"

David shook his head. "No way. I was the one who was in such a hurry to get married this summer, remember?"

"You know, Aunt Ollie can't be here for your wedding," Shirley said.

"She can't? Why?"

"She's in Boston, visiting her relatives. She'll probably be there for most of the summer."

David was quiet for a moment. "I'll miss her," he said.

"I know," Shirley said. "Why don't you give her a call up there and talk to her?"

David did. He told her, "Aunt Ollie, I always figured you were gonna dance at my wedding."

Aunt Ollie laughed. "I'll be thinking about you, Davey," she said. "I'll say a prayer for you and Gidget."

David and Gidget spent Friday night apart. For David, this was a last chance to be a bachelor, to talk man to man with Patrick, to be single. They drank beer and joked around. Patrick asked him, "Is this for real, David? Are you seriously, honestly planning to go through with this?"

"Yup. This is it, Pat."

"But what about all the other girls in the world? Think of all the girls we've known. What do you say we forget about this wedding and just hop on over to the skating rink and then maybe go check out Karen and Jenny, or some of their friends? What do you say?"

David laughed. "You better get it through your head I mean this," he said. "I want to marry Gidget tomorrow, and that's it."

"Yeah, but what about your *freedom*?"

"Drink a beer, Patrick. You're too sober to be any fun."

"I'm just trying to save you from making a mistake," Patrick said.

"Don't you like Gidget?" David asked.

"Course I do. I love Gidget. She's the classiest girl you ever went out with. I mean, when you think about it, a lot of those girls we used to run around with, a lot of them were trash, weren't they?" Patrick opened another beer. "Remember that time we almost got caught in that one girl's house, those sisters, when their father came home in the middle of the night?"

"Yeah, I do," David said. "We were running out the door pulling our clothes on while we ran. We kept on thinking their old man was chasing us."

"Yes, and he might have a gun. God, I'll never forget that, will you?"

David shook his head. "Christ, no. It scared a year off my life."

"What were those girls' names, anyway?"

David thought. He shook his head. "Damn if I know," he said finally. "I just can't remember anymore."

Patrick burst out laughing. "Wasn't it fun, though? All those different dates we used to have?"

David nodded. "Yeah, it was," he said. "It was a lot of fun, and the right thing at the time. But this is a different time for me. Now I want to settle down with Gidget."

For Gidget and Gladys, it was a quiet evening of reminiscence. They remembered the seventh grade, when they met, and the eighth grade, when they became best friends and also discovered boys. They laughed about the tribulations of growing up — their fears of unpopularity, battles against their parents' restrictions, moments of embarrassment in school. Gidget talked about her feelings for David, her hopes for the future, some anxieties about the changes she would face — "Where *is* Fort Campbell, anyway?" Gladys spoke seriously about her own mixed feelings — her happiness for Gidget, and her sadness at the inevitable change in their relationship, especially with Gidget about to move hundreds of miles away. They both wondered aloud whether marriage was everything it's cracked up to be and they both laughed at the triteness of their question. Finally, they noticed it was late, and Gladys pointed out that they would have a big day tomorrow — maybe the ultimate big day. They hugged each other as Gladys promised to come over tomorrow to help with everything.

On Saturday, June 8, the first thing that Gidget became aware of was the sound of knocking at her front door. She sat up in bed and glanced at the clock. It was after eleven. She threw on her robe and went to open the door. Warm sunshine bathed the front walk. On the porch stood Gladys, her lime green bridesmaid's dress folded over one arm and an overnight bag slung from the other. Gidget blinked.

"Gladys, oh my God!" she said. "It's today!"

The girls embraced as they went inside, laughing from nerves and anticipation. They had coffee and toast, and then Gidget showered and washed her hair. The hairdresser arrived and went to work on Gidget, who was hard to please; her hair was too curly, or not curly enough, the bangs should be feathered back or should come straight down. The hairdresser did her best, but after she left Gidget wet-combed it all out and started over. She finally attained a level of satisfaction, while Gladys, who had thrown up her hands over Gidget's hair, finished her own makeup. Finally, the two girls helped each other with their dresses. By the time the photographer arrived, Gidget was standing in the living room of the house wearing her white wedding gown. Gladys was almost speechless at how lovely she looked. Gradually, the rest of the family emerged — John Geisler in his rented tuxedo, Johnny in his good suit, Kathy in a pretty new dress for the occasion. The photographer took pictures in the living room, and more outside on the front lawn. He wanted Gidget alone, Gidget with John, Gidget with Gladys, Gidget with everybody, Gidget with her father putting a garter on her leg. By the time he had finished, Gidget was tired of standing up, bored with smiling, anxious about her dress and her hair, and generally a nervous wreck.

"When is this going to happen?" she asked wearily.

"Right now," Gladys announced firmly. "It's time to leave for the church."

There was a lot less detail to attend to at David's house. David, too, awoke late and with a feeling of awe that this day had come. He sat around, had breakfast, joked with his parents, looked at TV, and paced. When it was time, he took his shower and put on his Army dress greens. He asked what time it was at regular intervals. He called Patrick on the phone to satisfy himself that Patrick was up and sober. Patrick was. He and David agreed to meet at the church.

The Heideckers were struck with the beauty of the day as they stepped outside together. This was early June in Carroll County, when foliage grew thick and trees were dressed with pink and white blossoms. The semi-circle of pine trees that Dick and David had planted long ago stood tall and full, marking their original acre of land and seeming to embrace their home and family. The soprano songs of robins and sparrows resonated gently as rabbits and chipmunks darted about. There was just enough wind to let the American flag flutter gently above the house. David put one of his arms around each of his parents as they stood at the top of the hill. Dick was wearing a three-piece suit for the first time in David's memory. Dick had complained all morning about having to wear it; now he was fully dressed and David was astounded. He thought his father looked magnificent. Shirley was dressed in a pretty white dress that was new for this day, and she wore a corsage; she, too, looked lovely, David thought. He leaned down and kissed her.

"I hope not too many guys whistle at you, Mom," he said. "It might disrupt my wedding."

Shirley's eyes were beginning to well up with tears from the emotion of this day. David gave his father a hug.

"You look great, Dad," he said. "I hope Gidget doesn't want to marry you instead."

Dick chuckled. "Quit talking," he said. "It's my job to get you to the church on time."

At the church, David and Patrick stared at each other: neither had ever seen the other look so formal. They waited together in the wings, where Patrick reminded David that it wasn't too late to change his mind, they could still go out and get a beer and change their clothes and head for the skating rink. David ignored Patrick. He knew that Gidget had arrived when the minister asked him and Patrick to stand in front of the altar. Then Gladys began her walk down the aisle. She took her place at the altar, across from David. She had never seen David look so nervous. She kept smiling, and whispered to him, very quietly, "David, you said you wouldn't be scared." And David, who was almost trembling, whispered back, just as quietly, "Shut up, Gladys."

Gidget and her father started down the aisle. David's eyes were fixed on Gidget. He stopped looking as if he were about to faint. The minister came forward and placed Gidget's hand in David's. David whispered "Hi," and squeezed her fingers. He smiled down at her as she looked up at him. They heard the minister say:

"Dearly beloved, we are gathered together here in the sight of God, and in the face of this company, to join together this man and this woman in holy matrimony."

Gidget became aware of tension in David's body when the minister said if there was anyone who knew of a reason why David and Gidget should not be married, he should speak now or forever hold his peace. She felt, and then saw, David grasp Patrick's arm and press down on it. Gidget and Gladys exchanged knowing glances. If there was anybody in the world who would "speak now" as a practical joke in the middle of his best friend's wedding, it was Patrick Kenney. The moment passed, and David relaxed. Now Gladys turned to face the congregation, getting ready to sing "The Rose." She started softly, melodiously: "Some say love, it is a river . . . ." She sang it perfectly. David and Gidget exchanged vows, and then their rings. They said the Lord's Prayer with the congregation. And then they were married.

Outside in the warm sunshine, the solemnity of the ceremony gave way to joyful sounds. The bride and groom, holding hands and smiling, became the life of the party. Guests kissed and embraced and congratulated them as they left their nervousness behind and revelled in the happiness of the moment. They paused with the photographer for more pictures, this time including David and Dick and Shirley and Patrick. Then they proceeded to a reception in the parish hall adjacent to the church. There were tables of punch and lunch meat and rolls and salad, and a three-tiered wedding cake with a bride and groom on top. David told Patrick he was supposed to make a toast, and Patrick, who had never made a speech in his life, banged on the table and cleared his throat.

"Folks, ladies and gentlemen, can I have your attention? Please?" He paused as he tried to think of something to say. "Here's to David and Gidget, who just got married." He blushed. "Of course."

Dick Heidecker rescued him. "To the bride and groom," he said. "Long life, good health, and happiness."

There was dancing, and in the midst of the reception, a sudden rainstorm followed by immediate clearing. Gidget threw her bouquet to Gladys. Patrick ended up with her garter. Gidget was beginning to wear out. She went to the ladies' room with Gladys to change into her going-away dress. After they got her wedding dress off, she sat down in a lounge chair in her slip and put her head in her hands.

"Gidge, what's wrong?" Gladys asked.

"I'm tired of all this," Gidget complained. "I want to get away from everybody and be with David. I'm tired of talking and smiling and I have a really bad headache and I feel like I can't even talk to my own husband with all these people around."

Gladys giggled. "Gidget, your *husband*," she echoed. "That sounds so fabulous."

"It sounds better than it is, because I can't even *be* with him in this mob. Do you know that they want us to go back to the house and open our presents before we leave for our honeymoon?"

"Are you going to do it?" Gladys wanted to know.

"I don't know. Give me two aspirin, will you?" Gladys always carried aspirin in her purse. She handed two to Gidget. "It seems ridiculous, opening presents right now. I don't care about the presents, I care about getting out of here and being alone with David."

Gladys handed her a paper cup of water. "I don't blame you," she commiserated. "Parents are such a drag. Why don't they let you go?"

Gidget sighed. "They mean well," she acknowledged. "They don't realize what I'm feeling."

"Yeah, that's true."

"Maybe I ought to do it, Gladys. They gave me this nice wedding, after all."

"It was beautiful, Gidge."

"I know. I guess I can give them another hour of my time, right?"

"Well, if you look at it that way. After this, you'll have the rest of your life to be alone with David."

"I know." Gidget stood up and reached for her going-away outfit. "Will you help me with this? I want to look nice for David."

"And your folks," Gladys added. They both giggled.

Gidget rode with David to Bluebird Drive. Her father was there, and Johnny and Kathy, as well as Dick and Shirley and Patrick and a few close friends and relatives. Gidget felt better. The aspirin helped, and so did getting away from the crowd of people, and being able to sit down next to David. She and David opened presents while Kathy wrote down the gifts and the names of their donors. Nobody noticed that Patrick, Johnny, and Shirley Heidecker had disappeared.

The Heideckers' church, Ebenezer United Methodist, where David and Gidget were married June 8, 1985.   *Ann Turnbull*

The day before the wedding, David had had his car washed and cleaned inside and out. He had even paid for a wax job. It was spotless. Out on Bluebird Drive, just out of sight of the picture window in the living room, Patrick, who was no longer sober, was applying soap to David's shiny clean car. Across the sides, up and down the windows, around the back, he made thick white stripes. Shirley poured bags of confetti, salvaged from Webster Clothes, inside the car. Over the seats, onto the floor, into the ashtrays and vents, she left no spot uncovered. Johnny, sitting on the grass behind the car, attached empty beer and soda cans and other trash to a seven-foot link chain. He ran the chain around the bumper and attached the ends of it together. Weighed down by metal and debris, the chain touched the ground. The three conspirators worked silently, each intent on his or her task. When the chain was firmly in place, Johnny looked up.

"Are you guys finished?" he asked.

The three of them stepped back to appreciate the full impact of their handiwork. It was spectacular. Patrick had completed his job by writing "Just Married" in huge white strokes across the passenger side of the car. Confetti spilled through the windows, and the thick chain pulled at the bumper. Patrick, who was drunk from beer which he had smuggled into the reception, sat down on the grass. Shirley and Johnny went back inside the house to join the others.

David and Gidget were ready to leave. Gidget was saying good-bye to her father, who wanted to think of something profound to say but could only wipe away a few tears of his own. David hugged both his parents, leaning down to kiss Shirley and embrace Dick. He took Gidget's hand and led her out the front door of her house. Then he stopped in his tracks.

"My car!" he yelled. "Who in the hell did that?"

Dick Heidecker muttered, "Uh, oh!"

"Son of a bitch!" David shouted. "Patrick, did you do this? I think I'll kill you!"

Gidget put her hand on David's arm. "Don't get upset," she said. "It's just for fun, because we're married."

David took a step forward. "Damn!" he said. "And it was so clean, too!"

Dick said, "It looks good, son. What's the point of getting married if nobody knows about it?"

David went closer to the car. "Yeah, I guess so," he said grudgingly. "But who did all this confetti?"

Patrick had struggled to his feet and was leaning on the car. "You can't blame that on me," he said. "Your mom did that."

"Mom?" David looked over at Shirley, who smiled coyly. David started to chortle. "I don't believe it, my own mother! Who did the chain?"

"I did that," Johnny volunteered. "Do you like it?"

David punched him in the arm. "Yeah, I love it," he said. "Let me get rid of that thing right now." He yanked the chain in two directions, with no results. He dropped it. "What the heck, I'll keep it," he said.

He opened the passenger door and pulled armfulls of confetti onto the street before helping Gidget to get in. She lowered the soaped-up window and waved. Gladys stepped up to the car and leaned down. "See what you would have missed if you hadn't come back to the house?" she whispered.

Gidget laughed. "It's okay, I like it," she said.

David got into the car and turned the key. He and Gidget waved as they drove up Bluebird Drive. Behind them, Patrick had climbed into his own car and was pulling out into the road in an apparent attempt to follow David and Gidget. This was too much for Dick. He stepped into the middle of the road and put his hand up.

"That's enough, Pat," he said. "Park your car and get out."

Patrick rolled down his window. "Get outta my way, Mr. Heidecker!" he yelled. "My best friend just left and I'm going with him!"

"You're going nowhere," Dick told him. "Not unless you're willing to run me over."

Parick moved his car slowly forward. "I mean it, Mr. Heidecker, I'm coming through!"

Dick put his hands on his hips and stood there with his feet apart. Patrick blew the horn for a minute, and finally turned off the engine and slumped down in the seat. He was crying. Dick opened the passenger door and got in next to Patrick. Everybody else went back inside. Dick put his hand on Patrick's shoulder.

"You've had too much to drink," he said gently. "You need to sleep this off."

"Mr. Heidecker, David's the best friend I have in the world," Patrick sobbed. "When I was a kid, he was nice to me when nobody else was. I looked up to him, you know?"

"I know," Dick said sympathetically.

"He let his home be my home, too," Patrick went on. "I always had a place to go, and people to be nice to me. You and Mrs. Heidecker always treated me nice, too."

"We tried to," Dick said.

"I don't have any friends like that in the Army," Patrick said. "There's nobody like David in my life."

"David's still in your life."

"Yeah, but not as much," Patrick said. "I mean, it isn't going to be the same, is it?"

Dick thought a minute. "I guess it won't be quite the same," he admitted. "Things change, Patrick. You and David are growing up, you're not kids anymore. Things would be changing even if David wasn't getting married, wouldn't they?"

"I guess."

"But you and David will always be friends. You might be in different places, different parts of the country, like you are now, but you'll always be back in touch. I believe that."

Patrick was inconsolable. Dick, whose own feelings were in turmoil, continued to talk to Patrick, to try to persuade him — and himself — that David was still there. Dick had already undergone the pain of separation when David had left for Fort Benning; for him, David's marriage did not necessarily signal further separation. But for Patrick, who had been a bachelor with David, marriage was an event more significant than geographical distance. Dick understood that. When he was unable to console Patrick, he suggested that Patrick have a conversation with Gladys.

"You know, Pat, you and Gladys are more or less in the same boat," he pointed out. "You know how close those two girls have been to each other, Gidget and Gladys. They've been friends about as long as you and David.

David with Dick and Shirley on his wedding day.

David and Gidget on their wedding day.

I betcha that Gladys is moping around inside right now the same way you are, and maybe she needs somebody to talk to like you do.''

Patrick sniffed. "Yeah," he said.

"What do you say you come inside and talk to her?" Dick suggested. "I bet it would make both of you feel a lot better."

"Do you think so?" Patrick asked.

"Whatta you got to lose?" Dick asked rationally. "You're feeling lousy now."

Patrick said, "Okay. I'll come in."

"And drink coffee, bud," Dick said. "You don't need any more beer."

"I know," Patrick said. He looked at Dick. "Thanks, Mr. Heidecker. I'm sorry for acting like I was going to run you down."

Dick snorted. "I was a cop for sixteen years, remember?"

"Yeah, I forgot," Patrick said.

The two of them got out of the car and went inside, where Gladys sat alone in a corner. Patrick punched her shoulder. "Hey, I need a friend," he said. "Can I sit with you?"

Gladys stared at him. "Me, too," she said.

Out on the highway, David and Gidget were really alone for the first time since David's return from Fort Campbell, and certainly for the first time that day. They were alternately quiet and talkative, sharing the joy of each other and their new status, leaving the stress of the day behind. David drove confidently, his right hand on Gidget's left hand where he could feel her new wedding band again and again. He grinned and waved back at drivers of other vehicles who blew horns and shouted at his car. A lot of the confetti had blown across Carroll County, and somewhere on I-70 they lost the seven-foot chain, but the wide stripes of soap continued to advertise their status. Both of them enjoyed it as they rode inside the protective shell of metal and chrome, being greeted, but not entrapped, by friendly strangers. The radio played softly as Gidget rested her head on David's shoulder. Every now and then she reached up to kiss him on his cheek. Once he said:

"Hey, can't you wait until we get to our hotel? What are you, some kind of nymphomaniac?"

Gidget giggled. Nobody had told her of the wonder of sitting next to her husband, on their way to a hotel, with no curfew and no parents to account to. In retrospect, it had all been worth it — the separations from David, the long waits for his letters and phone calls, lonely Saturday nights, her parents' lectures, even this hectic, beautiful day. They sped through the night as if on a mission.

They were headed for Columbia, Maryland, a city of 60,000 people which was less than an hour away. David and Gidget had reservations at the Columbia Hilton, a new hotel on the outskirts. They checked in late in the evening as Mr. and Mrs. David W. Heidecker and were given the key to the first hotel room they had ever shared. It was perfect. They took a shower together, turned the TV on low volume in the dark, and made love most of the night. They slept until noon on Sunday.

David and Gidget spent three nights in Columbia, seeing the town and being together. Columbia had been David's idea. They had considered other places, such as Ocean City, but had worried that all their friends might be there, especially the weekend after Gidget's graduation. David had rejected out of hand any place that might be populated with anyone they knew. Columbia would be interesting, close to home, and probably devoid of acquaintances. He was right. They walked around Lake Kittamaqundi, the man-made lake which was the center of downtown, fed the ducks there, rented a paddle boat. They went to the movies, swam, had dinner at Friendly's, and played miniature golf. There was cable TV in their room, and they had each other.

David called his parents. "Hey, Mom and Dad, we're having a great time! Do *not* wish you were here, sorry." He winked at Gidget. "Here, say hi to my wife!" He thrust the phone into Gidget's hand and laughed as she blushed and finally managed a weak hello. He wanted to call Patrick, but Gidget put her foot down.

After three days in Columbia, they decided to wind up their honeymoon with a day at Hersheypark, Pennsylvania, about an hour north of Carroll County. Gidget had been there many times before, but David never had. The theme park had a variety of rides, including a terrifying roller coaster built to compete with the heart-stopping mechanical giants of larger and newer parks. David loved it there. He and Gidget sat in the front seat of the roller coaster and rode it three times, screaming and waving their arms in the air. Later they sat on a bench and ate hot dogs with mustard.

At last they were back in the car, heading south. It was nine o'clock at night when they pulled up in front of Gidget's house. David stopped the car, took Gidget's hand, and looked at her solemnly.

"Well, kid, the honeymoon's over," he announced.

Gidget said, "I love you, David."

"Me too, babe. But I have one question."

Gidget looked up at him, trying to read his face. "Yes?"

David winked at her. "Is your old man going to let me sleep in your bedroom?"

Gidget burst out laughing. They opened the trunk for their suitcases and walked inside.

CHAPTER 14

Summer of '85

Country and bluegrass music blared from the radio as David and Gidget headed for Fort Campbell in Gidget's green Impala. Gidget played with the radio buttons, but all the stations seemed to have the same sound.

"Forget it, honey," David told her. "This is Tennessee — you aren't gonna find any other kind of music."

Neither of them really minded. David had become accustomed to the sound of country music over a period of many years because Shirley loved it, and Gidget was open to all kinds of music. Besides, they were passing through some of the prettiest countryside they had ever seen, in very early summer when trees and shrubs and whole mountainsides were in bloom. A couple of times, they stopped on the side of the road just to take in the beauty of the scenery, but when David put his arm around Gidget and held her close to him, they hurried back into the car so they could reach their new home sooner. The date was June 14, 1985, exactly eleven months from the night they met at the fire house carnival.

Because David was scheduled to depart for Egypt in a month, he had arranged for them to move in with a fellow soldier, Harry Magrette, and his wife, Donna. He didn't want to live on base with Gidget, and there was hardly time to find an apartment to sublet. Besides, they had no furniture.

"It'll be company for you," David explained to Gidget. "I'll be gone most of the day while we're here, and a month from now I'll be in a foreign country. It'll be nice for you to have a girlfriend to show you around."

Gidget agreed. She was on her way to a different part of the country where she knew nobody except David. When they arrived, she found that the Magrettes seemed nice, especially Harry, who was friendly and outgoing; Donna, who was older than Gidget, semed somewhat quiet and aloof. The Magrettes rented a little yellow house on a rural road in Clarksville, Tennessee, just a couple of miles from the base; David had explained that Fort Campbell actually straddled the boundary between Tennessee and Kentucky. Gidget liked the house as soon as she saw it, although the kitchen was small and there was only one bathroom. There was a porch across the front and a medium-sized bedroom for her and David. Their bedroom was sparsely furnished with one double bed, an old chest of drawers, and no rug on the floor, but neither of them cared. They had privacy, and that was enough.

The double bed was barely large enough for David's lanky frame plus Gidget, but they made a joke of it. "This is all my mother's fault," David said, as they lay together on their second night in Clarksville. "She claims I grew eleven inches the first year she had me. Without those eleven inches, I'd have plenty of room in this little bed."

Gidget giggled. "Yes, but then you'd only be five foot six," she said. "Do you think I wanted to marry a shrimp?"

"You're a shrimp," David said, hugging her with both arms. "You're my shrimp and I love you."

"Me too, David," Gidget told him.

"You don't mind us staying here like this, do you, babe? Not having our own place right now?" David rolled over. "We can get our own place as soon as I get back from Egypt, how's that?"

Gidget nodded. "I'd like that," she said. "Maybe I should look around while you're over there and have a place all picked out when you come back."

"Yeah, you can get Donna to help you, too. You'll have fun doing that."

On her way to the bathroom, Gidget took care to put on her floor-length bathrobe which David said made her look like an old-fashioned china doll. On their first night in the house, she had encountered Harry Magrette as he left the bathroom with only a towel draped around him. Gidget hadn't really minded, but David told her to be careful, he didn't want anybody else looking at her half dressed. This time, she didn't see anybody. When she climbed back in bed, minus the bathrobe, David made love to her.

Clarksville, Tennessee is the county seat of Montgomery County and home to about 55,000 people. The Chamber of Commerce and other boosters like to refer to their town as "A history-rich city that stretches majestically atop the steep bluffs overlooking the Cumberland and Red Rivers." They call attention to its golf courses, swimming pools, and tennis courts, its special events and historical sites. They bill the city as "one of the most historic ports on the Cumberland River," "more than just a pretty place," "Tennessee's fifth largest city," and "close to everything — next to perfect." But if you spend a day in Clarksville, you come to know that its dominating feature is not its history, its recreational facilities, or its scenic beauty — its dominating feature is Fort Campbell.

Main Gate Four, Fort Campbell, Kentucky. These words greeted visitors to the Fort.

Ann Turnbull

Fort Campbell occupies over one hundred acres, all of them west of U.S. Route 41A which stretches north from Tennessee into Kentucky and is known also as Fort Campbell Boulevard. There are six gates to the base, all from that highway. The main entrance, known as Main Gate Four, is in Kentucky; hence the official address of Fort Campbell, two-thirds of which is in Tennessee. The Fort encourages visitors; there are tours, public events, and the Pratt Museum containing historical military items.

Running alongside the base, Fort Campbell Boulevard is a four-lane divided highway crowded with gas stations, cheap motels, fast food outlets, bars and lounges, video rental places, used car lots, and furniture stores. It is obvious that the economic target is not the tourist or the history buff but the transient military family. There is a huge market in rental homes, particularly in trailer parks, which are ubiquitous.

Leaving Fort Campbell Boulevard, one goes from the commercial to the rural in a matter of minutes. Less than a mile east of the highway are cornfields and cattle farms; the roads become narrow, winding, and sometimes dirt. Small wooden houses sit in broad fields, and unnamed roads lead to rows of mobile homes. Dogs run free, and clean wash flaps from clotheslines. The smells are of nature, not traffic, and the sounds of civilization are muffled or too far away to be heard. Such a place may be bucolic, or it may be lonely and deserted, depending on one's circumstances and perspective. In just such a place, David and Gidget started out their married life together.

David's military routine required him to be at the base by 6:30 in the morning. He would set the alarm for 5:45, shower and shave, and then wake Gidget to sit with him while he dressed and got ready for the day. He didn't eat breakfast there, but he enjoyed looking at Gidget's sleepy face and hearing her voice. She liked to watch him put on his fatigues and combat boots. By quarter after six, he was kissing her good-bye and hurrying out the door with Harry to get to the base. Gidget went back to sleep until later. Eventually, she got up, read the Garfield comics and articles of interest in the Clarksville *Leaf-Chronicle*, watched television. She and Donna got along, but they were not really friends. There was a washer and dryer in the house, and they did laundry. They also took turns planning and cooking dinner. By mid-afternoon, Gidget began to make herself ready for David's return at 4:30 or 5:00. She bathed, dressed, worked on her hair until she was satisfied, and then waited eagerly for the sound of David's footstep at the door. She greeted him enthusiastically, throwing herself into his arms and allowing herself to be picked up from the floor and squeezed.

"I don't believe it!" David would yell. "This good-looking chick cannot possibly be my wife! I can't be that lucky! Who are you, anyway?"

"I can't tell you," Gidget whispered. "My husband is a very jealous man."

David would put Gidget on his lap and tell her about his day — "Nothing much, same old stuff" — and ask her what was for dinner. Usually he would want to shower again after a day at the base, and then they would eat and sit down together in front of the TV. Sometimes they went for a ride, or went out to the stores to look around or buy an ice cream cone, but often they were content to be alone together. It was summer, and they could walk hand in hand without coats, down untraveled roads or through sweet-smelling fields, absorbing the novelty of their surroundings and each other. Neither of them cared much about meeting other people just now, and the many activities on base held no inducement for them; if they should have given more thought to the imminent condition of Gidget's life in Clarksville without David, neither of them did. The Magrettes, who appeared to be private people by nature, gave them space; sometimes the two couples spent evenings together at their mutual home, watching TV or playing a game of Monopoly, but often Harry and Donna stayed in their bedroom or went out alone.

It was a special time for David and Gidget, but not a time that could be characterized as smooth. Not only were they paying guests in somebody else's house, but they had almost nothing with them except clothes. All the wedding presents were back at Dick and Shirley's house, waiting until David and Gidget had their own place. There were hours of boredom for Gidget, alone in a strange place, and times of stress for David, when he felt burdened with a heavy sense of responsibility. There were arguments, some of them tumultuous, most of them brief and petty, nearly all of them born of anxieties engendered by a combination of their situation and their youthfulness. But arguments gave way to reconciliation, and their fears to their sense of joy, so that days began and ended happily, for the most part, despite pressures which were serious and to which both David and Gidget were unaccustomed.

One Friday afternoon, David called from the base to say they had plans for the evening. "Make yourself pretty, babe," he told Gidget. "Two of my buddies want us to go out on the town tonight."

"Are they married?" Gidget asked.

"One is, the other has a girlfriend," David said. "There'll be six of us. I'll see you in a while, okay?"

Gidget showered and went to work on her hair. She put on her brightest summer skirt and blouse, and fixed her makeup. At 5:30, David and two couples appeared at the Magrettes' house. Gidget opened the door. David kissed her.

"Wow!" he said. "You look terrific! Want to meet my friends?"

Gidget asked them to come in. Alex was a young soldier about twenty-two years old, and Ann, his girlfriend, was a local Clarksville girl who lived with her parents and went to Austin Peay State University. The other people were Paul and Penny, a black couple in their mid-twenties. All six of them piled into the Impala with David behind the wheel.

They headed south on Fort Campbell Boulevard, in the direction of Tennessee. There was a reason for that: the drinking age in Kentucky was twenty-one, whereas it was only nineteen in Tennessee. Gidget was underage in both states, but she didn't drink anyway and didn't care. David was legal in Tennessee but not in Kentucky.

David asked, "What does everybody have in mind for dinner?"

His question brought several responses: Kentucky fried chicken, Chinese food, the House of Pancakes, and Western Sizzler, but David pulled into the parking lot of Bernie's Bar and Restaurant and suggested that somebody check it out. Alex jumped out of the car and was gone for a few minutes. He came back to report that the place looked fine, there definitely was a bar, and the prices were low. Everybody piled out and headed into the restaurant. They found a table for six, and everybody but Gidget ordered a beer. Ann asked her how old she was.

"Eighteen, how old are you?" Gidget replied.

"I'm twenty."

"Do you like living in Clarksville?" Gidget wanted to know.

"Sure, it's fine. I'm an Army brat, so I've lived lots of places. The best thing about this place is Alex."

Alex toasted her with his beer can. "That's my girl," he said. He turned to David. "How long have you guys been married?"

David grinned. "Two weeks, give or take," he said proudly.

"Two weeks, really?"

Now everybody toasted David and Gidget. Paul touched his can of beer to Gidget's glass of Coke so hard that some of the soda spilled over the edge; he apologized and wiped the table with a napkin. Ann suggested that they order champagne, but nobody could afford it, and Penny said that what they really needed was something special like a belly dancer or a gorilla jumping out of a cake. Paul asked David how long he thought the honeymoon would last, and Gidget blushed when he answered that he expected it to last forever. Alex started on his repertoire of newlywed jokes, but Ann made him stop after the first two. A bored-looking waitress came to take their order. Gidget asked for a hamburger and french fries, and David wanted fried chicken. The service at Bernie's was efficient, if not especially gracious, and afterwards the three couples divided up the check and left a tip. They headed for the car, and David continued south on Fort Campbell Boulevard. They stopped at a lounge down the road, but Alex, after going inside to check, reported that the cover charge was seven dollars apiece. It was too much, so they drove on. Another place had no cover charge, but had a three dollar minimum per person. Everybody agreed that that was okay, and they all went inside. They sat at a crowded table in a dingy room and drank two beers apiece (except for Gidget), as a musical group with three men and a girl played guitars and sang pop tunes with a country sound. It was too loud for them to talk, and there was a lot of noise and smoke. After a while, they were ready to move on.

In the car, they had a discussion about what to do next. It was not even ten o'clock, and the next day was Saturday. Paul and Penny suggested that they all go to their place, which was on the base. David drove to the base, and Paul directed him to his home. It was an apartment in the married housing section. Gidget was surprised at what a nice place it was. Although small and modest, it was fixed up nicely and seemed comfortable and private. She began to wonder if living on base might not have been a better idea; there was so much more to do there, and there were neighbors and people to be friends with. She asked Penny about it.

"I like it here," Penny said. "You can always find somebody to do things with or to drive you somewhere, and the base has everything you need."

"It's noisy, though," Paul said. "And sometimes you feel shut in by everything around you. I'd like to have a little more space, maybe a little yard and a garden or something."

David volunteered, "We'll be getting our own place as soon as I get back from Egypt. Gidget's going to pick out a place while I'm gone."

"You ought to look at the mobile homes, then," Ann said. "A lot of them are nicer than apartments, and don't cost any more."

"Really?" Gidget asked.

"Sure. They're spacious, and you have a little grass outside, but you're close to other people, too."

Gidget asked David, "What do you think about that?"

David was pouring himself a soda. He nodded. "Fine with me," he said. "I don't care too much where I live, as long as it's with you and doesn't cost too much money."

Paul and Alex exchanged glances. "Newlyweds," Paul said. "I bet you don't even fight yet."

Gidget smiled shyly. "Once in a while," she offered.

When it was time to go, David and Gidget dropped Alex and Ann at their homes, and finally pulled up in front of the Magrettes' little house. They held hands in the car while the radio played softly.

"Did you have fun tonight?" David asked.

Gidget nodded. "I did," she said. "I didn't enjoy the lounge too much; it was kind of noisy."

David shrugged. "That's just the kind of joints soldiers go to," he said. "I don't know if anyone really enjoys them, you just go there for something to do."

"Oh," Gidget said. "Well, everything else was a lot of fun. I liked your friends."

"Yeah, it was good to be with people for a change," David acknowledged.

"What did you think of Paul's place? I liked it. Did you?"

"I did, but I really don't want to live on base. It's like Paul said, you want a little more space, maybe a yard. You'll find the right place for us; I trust you."

"Do you think we should consider a mobile home?"

"Why not? Look around and pick whatever you want."

Gidget leaned up and kissed his cheek. "I love you," she said.

They spent another Friday evening at the Two Rivers Mall in Clarksville. They walked around, looking at merchandise, stopping now and then to look at a price, not actually buying anything. They had a hamburger, and later went to Baskin-Robbins for an ice cream cone. David sat by the window, watching the ceaseless traffic.

"You know, Gidge, we're only an hour away from Nashville," he said. "We could drive down there sometime, go to Opryland, maybe see the Grand Ole Opry."

"I'd like that," Gidget said. "Maybe Minnie Pearl is there."

"Yeah, and we could hear Roy Acuff do Wabash Cannonball. It'd be fun."

"It would be."

David said, "You know what, honey? There's this fantastic hotel down there, right next to the Opry, called the Opryland Hotel. I was there for about a half an hour last spring, before we got married. It has these gardens that are indoors, under a glass roof, like, with waterfalls and everything. And it has all these lounges, a bunch of different ones where you can go and see entertainment practically all the time. Anybody can come to the entertainment, but if you stay at the hotel you can just go from one lounge to another and then go to your own hotel room whenever you're tired."

"Is it good entertainment?"

"Yeah, it's mostly country, and it is good. Then they have a swimming pool and a bunch of restaurants right there in the hotel so you don't even have to leave the building if you don't want to."

"It must be expensive," Gidget said.

"Sure it is," David replied. "And right next door is this gigantic amusement park, like Hersheypark, called Opryland, with rides and everything."

"Sounds like fun," Gidget agreed.

"We have to get down to Nashville, honey. There's a whole lot I want to do with you."

"Me, too," Gidget said.

"And places to see. I want to take you to California, see the Pacific Ocean, go out west to the Grand Canyon and all. There's mountains all over this country we haven't seen yet."

"All over the world," Gidget reminded him.

"That's right. I want us to see Europe someday, and Japan, maybe even some of Africa. There's at least a thousand things I want to see with you."

"We have time," Gidget said. "We have our whole lives."

"Yeah, I know. After I get back from overseas, we'll do all those things. We'll do it all."

They walked back to the car with their arms around each other.

The most protracted argument they had that summer had to do with their automobile. They had arrived in Clarksville in Gidget's dull green Impala which, according to Gidget, ran perfectly but which, according to David, was not sporty looking at all. A week after their arrival, David heard about a blue Monte Carlo that was available. He checked it out; it was sporty looking, all right, but it didn't run. David took Gidget and Harry Magrette to see the car.

"Gidge, how would you like to drive that instead of your Impala?" he asked, pointing proudly to the pretty blue Monte Carlo.

"I'd love it," Gidget said. "It definitely looks a lot better than my car. But my car runs and this one doesn't."

"Hey, no problem," David announced. "I can take the engine out of the Impala and put it in the Monte Carlo. We'll have a great looking car that runs well, too."

Gidget was dubious. "Are you sure?" she asked. "What if you can't get it in right?"

David looked hurt. "Are you kidding? I've been working on cars all my life, you know that. Harry'll help me. We can do it in two days."

"How much do we have to pay for this other car?" Gidget wanted to know.

"$300. But we don't have to pay it until 1986. That's the deal I made with this guy. His name is Joel. By next year, we'll have that money saved up easily. It'll all work out great, you'll see."

"He's right, Gidget," Harry chimed in. "I'm gonna help him switch the engine."

Gidget looked at Harry. "Do you know anything about cars?"

"Yes, ma'am!" Harry assured her. "Been around cars all my life, same as David."

The two days they expected the job to take turned into four, and then there were extra hours required for fine tuning. They started early on a Saturday morning, David and Harry and Joel with assorted tools from various sources, cans of cold soda to drink, and a pile of rags and old towels on the grass. The day was hot and sticky and the Monte Carlo's engine more obstinate than they expected; by three o'clock the three of them had traded in their sodas for cold beer. By nightfall they were tired, filthy, a little tipsy, and not nearly finished with the job. They started again on Sunday, this time without Joel, who had lost interest and said that his labor was not part of the deal, even though he had touted his knowledge of engines and his willingness to help in the first place. By Sunday evening, David and Harry were confronted with two motorless automobiles, engine parts spread all over the grass, a threat of rain, and no way to get to work the next morning. Gidget was upset.

"David, we came here with a perfectly good car, and now you've torn it all apart and spent the whole weekend, we don't have a car that runs, and we owe $300!" she fumed. "What are we going to do?"

David touched her arm with black greasy fingers. "Hey, it'll be all right," he said. "It's just taking a little longer than we thought, that's all. We'll have everything A-OK by tomorrow night."

"Tomorrow night! You have to go to work tomorrow," Gidget reminded him. "How will you get there?"

"Yeah, we better do something about that," David said. "Come on, Harry, let's go inside and make some calls."

They called Alan O'Sullivan, the company clerk, whom Gidget had met twice, and were able to secure a ride to and from the base for the next day — and the next — but the Monte Carlo was not running by Monday night. By now Gidget was convinced that her Impala had been destroyed for no purpose, that they would never have transportation again, and that they were needlessly in debt. Her anxieties began to get on David's nerves; he told her finally that he would get the goddamn car running if she would just get the hell off his back, and Gidget went to bed alone and in tears. David came in later, considerably cleaned up and calmer, and kissed her awake to say he was sorry and that everything was going to work out after all. The next night, Tuesday, his faith and diligence were rewarded by the sound of the Impala engine turning over in the Monte Carlo; the car still needed work, but at least it was running.

He bounded into the house, calling for Gidget. "Hey, baby, come on out and see what we got!'

Gidget wandered outside warily. "Is it running?" she asked.

"You bet your life, and it's running pretty good, too! Come see!"

He put Gidget into the passenger seat and drove the car up and down the road for a few minutes. "See, what do you think?"

"I guess it's okay," Gidget said hesitantly. "Will it keep running?"

"Yeah, but it needs some more work. We'll get it shipshape before long, you'll see."

"More work!" Gidget sighed. "I think you should have left well enough alone with my Impala."

"But it wasn't well enough," David insisted. "The new car looks terrific."

"But you won't be here in a couple of weeks!" Gidget wailed. "I don't care if the car looks terrific or not! I just want to be able to get around!"

"Honey, you will," David assured her. "I'm getting it in tip-top shape for you to use while I'm overseas. This is for us, don't you see?"

Gidget said nothing. She felt that all of it had been a waste of time, but on the other hand, David did seem to enjoy it — the work itself, as well as the sporty look of the Monte Carlo. She supposed it was all right as long as the car ran. Besides, she liked sporty cars, too, and it *was* pretty. She put her arms around David's neck.

"It's neat," she told him. "I like it a lot."

A couple of days later, David came home from the base in a rage. Donna Magrette, who was cutting grass in the yard, ran inside to alert Gidget. Harry and David were home, Donna said, and David was standing alongside the Monte Carlo slamming the car door over and over while Harry hollered at him to quit it before he damaged the car. Gidget, who had just started to cook dinner, looked out the window and saw David pounding his fist on the roof of the Monte Carlo. She could hear him yelling obscenities as Harry Magrette made futile efforts to calm him down. She ran out of the house and put her hands on David's shoulder.

"David? What is it?"

David looked at her and continued to beat on the roof of the car. Then he held out his left hand for her to see. "Look at that!" he yelled.

It took Gidget a minute to realize that what he was showing her was his left hand without his wedding ring, which he always wore. Gidget was appalled. "Oh, David, your wedding ring! Where is it?"

"Do you think if I knew where it is it wouldn't be on my finger?" David shouted. "It's lost, that's where it is!"

Now Gidget was upset. "It's really gone?" she whispered.

"That's right, my wedding ring is in the fucking dirt somewhere in Kentucky, and one day some shriveled old archeologist will dig it up and say, hey, look at this!"

"Whereabouts did you lose it?" Gidget asked.

"In a field, that's where." David was shouting directly in Gidget's face now. "We were out in the field, digging, and I lost it. Have you ever heard about a needle in a haystack? Have you?"

"Yes," Gidget whispered. She was starting to cry.

"Well, that's the haystack, that field, and my ring is the needle. You figure it out."

Gidget was crying hard now. "Maybe it'll show up," she managed.

"Fat chance!" David yelled. He slammed his hand against the roof of the Monte Carlo one last time. "Damn!"

Gidget touched his arm. "David, please," she implored tearfully. "Maybe we'll find it."

"Yeah?" David walked rapidly towards the house, away from Gidget. "Where, in China when some kids dig there?"

Gidget stood forlornly by the car. "I don't know," she said.

David disappeared into the house. He yelled out to her, "Of course you don't know! You don't know anything!"

Now Harry Magrette was running towards the house, shouting at David. "Goddamn it, David, quit this noise!" he hollered. "You're being completely irrational! We know you're upset, but cut all the racket and stop yelling at Gidget!"

Gidget, now alone outside, cried bitterly. She walked slowly towards the house and inside the door, where David stood with his back to her. "David, it'll be all right," she sobbed. "We can get another wedding band."

"But you don't understand!" David hollered, hitting his open hand against the wall of Harry Magrette's house. "Then they won't *match*!"

"What?"

"Our bands. If we buy a new one for me, it won't match yours anymore."

David walked into the bathroom and closed the door behind him. The only sound in the house for the next five minutes was the sound of Gidget crying. Harry put his arm around her shoulders, and Donna brought her a glass of water. Gratefully, Gidget pulled herself together. She walked hesitantly to the bathroom, knocked cautiously on the door, and opened it. David sat on the side of the bathtub, his face in his hands. Gidget put her arms around his shoulders and kissed the top of his hair.

"It'll be okay, David," she said gently.

David said nothing. Finally, he reached for her hand and squeezed it. "I'm sorry, babe," he said. "It's just that I got so upset about losing the ring you gave me. Nothing ever meant as much to me before."

Gidget rubbed his back. "I know," she said. "But it's just something you buy. We can both buy new ones, if you want. Then we'll match again."

David's face brightened. "Yeah, you're right," he said. "Of course we could do that." He pulled Gidget onto his lap. "Can you imagine what I felt like out there, Gidge, crawling around in the dirt with about five other guys, praying to God that little band of gold was gonna turn up? I felt like screaming, crying, and I couldn't because of all those guys. It was about the most terrible thing that happened to me since I was a little kid in the institution, when people were ganging up on me and I didn't have anybody."

Gidget was puzzled. "Who was ganging up on you today?" she asked.

"Nobody," David said. "I'm telling you what was in my gut, not my head, silly." He almost smiled. "I love you, babe," he said. "You mean more to me than anybody, do you know?"

Later that night they talked about having a baby. They had talked about children before; David had always said he wanted to have a big family. Now he thought it was time to get started.

Gidget had doubts. "We're kind of young for that, David," she said. "There's plenty more time."

"So what?" David said. "I want a lot of kids, don't you? What's wrong with getting started? If you got pregnant right now, I'd be back from Egypt before the baby was born. It'd be perfect."

"I'll become fat and shapeless," Gidget reminded him.

"No, you won't. You'll be the only woman in the world to give birth with a twenty-four inch waist. Besides, you'd be beautiful to me anyway."

Gidget said, "I think you want to make me pregnant so that nobody else will be interested in me while you're gone."

"No, I trust you," David told her. "I don't trust the other guys, but I trust you."

"That's good," Gidget said.

"See honey, I feel like I owe something for what my parents did for me. Everything I have, even you, is because of them. It was their being there for me that made everything else possible, especially my life with you. Do you think I would be anything if they hadn't come along for me?"

"I know," Gidget said.

"Well, I have to give something back for that. What I mean is, I want to have a family with you, kids and all, that'll be the best family ever. Our kids have a right to grow up with two parents taking care of them from the time they're born. That's what I owe to them because of my mom and dad."

Gidget lay next to him in the skimpy double bed. "I know," she said. "I want that, too. But we have to have our own place to live when we have children."

"Sure," David said. "We'll have our own place to live by the time I get back from Egypt. That's no problem."

"But we don't know where you'll be stationed next," Gidget pointed out. "What if they send you to Germany or someplace like that?"

"What if they do? Dependents can come to Germany. We'd all be together."

"But it's a foreign country!"

David said, "Silly. Don't you think they have kids in Germany?"

"I guess so." Gidget nestled against his warm body. "But what about all the money it takes to support a family? You don't even know what you want to do when you get out of the Army."

"Yeah, but I'll do something. You know I'll get a good job. I'll probably go back to school, get more education, and then get started on a career." David leaned over and kissed her gently. "Besides, babies don't eat much."

Gidget sighed. David was wearing her down. It was hard for her to look into his face and say no to anything he asked for. Besides, she understood what family meant to David. Maybe he was right.

"Okay," she said. She was not entirely persuaded, but from then until David's departure, neither of them took any precautions.

The next day, Gidget called the jeweler in Carroll County who had sold her their wedding rings. The store had another one in stock, they said, but they couldn't send it until payment was received. Gidget did not have a credit card, and her check could not get to Maryland and clear in time — David would be leaving in a week. She reluctantly decided to wait until her next trip home to buy it.

David called his parents collect at least once every week. Sometimes they called him, too, usually around dinner time when they knew he would be there. Gidget called her parents, too, although that was not as simple because they didn't live together. She liked to talk to her mother, to tell her how she felt about being married, how she enjoyed waiting for David to come home in the afternoons. She liked to tell her father about Clarksville and Fort Campbell and the things she did with David. Gidget found that the person in Carroll County that she missed most of all was Gladys. She called her a couple of times, but they couldn't talk long because of the expense. She had to pay Donna for the calls.

The Magrettes did not have a VCR. Harry and David decided to rent one for the last weekend before their scheduled departure to Egypt. They got one from a video store on Fort Campbell Boulevard and hooked it up. The two couples selected a group of movies and spent the weekend in front of the television set in the little yellow house. The men wanted at least some horror movies, but Gidget protested; they compromised with The Incredible Shrinking Man and Alfred Hitchcock's The Birds. They also watched Bite the Bullet, with Gene Hackman and James Coburn, and The Flim Flam Man, a comedy about a con man and a military deserter which David and Harry particularly enjoyed. They finished up with Flashdance. On Monday, David and Harry took the films and the machine back to the video store. They had one night left in town.

Approximately 750 soldiers from the 101st Airborne Division were scheduled to take part in the international peacekeeping mission in the Sinai Desert in July of 1985, including virtually all of the Third Battalion's Alpha Company. They were to leave on three flights, each about a week apart. David Heidecker and Harry Magrette were assigned to the second flight, due to depart on Tuesday, July 16.

David and Gidget spent their last night together at the Magrettes' house. David asked Gidget to write often. "There won't be anything to do there," he told her. "All I'll do is sit around and look at the sand and wait for your letters."

"Are you sure about that?" Gidget asked. "What about all those sexy Arab women? Maybe you'll meet one of them."

"Hey, watch your mouth," David said. "You're the only sexy woman in the world for me."

"But it seems so long until you'll be back. I don't know what I'll find to do, either."

"You might be able to find a job," David suggested. "The car's running fine, you'll be able to get around. You need to get into some things. They have a lot of classes and stuff at the base, you know, things to do. You should go up there and find out what you want to do."

Gidget nodded. "I will," she said. "And later I'll find a place for us to live for when you get back. I'll get it for December, then I can move in and fix it all up before you get here."

David leaned down and kissed the top of her head. "You know, this is crazy, me going to a foreign country right after we got married," he said. "I wish I didn't have to."

"Me, too," Gidget said.

"I want to go to bed every night with you beside me and wake up with you next to me every morning," David told her. He got up for a soda. "Let's figure out how much time we've actually had together so far," he said. "We met July 14 last year, and I left for Fort Benning on August 21, I remember those dates. That gave us about five weeks when we were dating all the time, right?"

"Right, and then you came home for Thanksgiving. That was about one week."

"Okay, that makes six weeks. Then I got back for Christmas, but it was only a few days. Call that half a week."

"You came home for my birthday in May, that was another week," Gidget said. "That puts us at seven and a half weeks, right?"

"We got married June 8, and tomorrow is July 16. That's five and a half weeks. Seven and a half plus five and a half is thirteen, is that right? Thirteen weeks that you and I have been together out of a whole year!"

"Yes, and only five and a half of those we were living together. The rest was more or less dating," Gidget said. She took some of David's soda. "A year has fifty-two weeks in it. Thirteen weeks is only one quarter of a year, and that's what we've had together so far. Can you believe that's all?"

David kissed her. "Yeah, well just think what we have ahead of us."

"What?"

"We have the whole rest of our lives to be as happy as we've been for our thirteen weeks. I'm only twenty. You're eighteen. What do you think thirteen weeks means out of, say, the fifty or sixty years we have to go?"

Gidget laughed. "Well, when you put it that way," she said.

David put his glass down. "Come on, baby, let's make love," he said. "It's our last chance for five months, and five months is going to seem like forever!"

Gidget whispered, "I love you, David."

"Me, too, Gidge," David said. "No matter what, I love you forever 'n' longer."

CHAPTER 15

The Sinai Desert

The mission that brought David Heidecker to the Sinai Desert in July of 1985 had its roots in the Camp David Accords of 1979. That year President Jimmy Carter established a sort of peace between Egypt and Israel through those Accords, whose concept was that Israel would give up the Sinai through a phased withdrawal in return for international guarantees of security.

As world events unfolded, objections by the Soviet Union and certain Arab countries prevented the United Nations from mounting its own force to oversee security arrangements. In 1981, therefore, the Multinational Force and Observers (MFO) with headquarters in Rome was created for that purpose. Eleven countries were represented in the MFO, but the United States supplied nearly half of the 2,500 soldiers based there. The bulk of them came from the 82nd and 101st Airborne Divisions.

The Sinai Desert forms a triangular peninsula bounded by the Mediterranean Sea on the north and the two northern tributaries of the Red Sea — the Gulf of Suez on the Egyptian side, and the Gulf of Aqaba on the Israeli side. The Gulf of Suez, of course, leads to the Suez canal. The American military contingent is located at South Camp, near Al Aresh, in the southeastern part of the desert on the Gulf of Aqaba. This particular area of the Sinai is mountainous, arid, and intensely hot, with an average summer temperature of 95 degrees. Winter nights can be cool; ice occasionally caps the highest mountain peaks, but there is almost no rain. Scrub grows in a few places, although there are no trees as such. Wildlife is sparse. There is virtually no settled human population. Wandering Bedouin tribes make an appearance in this part of the desert from time to time. Across the Gulf of Aqaba is Saudi Arabia.

David and the contingent from his 3rd Battalion of the 502nd Infantry were transported to the Sinai on three planes spaced about a week apart.

David was assigned to the second plane, which departed Fort Campbell on July 16. It was a long and grueling flight, finally landing at Cairo where the soldiers were flown to South Camp by military transport. From there, buses took them to the base itself, where the 250 tired soldiers were confronted with the anomaly of a modern village in Biblical surroundings. Buildings, trailers, plumbing, and air-conditioning units rose from the dunes, giving the impression of having been plunked down randomly like a child's sand castle, quite literally in the middle of nowhere. Young American soldiers who took modern conveniences for granted failed to perceive — much less appreciate — the miracle of modern technology in the sand. They were disappointed at the quality of the facilities compared to those stateside, although there were barracks, a mess hall, recreational facilities including a gym with a basketball court and weight-lifting rooms, a library, and a movie room. Everything was air-conditioned. In the barracks, two soldiers were assigned to each room, which contained bunk beds, two bureaus and two desks. The bathroom was in a separate building. The Gulf of Aqaba was visible from South Camp, and accessible by jeep in about ten minutes.

In the Sinai Desert, 1985. David Heidecker is the tall soldier in the middle.

Military routine at South Camp combined the familiar with the unfamiliar. The soldiers wore a different uniform in the desert — khaki and brown pants and jacket, and a rust-colored beret. The focus of their duty in the Sinai was not at South Camp at all, but at the many observation posts which had been constructed within miles of the base in several directions. These isolated outposts, often made primarily of trailers, were designed to be manned by a squad, whose principal function was to observe, or to look for trouble. Each soldier was assigned a primary job — David's was automatic rifleman — and additional duties — David's were generator operator — but all of them nonetheless spent huge amounts of time "on guard," sometimes all night, or "observing." They rotated between South Camp and various observation posts, where they sometimes stayed for as long as thirty days.

The mail in and out of South Camp was sporadic. It came and went on trucks, which did not always appear. David's letters to Gidget took anywhere from six to twelve days to arrive in Clarksville. Gidget's letters back were even less predictable, depending partly on whether David was in South Camp or at one of the observation posts. He now had a new address: after his name, social security number, company, battalion, regiment and division, Gidget had to write: "MFO South Camp, APO N.Y. 19679."

On July 29, when David had been in the Sinai for nearly two weeks and had not yet heard from Gidget, he was permitted to telephone her. Calling home from South Camp was a complicated and expensive undertaking involving a time difference of seven hours. When David finally did reach Gidget, he spent the entire phone call telling her how much he missed her. He realized only later that he had told her almost nothing about life in the desert. Afterwards he wrote:

Dear Gidget:

Hi, honey, how's everything going? I felt a lot better after I heard your beautiful voice. After our conversation my sergeant handed me your first letter. It took 10 days for the letter to arrive. One question — why did you put four stamps on it?

After I talked to you I came back to the guard shack and read your letter four times. I cried myself to sleep. The next day we didn't do much. For PT we played volleyball.

On the day after that is a different story. We didn't have PT but God knows I wish we did. All we did do is fill sand bags all day. It was hotter than hell out. The sergeant thought he was hurting us but I laughed in his face and told him, personally I didn't care what he had us do, we were all going home the same day no matter what we did.

There is nothing to do at South Camp. You can lift weights, play basketball and drink. I know I don't need to worry because you will be fine, but I still do. I love you so much it hurts sometimes. There have been times when I just stop what I'm doing and think of you and wonder what you are doing, just remembering the good times and wishing I could be with you.

Write a lot — I miss you!

> Love you 4-ever-n-longer,
> David

Each soldier had to develop his own methods of coping with the loneliness and monotony of duty in the Sinai. For David, weight lifting became a regular part of his life — not because he liked it, particularly, but because it was something to do and a way to stay in shape. He played some sports, too, including basketball and volleyball, but those depended on the availability of other people. The companies formed softball teams, and David played for his company, which won its opening game 15 to 4. It was the first time David had played since high school; he wrote his father, "I did pretty good — three hits and no errors!" He also played cards, and occasionally saw a movie. Shirley sent him copies of *Sports Illustrated*, which always came late, but were more up to date than the issues available in South Camp's library, which David also frequented.

It was not easy to give the barracks a touch of individuality, but the men tried. Upon arrival, David tacked his photograph of himself and Gidget, taken at Gidget's senior prom, to the wall next to his upper bunk. In the fall Dick and Shirley sent him newspaper clippings about South Carroll's football games, and he tacked them up, too. Finally, Gidget sent him a wedding picture, and that joined the other memorabilia above his bunk.

Small incidents broke the routine. Occasionally they went swimming for the afternoon in the Gulf of Aqaba. Once they went on patrol to some Italian ships in the Gulf of Aqaba, and David tried wind surfing. He wrote to Gidget:

> I fell every time I got the surf up, but I had fun. We stayed over there all day and swam. It was so embarrassing falling off that surf but what was worse was when we got done the Italian captain got on it and rode it all the way across to the other shore. He acted like he was born on it!

At other times they encountered Egyptian soldiers who were not, of course, part of the international peace-keeping mission, but were there because this was their country. Sometimes, too, they saw Bedouins, the wandering desert people who often dressed in red and black robes and lived in tents with camels outside.

David did his best to keep occupied when at the observation post, where there were fewer diversions. He wrote to Gidget prolifically. On August 4, he wrote:

> When I woke up it was lunch time and both of the cooks were on a patrol. So a buddy and I went to work. First we made hot dogs. Start off easy. Second we made french fries and onion rings. That was it for lunch. Everyone liked it and we made a lot so there was no complaining.
>
> For dinner we made barbecue chicken with homemade barbecue sauce, with beans and rice. We experimented with the sauce. First it was too hot, then not hot enough then back to hot, although we thought it was fine. Oh well, it turned out great, no complaints. I had 5 pieces.

Some of his letters were less upbeat: "I hate the way the mail is here, one day they'll deliver mail and the next day they won't." "Every night I lie in bed and think about you." "We didn't do much today, as usual. All I want to do anyhow is hold you in my arms." On August 8 he wrote, "I know this will get to you late, but happy second month anniversary. I love you more now than when we got married."

For Gidget, life in Clarksville without David seemed hardly less desolate than David's life on an observation post in the Sinai Desert. She had found out almost immediately that she was not pregnant; she was partly relieved, but surprisingly disappointed, too. She knew almost nobody except Donna Magrette, who seemed increasingly remote, as well as more and more annoyed to be sharing her home with a stranger. Gidget slept late, read the comics, watched television, did laundry, wrote to David. She had no pressing financial worries. The Army deposited most of David's check directly into their joint checking account, while some cash was paid directly to him twice a month. Gidget was able to write checks on the account, and to pay Donna $100 each month. But she had nothing much to do. Soon after David left she called Penny, the woman she had met socially who lived on base.

"What do you think about the possibilities of my getting a job?" she asked Penny. "Are they hard to find here?"

"What kind of work can you do?" Penny asked.

"Well, I had some experience as a waitress back in Maryland. That would be one thing."

"Those jobs could be hard to get," Penny told her. "Especially in Kentucky where you have to be twenty-one wherever they serve liquor. What else could you do?"

"Receptionist, clerk-typist maybe, something like that?"

"But, see, Gidget, those kind of jobs are permanent positions, and you won't be here permanently. After David gets back you might be here a little while, but then you'll go somewhere else, maybe even to a foreign country. Nobody will want to hire you because of that."

Gidget was discouraged. "It was just an idea," she said.

"Well, if you need something to do, why don't you come on over to the base and sign up for some classes or activities?" Penny suggested. "They have lots to do. I'll go with you."

Gidget perked up. "That's a good idea," she said. "Maybe I could come up tomorrow?"

They made definite arrangements. But before the appointed time, and less than a week after David's departure, the Monte Carlo broke down, and Gidget was unable to go.

The car, which had been a bone of contention from the beginning, developed problems almost as soon as David left. The very next day, the lights had failed, making it impossible for Gidget to drive after dark. This information brought the following response in a letter from David:

> About the car. The reason why the lights won't come on is probably because the alternator wires disconnected when I tried to fit the belt on. If so, to fix it all you have to do is slide the connector back onto the slits on the back of the alternator. (Here David drew a diagram.) As you can see the alternator is on the left of the fan. Don't forget to let the car run awhile before moving. Most important of all is to be careful. I would rather have you safe than the car fixed.

By the time Gidget received this information, which was in August, the car had died completely, making it impossible for her to drive anywhere in the daytime, either. For over a week, the car was in a repair shop in Kentucky, to which Gidget had it towed; she paid a man there a hundred and twenty dollars, but the car ran for only three days after that. In desperation, she called Joel, the original owner of the car. He was able to get it to his house, where he promised to work on it. In the meantime, Gidget was stuck.

Donna had a truck which she allowed Gidget to use occasionally. Once in a while, Gidget took the truck, went up to the base to cash a check, and bought a few groceries, or lunch at Kentucky Fried Chicken. She gave up on joining any regular activity or class; without reliable transportation, she was just too far away from the base. Once she heard about a chance to work selling ice cream from a truck; the lady who owned the business needed temporary help and was willing to pick Gidget up for work. Gidget liked that job. She worked for a whole week and made twenty dollars a day. More important to her, she was able to speak to people all day long, exchanging pleasantries and small talk. It was a welcome change from the solitude of the Magrettes' house in the country.

But the job came to an end, and again there was nothing to do. Gidget occasionally called her parents, and David's parents; she and Shirley compared David's letters. Late one Friday night, Gladys Nunn called. She had a weekend job as a night dispatcher for a trucking company, she said, working from midnight until 8 a.m. every Friday and Saturday night. Her company had something like a WATS line, she told Gidget, where you could call long distance for nothing — Gidget could call collect every weekend and they could talk as long as they wanted. Gidget was thrilled. Her telephone calls to Gladys became the high point of her week.

"Gladys, it's me!" she would squeal. "How're you doing?"

"Gidget, I could die of boredom here, and I just came on! Thank God you called! How are you?"

"Boredom, you want to talk boredom? You should be sitting here in the middle of nowhere in somebody else's house, who doesn't even like you much, with your husband 9,000 miles away! Is that boredom?"

Gladys laughed. "You're right, you're the one who needs cheering up," she said. "Want me to tell you about my boyfriend, that should be good for some laughs."

As usual, Gladys was in a romantic crisis, either in between boyfriends or about to be. They discussed her social life for forty-five minutes, giggling the way they used to. Then Gidget talked about her life in Clarksville, its tedium and loneliness, her letters to and from David. They talked about Christmas, when David would be back and the three of them could be together again, and usually they got around to talking about whether Gladys could drive down to Tennessee for a visit.

"Gladys, you have to!" Gidget entreated. "I'll die of boredom if you don't, and besides, we could go to Memphis. Think how much fun we'd have!"

"I know. I need to figure out my working hours, and money and stuff. Maybe I can work it out."

On September 4, Donna went off to Illinois to stay with her parents until Harry came back from the Sinai. This left Gidget alone in the little yellow house in Clarksville, and more isolated than ever. Now she had to depend on the few friends she had made for transportation, or walk a couple of miles to Fort Campbell Boulevard. She called her mother.

"Even if I didn't like Donna much, it was somebody to talk to!"

"Why don't you get Gladys to come down for a visit?" Linda suggested.

"I keep on asking her, Mom. She always has to work, or can't afford it or something."

"Tell her you need her. I bet she'll come."

Linda was right. This turned out to be a propitious time for Gladys, too; she had recently broken up with a serious boyfriend and needed consoling. She had even received a sympathetic letter from David, who wrote: "Right now, you and Gidget need each other, even if it is only talking on the phone. At least you know there is always someone who will listen." The two girls made their plans: Gladys would leave on Sunday, September 15, right after work, and stay until the following Friday.

Gladys left Carroll County in her red Ford Pinto stickshift, equipped with a CB, and drove uneventfully to Clarksville, where she arrived at midnight after a sixteen-hour drive. Gidget, who was watching from the window, ran out of the house, and in a minute the two girls were jumping up and down with excitement. It had been over three months since they had seen each other.

Having Gladys around changed Gidget's outlook dramatically. After a long sleep well into the next day, they got up and chattered without stopping; there was so much to catch up on. Now that they had a car available — Gladys's car — they could drive everywhere. Gidget showed Gladys the base, and Clarksville; they ate all their meals at McDonald's or Kentucky Fried Chicken.

In the middle of the week, they set out for Memphis to visit Graceland, the home of Elvis Presley. Gidget had no idea how to get there, but Gladys was good with maps.

"Look, Route 40 goes directly into Memphis," she said, showing Gidget. "Somewhere outside of Clarksville, we'll pick up this Route 48 and stay on it to Route 40, see? Then we just head west and we'll be in Memphis."

Route 48 turned out to be a little country road, but it did, indeed, intersect U.S. Route 40. The girls had selected a lovely time of the year for their trip, quite by chance. Fall had come to Tennessee. The countryside was green and red and yellow, the air pleasantly cool. As Gladys drove, she asked Gidget to take pictures.

"It's pretty," she said. "Besides, I have to prove something to my father."

"Prove what?" Gidget asked.

"He said I shouldn't drive out here to see you because it is all deserted road, with nothing but mountains, no water or people or anything, and if my car broke down, I'd be stuck in the middle of nowhere. Any time you see a river or a lake, take a picture, okay?"

Gidget did. They continued to drive southwest, with Gidget watching the map and remarking that she had never realized what a long state Tennessee was — it must be more than 400 miles across, and they were only coming from the center of the state, which still made it 200 miles for them. They stopped a couple of times for a drink, and once Gladys pulled over so that Gidget could take a scenic photograph. Both girls got out of the car at a mountain overlook from which they could see a panorama of farm houses, tiny roads, trees and blossoms, all decorated with the colors of autumn.

Gladys caught her breath at the view. "Gidget," she said dramatically, "I think we're in the Deep South."

Route 40 took them directly to the beltway surrounding Memphis. They found their exit and then Elvis Presley Boulevard, where signs directed them to "Parking for Graceland," an unpaved lot across the street from Graceland. Gidget and Gladys were momentarily speechless as they observed the tacky commercialism of the area — the street was lined with gas stations, fast food places, signs, parking lots, and, of course, advertisements for Elvis Presley souvenirs. After the pastoral beauty of their five-hour drive from Clarksville, the scene was disappointing.

"Look at this!" Gladys exclaimed. "I thought Graceland was out in the country somewhere, or at least in the suburbs. Didn't you?"

Gidget nodded. "I always did," she said.

"This looks like junk city!" Gladys said. "Don't you think they have any zoning laws?"

"It probably was out in the country when they bought it," Gidget said. "Then they had all this development later."

"I guess," Gladys said.

She pulled into the parking lot and paid one dollar. At the ticket office, they were confronted with several choices: they could visit Graceland only, or Graceland plus Elvis's airplanes (the Lisa Marie and the Jet Star Hound Dog II), or all that plus Elvis's recreational bus from the sixties, or all that plus Elvis Up-Close, described as "a glimpse of the private side of Elvis Presley, including never before displayed items from the Presley collection," or any combination of these attractions. After some discussion, Gidget and Gladys decided on the tour of Graceland only, and paid seven dollars each for that ticket, which contained an aqua-bordered photograph of Graceland, a tour number, a time designation, and an announcement that there would be no refunds or rainchecks. As they waited in line with their tickets, they read the brochure which explained how the tour worked. How long you had to wait for your tour to begin depended on how many people were there ahead of you. Gidget and Gladys had about a thirty-minute wait.

When their tour number was called — at exactly the time designated on their tickets — they boarded a blue and white shuttle bus for the three-minute ride through the famous music gates, up the winding driveway to the front steps of Graceland. As the shuttle bus stopped, the sixteen tourists stepped out of the bus and onto the driveway, where they were greeted by a serious young tour guide. They were welcomed to Graceland, reminded that it is a private home still occupied by Elvis's aunt, and asked to keep off the grass. The guide told them that there would be a brief delay while the group ahead of theirs finished up. Gidget and Gladys took pictures of each other in front of the impressive doorway. They persuaded the guide to photograph the two girls together, and after that they took pictures of each other with the guide, whose name was Dean. As their time came to enter, light-hearted banter gave way to solemn anticipation. The door opened. Twenty-nine years after Blue Suede Shoes, Gidget and Gladys, who were only ten years old on the day that Elvis died, stepped inside the home of the King of Rock and Roll.

The guide directed them to the various rooms, including the dining room, the living room with the gold laminated grand piano, and the clubroom downstairs which was reached by way of a mirrored staircase. Dean pointed out the huge chair where Lisa Marie used to take her nap, and the fabric-covered ceiling which improved the acoustics of the room so that Elvis had been able to record there. Large parts of the house, including the entire upstairs, were off limits to the public, but after leaving the house itself they were directed to other areas, including a parking area which contained several vehicles. The girls' favorite was a pink jeep which had been used in the movie Blue Hawaii and which the public was allowed to enter. They took turns sitting in the car and being photographed by each other. Afterwards, Gladys wondered aloud how many photographs might be in existence of people sitting in the pink jeep, and they laughed about it. They visited another building containing Elvis's gold records and countless trophies, including his diploma from Humes High School, and finally the so-called "Meditation Gardens" near the swimming pool, where Elvis, both of his parents, and his grandmother were buried. There were flower arrangements on the graves, sent from fans; one announced, "From Debbie, the No. 1 Elvis fan in Pennsylvania."

Gidget shook her head at Gladys. "Weird," she said.

Gladys touched her arm. "Hush, look behind you," she murmured.

The middle-aged lady behind them was praying, her hands pressed together and tears streaming down her face.

"Let's get out of here," Gidget said.

The tour was over. The bus drove them down the circular driveway and delivered them to a shopping strip across the street. All of the stores there sold Elvis Presley souvenirs, records, or memorabilia. Gladys bought a cassette tape, Elvis' Golden Records, and a poster of Elvis with a Hawaiian lei around his neck. Gidget looked for something to bring back for David. After a careful search, she decided on a man-sized stein with a picture of Elvis from the movie GI Blues.

"What do you think?" she asked Gladys.

Gladys nodded. "He'll like that," she said. "It's his size, and he'll dig the picture."

Gidget bought it, and they collapsed at the Heartbreak Hotel Restaurant with cheeseburgers and sodas.

"I'm worn out!" Gidget exclaimed. "Aren't you?"

"Yup," Gladys said. "You know what I'm really glad of?"

"What?"

"I'm glad we didn't pay to go through those silly airplanes!"

"Me, too," Gidget said. "I liked seeing the house, but enough is enough. Besides, what could be in an airplane that you would care about?"

Gladys shrugged. "Nothing, you're right. We've seen enough."

Gidget sighed. "And it's a long drive home, too."

Gladys pulled her road map out of her purse and studied it. "Look, Gidge," she said. "On our way back, we could stop by Loretta Lynn's Dude Ranch. What do you think?"

"What is that?" Gidget asked.

"It's where Loretta lives. Remember when we saw the movie, Coal Miner's Daughter, and Loretta and her husband live on this ranch so that her husband will have something to do?"

"Yes, I remember that."

"Well, this is the ranch. It's called the Loretta Lynn Dude Ranch and it's open to the public, according to this map. You can go there and look around."

"Okay, why not?" Gidget said. "We're being tourists today, we might as well do it all."

They paid for their lunch and walked slowly back to the car with their purchases. "It's okay if we get really tired, Gidge," Gladys said. "The dude ranch has, like a motel on it. We can sleep there if we want."

Back on Route 40, heading east, Gladys picked up a friendly trucker on her CB. Gladys's handle was Sugarbritches; the trucker's was Funky Monkey. He was driving a heavy eighteen-wheeler and said he was bringing it east from Little Rock, Arkansas.

"Where you girls headed?" he asked them.

"Fort Campbell, Kentucky," Gladys said.

"What all for?"

Gladys looked over at Gidget. "We're looking for boy friends," she said. "Don't you figure an Army base is a good place for that?"

"If you like 'em big and dumb," Funky Monkey answered. "I guess there's no accounting for taste."

Gidget took the mike indignantly. "You don't know what you're talking about," she told him. "I'm married to a soldier and he's not dumb!"

The trucker chuckled. "Well, ma'am, you'll have to pardon me, but then again you should have told me straight off that you're married. And anyhow, unless there's something awful durn wrong with my rearview mirror, there ain't no way you ladies are married to anybody."

Gladys took the mike. "Well, look again, Funky Monkey, my girlfriend really is married. But I'm not. I'm just visiting because her husband is overseas."

"Okay, then," said the fellow-traveller. "What's your name, miss?"

"It's Gladys." She looked warily at Gidget. Her father, who was a trucker himself, had always told her not to give her real name over the CB. Of course, he had also told her not to have a conversation with a driver who could see her car, and she was paying no attention to that instruction either. "Gladys Jones," she added, in last-minute recognition of her upbringing. "And I'm from Baltimore." She grinned at Gidget.

"Okay, Gladys, my name is Darren," the trucker said. "And I'm from Dixie, can't recollect exactly which part just now. So you're a Yankee girl."

"I never quite thought of it that way," Gladys said.

"What about your girlfriend, what's her name?"

"That's Gidget."

Gidget punched Gladys's arm, but it was too late. The trucker guffawed loudly. "Gidget, huh? You mean those old movies? Gidget Goes Hawaiian, and stuff like that?"

"Same name," Gidget told him, throwing caution to the wind. She was beginning to enjoy herself. "My name's Gidget Brown, and I look quite a bit like Sandra Dee."

"Yeah? It seemed like to me that Sandra Dee was a blond, either natural or not, I wouldn't know, and you look like a redhead in my rearview mirror."

Gidget glanced over at Gladys. "I didn't think he could see us that well," she said. "Maybe we should cut this out."

"Why?" Gladys said. "We're on a public highway. We can stop talking to him anytime we want, pull in somewhere if we like."

Gidget nodded. She pushed the button on the CB. "I am a redhead," she said. "But Gladys is a brunette, and she's single."

Now Gladys was blushing. "I'm a bottle brunette," she said into the CB. "I was born blond."

"Likely, huh," Darren said. "Say, where have you girls been today, anyhow?"

"Memphis," Gladys told him. "We went to see Graceland."

Darren spat out his window. "Graceland, huh? You mean the home of ole Pelvis with the grease in his hair? That place?"

"I guess we mean the same place," Gladys said hesitantly. "Did you ever go there?"

"I ain't that desperate for something to do," Darren told them. "I never liked ole Pelvis when he was alive, what do I want with him dead?"

"Well, sorry," Gladys said.

"What do they charge to let folks traipse through his house and snivel at his graveside anyway?"

"Seven dollars," Gladys told him.

"You all paid seven dollars just to look through somebody's house?"

"And they don't even let you go upstairs because his aunt still lives up there."

"What, in a cage?" Darren chortled through the CB. "Gimme a break, girls. Change the subject."

"You asked us!" Gidget said indignantly.

"So I did, ma'am, so I did. Then I'll ask you something else. Where're you all going now?"

"We're on our way back to Fort Campbell, but we want to stop off at Loretta Lynn's Dude Ranch," Gladys told him. "Ever been there?"

"No ma'am, I'm not no groupie."

"Neither are we," Gladys said indignantly. "We're just looking for something to do."

"Okay, okay," Darren said. "I surrender. Let's be friends, it's a lonely highway out here."

"All right," Gladys said. She looked over at Gidget, who was mildly horrified at what they were doing.

"Gladys," she said, "you're telling him too much! And he's a complete stranger!"

"So what?" Gladys said. "We're not doing anything. We're just having a conversation with somebody to pass the time."

Gidget nodded. It was true; they weren't doing anything wrong, and it was fun to talk to somebody. Darren told them he was thirty-five years old and single. The girls didn't believe him; he sounded older, and all men claimed to be single. But as Gladys said, so what?

Somewhere along Route 40, Darren asked them, "Where all did you girls say you wanted to stop off at?"

"Loretta Lynn Dude Ranch," Gladys told him.

"Uh-oh, you missed it," he chuckled. "We passed that place some ways back."

"Why didn't you tell us?"

"I forgot where you said. You want to turn around?"

Gladys looked at Gidget. They had had a long day. "No," she told Darren. "I guess we'll just head on back to Fort Campbell."

"Okay, I tell you what," Darren said. "Your turn-off for Fort Campbell is Route 48. There's a truck stop there called Reed's. It comes up around time for my dinner, so I reckon I'll stop there. You girls want to join me?"

Gladys looked at Gidget. "What do you think, Gidge? Let's do it."

"I don't know. We don't know anything about him. I think we should keep going."

"We're only going to be talking to him while we have something to eat. We'll be in a public restaurant with lots of people around. Maybe he'll even treat us to dinner."

"I don't want any stranger to treat me to dinner."

"Oh, come on, Gidget. Nothing's going to happen. Don't be a wet blanket."

Gidget sighed. This conversation felt like part of an ongoing dialogue that she and Gladys had had for years, ever since they discovered boys. "Okay," she agreed finally. "If you really want to."

Gladys pushed the mike button. "All right, Funky Monkey, you're on," she said. "Just remember that Gidget's married and there's two of us."

"Yes, ma'am," Darren promised.

At Route 48, he made a wide swing to the left and led them into Reed's Truck Stop, where he parked in an area designated for trucks. Gladys parked her Pinto. She looked over at Gidget. "Okay, now, let's stick together," she said.

In the distance, they could see Darren opening the door of his truck and climbing down. They approached hesitantly. Up close, Darren was tall, nice-looking with dark hair, and at least forty. He shook hands with both of them. "Well, I feel like I know you, after all our conversation," he said. "I even know which of you is which. You're Gladys, and you're Sandra Dee." They all laughed. "*Damn* if you're not a redhead," Darren added. "That ain't nothing from a bottle, not with those freckles."

Gidget smiled shyly. "I'm the married one," she reminded him.

"Yes, ma'am," Darren said. He turned to Gladys. "You're the brunette," he said.

Gladys gave him her brightest smile. He was way too old for her, she knew, but it didn't matter; they were on a lark, playing a game with somebody they would never see again. It was a harmless game, one she and Gidget had played for years in different ways. Darren asked them if they had ever seen the inside of a cab of an eighteen-wheeler. They shook their heads. Would they like to? They hesitated. Darren laughed. "Hey, we're in a public parking lot in broad daylight," he pointed out. Gladys and Gidget followed him inside the cab.

They were amazed. Neither one of the girls had been inside a cab like this before. It was like a compact bedroom — "Fully equipped," Darren told them. He was obviously proud of it. After they had seen everything, the girls were reassured when Darren was the first to suggest they get out of the truck and go in for dinner. The three of them sat at a table and had the day's special, a hot turkey sandwich with french fries and gravy. Darren told them, "You know those stories about how truckers always know the best places to eat on account of they're on the road so much? That's a lot of crap."

When the waitress handed them separate bills, Darren made no move to pay any but his own. Gidget and Gladys each paid theirs. Outside the diner, Darren looked at the girls solemnly.

"This here's where we part company," he said "You all are heading north up 48, and I'm going east on Route 40. So I'll say good-bye to you here." He hesitated. "You all be real careful about who you talk to, okay?"

Gladys leaned towards him and kissed him lightly on the cheek. "We'll be careful," she said.

Darren turned and sauntered away towards his huge eighteen-wheeler. The girls watched him climb in, and then headed for the Ford Pinto. Gladys sighed. "He was nice," she said wistfully.

Gidget said, "He was too old, Gladys. Besides, easy come, easy go."

"I know," Gladys said ruefully. "It's the story of my life."

They headed north on Route 48 and made it all the way to Clarksville in an hour.

On Friday, September 20, Gladys got up at five o'clock in the morning to prepare for her trip back to Maryland. It was a sixteen-hour drive and she needed to be at work at midnight. As usual, she had made a list of things to do before she left. The last item she had written on the piece of paper read, "Put coat in car." But as she looked at the list in the morning, she saw an entry below that one, which said, "Gladys, I'm riding home with you, Gidget." Gladys began to shriek with joy.

"Gidge, are you serious? Will you ride home with me?"

Gidget was in the shower. She stuck her head through the curtain and called out, "Will you take me?"

"Will I take you, oh, my God!" Gladys yelled. "We'll have a couple of months at home before David comes back. It'll be just like old times!"

"Good, I'm almost ready," Gidget said.

Suddenly, during the night, she had realized that there was no reason for her to stay in Clarksville from now until December. She had no transportation, very few friends, no job and nothing to do. Why not go back to Carroll County and stay with her father until Thanksgiving, then come down and find an apartment for her and David? She could ride home with Gladys, and later she could come back by plane, or even by bus if she had to. It made perfect sense.

The two girls loaded their possessions into the Pinto and took off. Gidget rolled down her window and called, "Good-bye, yellow house! I won't miss you!"

She and Gladys laughed deliriously at the sheer adventure of it all. As they drove out of Clarksville, Gidget settled into a thoughtful silence.

"Gladys, there's one thing you have to promise me," she said.

"What's that?"

"You won't tell David about going inside that truckdriver's cab."

"Okay," Gladys said.

"Don't even tell him we talked to anybody on the CB," Gidget insisted. "I mean it, Gladys. David would get really jealous and mad. The only thing we need to say is that we went to Memphis, we saw Graceland, and we came home."

"But we didn't do anything wrong, Gidget."

"I know that. But he'll get mad anyway. Just promise, all right?"

"All right," Gladys said. "I promise."

She decided to try a different route home. Instead of leaving Route 81 at Winchester, Virginia, and heading east, they could go up to Harper's Ferry, West Virginia, and home from there by way of Frederick, Maryland. The trip went uneventfully, with Gladys driving all the way and Gidget, who could not drive a stickshift, talking to keep her awake. One hour west of Carroll County, in the mountains near Frederick — just after Gladys announced that they would be pulling into the Geislers' driveway by 9:15 — the Pinto nearly died. To the girls, exhausted from the long trip but keyed up from excitement and a day of non-stop chatter, their predicament became hilarious. Every time the speedometer exceeded ten miles an hour, the car bumped and jerked with a terrible noise that sent the girls into spasms of laughter. At a roadside rest stop, Gladys checked the oil and radiator; everything looked normal. They started the car again and drove it ten miles an hour up each hill, then let it drift down the other side with the clutch to the floor. They tried unsuccessfully to summon help: Gladys's mother was not at home, AAA said they were allowed only to tow to a garage, and the state police were willing to drive the girls home only if they could get as far as Frederick barracks. Gladys wanted to call Gidget's father, but Gidget refused because she intended to surprise him. And so Gladys called her employer to say she was not going to make it to work, and then they limped and coasted through the mountains into Carroll County, finally arriving at Gladys's house at two o'clock in the morning.

Gladys spoke wearily. "Gidge, it's the middle of the night," she said. "Will you sleep here with me and let me take you home tomorrow?"

Gidget shook her head. "I want to sleep in my own bed. Can't we borrow your father's truck?"

Gladys sighed. "Phew, I'm beat," she admitted. "But okay, I guess we've come this far, another mile won't kill me."

They took her father's pickup truck and made the short trip to Bluebird Drive. Gladys watched while Gidget tried to unlock the front door; her key no longer worked. She turned helplessly to Gladys, who got out of the truck. The girls began to throw handfulls of gravel at Johnny's bedroom window, calling his name: "Johnny, wake up! It's Gidget, can you let me in?" The girls laughed hysterically as their continuing efforts to arouse somebody failed.

Suddenly the lights in the house came on. They heard footsteps approaching the front door, then John Geisler's voice. "Who is it?" he called gruffly. "Who's there?"

"Dad, it's me, Gidget!"

Her father opened the door, somehow took in the fact that Gidget and Gladys were standing there at 2:30 in the morning, and embraced his daughter.

"Hey, everybody, Kathy, Johnny, wake up!" he called. "Gidget's home!" He looked over at Gladys. "Young lady," he said sternly, "do your parents know where you are?"

The girls dissolved in laughter before Gladys started back to the truck for the short drive home.

In the Sinai Desert, David was approaching the halfway point in his time there. Promoted in September to PFC, he celebrated with a buddy from Philadelphia, Kenny Yeatts. They had a couple of beers, shot a few baskets in the gym, and ended up at the PX where David made a major purchase.

"Hey, Kenny, look at this — they have stereos."

Kenny took a look. "Yeah, and the prices are good, too."

"Are they?" David stooped down to examine the merchandise. There were portable stereos with radios and cassette tape decks. Suddenly, he wanted one. Since leaving Fort Campbell he had bought nothing other than toilet items; he had used only the cash which the Army gave him every month and had not written any checks on his joint account with Gidget. He had not wanted to, really. Out there in the desert, away from commercial television stations and shopping malls, one was not subjected to the same pressures to buy that bombarded the public in the United States. One tended to crave the simplest things: McDonald's cheeseburgers, for instance, or drive-in movie theaters. Until now, David had not even considered buying anything for himself.

The item that he suddenly wanted carried a price tag of $240. David looked and looked at it. He glanced at Kenny. "What do you think?"

Kenny saw the price tag. "Well, it's a lot of dough," he said. "But it's a good buy, too. You could enjoy it here and then have it back home."

"That's what I'm thinking," David said. "I'm just not sure if I should spend that much money."

"Do you have it?" Kenny asked.

"Sure, I have it. Most of my pay goes into my joint checking account back in Kentucky where my wife is. She pays the bills and all."

"Does she spend a lot?"

"I don't think so, no. I think she's pretty careful. See, we just got married a month before I came over here, and we want to get a place of our own as soon as I get back. So of course we're trying to save as much as we can."

"Is she living pretty cheap now, while you're over here?"

"Yeah, absolutely. She's living with Harry Magrette's wife, in their house in Clarksville."

Kenny thought a minute. "It sounds like you can afford it," he said. "Actually, you could buy it for the both of you, sort of a Christmas present."

David grinned. "You talked me into it," he said. "I'm gonna buy it."

He wrote a check and left the PX with his stereo. Back at the barracks, everybody put cassettes into it and tried it out. David thought it sounded great. He slept soundly that night, dreaming of home and Gidget. The next day, he wrote her a long letter.

> Dear Gidget,
>
> Guess what, I got promoted. That's right, I am now officially a PFC. Hope you're proud of me.
>
> To celebrate I did something kind of reckless. I bought a portable stereo with a cassette deck. It's really great. I bought it for both of us, really. It cost $240, which is really a good price, so please make an entry of that in our checkbook so you don't bounce any checks, okay? I can't wait to show you the stereo!
>
> We had two inspections this week. The first one the sergeant messed up. He made us leave our extra boots outside instead of having them under our bed where they should have been.
>
> The second one we did great on. Everybody has to say who they are and what they do, like this: Private David Heidecker, born and raised in Woodbine, Maryland, primary duties, automatic rifleman, additional duties, generator operator. That last part sucks because I also check gas and water levels along with getting the chlorine level, but I can only say one thing for additional duties. Well, anyway, everyone said that right. Then we did our red alert drill, which is the sergeant bangs on metal and we say 'Red alert,' 'Red alert,' and take off to our bunkers, where we put on our flight jacket which is a bullet proof vest, which I don't think could stop a pellet, and our steel pots.
>
> After this we go to our additional duty station, where the VIP, who is the person inspecting, comes around and asks questions. A funny thing happened on that. The VIP

came up and asked me how much brake fluid and transmission fluid my generator took. The funny part is that a generator doesn't have brakes or a transmission.

We went on a patrol the next day, and as usual it was a waste of time. We got trucked out to a point in the middle of the desert. When we got off the truck I saw a Bedouin (desert person) hitchhiking. He came up to us and asked for water. We're not allowed to give him any so when he left he said in perfect English, 'Fuck MFO, piss on them all.' We all got a laugh at that.

After we got left off we walked 4 miles and set up. We took some good pictures, I'll send one home for you. We didn't see anything except for a Bedouin village. When morning came we walked back in and got picked up by the truck. I'll tell you, after seeing the way Bedouins live I'm glad that I'm an American. They live in cardboard boxes with no electricity and no bathrooms.

Well, I hope your week has been more fulfilled. I love you very much and miss you more than ever. I'll write more tomorrow.

> Love you 4-ever-n-longer,
> David

For Gidget, life had taken a sudden turn for the better. Now she could see her family and friends every day, and she had transportation. Shirley helped her get part-time employment at the Half Shell again; both of them enjoyed that. And of course, Gladys was a mile away. Gidget wrote to David:

> I realize I should have come back sooner. It was great in Clarksville when you were there, but without you it was terrible. Don't worry, I'll go back down at the end of November to get a place for us and have us all set up before you arrive. That will be the most fun of all!
>
> Don't forget to send your letters to Maryland for the next few weeks. Write to me a lot — I love to get your letters more than anything else.

> Love you 4-ever-n-longer,
> Gidget

Two days after they got back to Carroll County, Gladys met Jim, her newest boyfriend and future husband. A whirlwind romance ensued. Gidget became caught up in the dynamics of her best friend's relationships, which included serious estrangement from Gladys's own family, who did not approve of Jim. The two girls spent many hours together, talking over the pros and cons of marriage to Jim and the possibility of reconciliation between Jim and Gladys's parents. On several occasions, Gidget and Gladys spent the night at the Heideckers' house, where the two girls occupied David's room.

Gladys asked Dick if he thought it was necessary to know somebody for a long time before you got married. Dick shrugged. "You got a lifetime for that after you're married," he told her. "What's the difference?"

"That's exactly what I told my folks!" Gladys said confidently.

Shirley said, "He's teasing you, Gladys. You have to know somebody long enough to make sure you want to be married to them."

"I already know that," Gladys sulked. "I know I want to marry Jim, but nobody will believe me."

"That's just because it's happening so fast," Gidget told her. "My folks were the same way about David and me in the beginning."

"But you and David knew each other longer than Gladys and Jim, Gidget," Shirley said. "You knew each other long enough to be pretty confident about your feelings."

"I am confident!" Gladys insisted.

"Well, I'm thirsty," Dick said. "Can anybody hand me a beer?"

Shirley winked at Gladys. "If you want a good look at marriage, this is it," she said.

"What is?" Gladys asked.

"What you just saw. A middle-aged fat man sitting ten feet away from the refrigerator saying, Can anybody hand me a beer?"

The girls laughed. Shirley got up and handed Dick a National Premium.

Gidget spent more and more time at the Heideckers'. Often she spent the night there, and sometimes she went to work with Shirley, although they did not always work the same hours so that on those occasions, Dick came and picked her up. She and Dick went bowling together. The three of them shared David's letters with each other, and once they wrote him a communal letter, with each of them adding a section.

If Dick was home from work, Gidget often fixed him lunch. Dick liked to tease her because she didn't approve of alcohol.

"Did you ever stop to think," he asked one day as he popped the top of a can of beer, "that our country was built by beer drinkers?"

Gidget looked at him skeptically. "It was?"

"Sure. All great Americans are beer drinkers."

Gidget said, "Richard, you're just being ridiculous."

"Can you name one who wasn't?"

"Of course I can!"

"Who?"

"Well, I have to think. I mean, when you study history in school, they don't usually tell you about the person's drinking habits."

"Aha!" Dick shouted gleefully. "That's right! Do you know why?"

Gidget looked up from the corned beef sandwich she was making for him. "Why?"

"Because everybody but you already knows. They don't have to tell the rest of the world."

"Richard!"

"Yeah, it's true. Do you know that every President of the United States was a big beer drinker?"

"That is not true."

"Sure is. It's even in the Constitution."

Gidget handed him his lunch. "I don't believe a word you say," she told him. "Here, eat your lunch."

Dick laughed and laughed. Not since he had met David had Dick found such joy in a new relationship with another human being. If he had been capable of verbalizing his feelings, he would have told that to Gidget; if he had been a creative man, he would have written a song to her, or a poem. Being who he was, he had to content himself with telling her silly jokes and stories. He did once say to Shirley that Gidget was like the daughter they had never had. Shirley, also not given to expressing herself, only nodded. She and Dick seldom talked about their feelings, even to each other, but after twenty-seven years of marriage, each of them usually knew how the other felt.

Gladys and Jim continued to see each other throughout October, and finally they scheduled a church wedding for November 23, the Saturday before Thanksgiving. It was to be a sparse affair, since Gladys's father refused even to attend; Gladys and Gidget had to do all the work themselves. There were financial considerations, too. In mid-October, Gladys was notified by the trucking company for which she still worked on weekends that numerous unauthorized long-distance telephone calls to and from Clarksville, Tennessee had appeared on the company's bill, apparently made during the hours of Gladys's employment. She called Gidget to tell her about it.

"Gidget, you aren't going to believe this," she said, giggling. "Remember all those calls we made to each other when you were in Tennessee?"

"The calls on your WATS line at work, you mean?"

Gladys burst out laughing. "That's just it, Gidget!" she shrieked. "It isn't a regular WATS line! Those calls weren't free!"

"Oh, my God!" Gidget said. "You mean we were supposed to be paying for those calls?"

"Yes!"

"But we used to talk for forty-five minutes or an hour, Gladys! Remember, we'd ramble on and on about nothing in the middle of the night, thinking it was free?"

"I know!"

Gidget started to laugh, too. "You mean your company has the bill for those calls?"

"Yes!"

By now, the girls were laughing so hard they could barely talk. "Gladys, how did they find out it was you who made the calls?"

"Because I was the only one working during those hours."

"Oh, my God! What did you tell them?"

"Well, I thought about telling them it was the cleaning lady."

"Why didn't you?"

"Because there is no cleaning lady!" Gladys gasped.

"Oh, Gladys! What else?"

"I could have said it was a burglar, but I don't think they would have believed me."

Gidget teased, "Could you say it was a wrong number?"

"For forty-five minutes a call? To the same number every time?"

"Computer error?"

"I don't think so."

"An obscene caller?"

"But why would I stay on the line with an obscene caller for forty-five minutes?"

"Maybe he turned you on!"

Gladys said, "Gidget, I don't know why we're laughing like hyenas over this. The company said I have to pay for the calls."

"Really? Do you have that much money?" Gidget asked, suddenly serious.

"Of course not. They said I can work for nothing until it's paid off."

"Work for nothing? What if you quit that job?"

"Then they'll sue me."

"Oh." Gidget thought a minute. "Gladys, I should pay half of the bill," she said. "I was on the phone with you as much as you were with me, right?"

"No," Gladys said. "I told you the calls were free, I'm going to pay."

"Please let me pay you back."

Gladys was adamant. "No," she insisted. "I enjoyed every minute of those phone calls. I'll pay for them."

Gidget wrote to David about Gladys's upcoming wedding, and on November 18 David called Gladys from the Sinai.

"Hi, there, sexy, how's the Pips?" he demanded.

"David! I don't believe this! Are you calling me from Egypt?"

"Yup! I'm calling you to say best wishes, congratulations, and all that. What is this guy like?"

"Oh, David, he's great. I really love him. I can't wait for you to meet him."

"I can't wait either. Does he know he's the second luckiest man in the world — I'm the first?"

"I don't know," Gladys said. "I guess he and I are both pretty lucky."

"Well, you know how I feel about you, Gladys. You really are a very special person, and Gidget's closest friend, and you deserve to be happy. That's really what I wanted to tell you."

"Oh, David, thank you. That is so sweet of you. I miss you, too!"

"But I do have one regret," David said.

"What's that?"

"Well, my next assignment after this might be Germany. I always kind of figured you might come along with Gidget and me. We could be like Three's Company, only I wouldn't act gay. I always did want a live-in mistress. Wouldn't it have been fun?"

"It sure would," Gladys admitted. "But I'm taken now."

"Listen, you gotta give me some help about Christmas," David said. "By the time I get back to Fort Campbell it'll be too late for me to shop for Gidget. I think I should get her stuff here. But I'm not sure what to get."

"What do they have?" Gladys asked.

"There's a PX, so they have most everything," David said. "There's also a place to get Egyptian stuff, you know, Aztec statues and stuff like that. Do you think Gidget would like something like that?"

Gladys thought about it. "Sure," she said. "What do they look like?"

"Well, they have these ceramic statues about eighteen inches high. They're really detailed and all. Do you think Gidget would like one?"

"She'd love that, David, I'm sure of it."

"Great, then I'll get one for her. Maybe one for my mom, too. Listen, I'm going to have to go."

"David, thank you so much for calling. It is so great to hear your voice."

"Thanks, babe. I'll be thinking about you on your wedding day. I know you'll be the most beautiful bride in the world, after Gidget, anyway."

"Oh, I hope so!" Gladys said. "Good-bye, David."

"Bye, sexy. I hope Jim loves you as much as Gidget and I do."

On November 23, Gladys was married in a small church ceremony in which Gidget was her maid of honor. The ceremony was followed by a simple reception in the parish hall, and after that Gladys and Jim left for a brief honeymoon. Gidget went over to Dick and Shirley's house to go through her own wedding presents, which were still there.

"We might want some of these things in Tennessee when David gets back," she told Shirley.

"You can take whatever you want, they're your things," Shirley said. "But won't your place be furnished?"

Gidget nodded. "That's true," she said. "I guess I might want just a few knick-knacks and things."

"It might be hard for you to take much without a car," Shirley said. "You might want to wait until you and David come back in the car sometime, and take whatever you want then."

Gidget thought about it. That did make sense. There wasn't any way to know how long they might be staying in Tennessee before David was assigned to another place, possibly even a foreign country. It was just that the idea of having some of their very own things seemed nice.

She had Thanksgiving dinner with the Heideckers, and David, knowing that, called there to speak to everybody. His call came just as they had finished dinner, when everyone was in a good mood. Shirley talked first, telling David that she had made enough pumpkin pie for him, but that his father had just eaten it. Then Dick took the telephone and asked David if they had any snow there; he winked at the women and acted surprised when David said, of course not, the temperature was 81 degrees. Dick suggested that they have a sand fight for fun; it was the next best thing to throwing snowballs. When it was Gidget's turn, she told David that she would be leaving in two days to return to Fort Campbell.

"I'll be finding a place for us," she told him. "When you get back, it'll be all ready."

"That is going to be so great," David told her. "I can't wait to be with you in our own place."

"How much do you think it's all right to spend for rent, David?" Gidget asked.

"$200," David told her. "That way we won't be spending all our money for rent, and we'll be able to do other things and save for the future. What do you think?"

"Okay," Gidget said. "I'll look for something that costs $200."

"Are you going to fly down?" David asked.

"Uh-huh. I saved up the money from working at the Half Shell. It'll be my first time on an airplane."

"You'll like it," David told her. "The best part is, it's so fast!"

"I know."

"Speaking of money, there's something I've been thinking about," David said. "You know my wedding band that I lost?"

"Yes."

"Don't get a new one just now. I'd probably lose it again anyway, and it's expensive. Let's put it on hold for a while and think about it when our finances are more secure."

"Are you sure?" Gidget asked.

"Yes. I've thought about it a lot. I still feel bad about the ruckus I raised with you that day when I lost it, remember? Especially since I figured out that whether I have a ring or not doesn't have anything to do with how much I love you."

When they all finished, passing the telephone among them to say good-bye, they felt elated. David would be at Fort Campbell in exactly two weeks.

On Saturday, November 30, Gidget arrived at the Baltimore-Washington International Airport carrying two suitcases with all of her clothing and two or three small wedding gifts from the Heideckers' house. She was accompanied by Dick and Shirley, her mother, her brother Johnny, and Gladys, who was just back from her honeymoon. The flight departed late, lost time on the way, and hurt her ears, but it got her to Nashville, where Donna Magrette picked her up and drove her to the little yellow house in the country.

The search for a place to live did not begin propitiously. The first thing Gidget needed was transportation. She called Joel, who still had possession of the blue Monte Carlo.

Joel told her, "Listen, I had to repossess that car."

"What!" Gidget was shocked. "What do you mean, repossess?"

"See, you and David never paid me the $300 for the car, so I repossessed it."

Gidget started to cry. "I don't believe this!" she yelled into the telephone. "You told David we didn't have to pay anything until 1986! This isn't 1986, is it?"

"Uh, I don't recall making a statement like that," Joel told her. "I recall telling David the car was $300, period. And nobody's paid me."

"Is the car running?" Gidget demanded.

"Yes, ma'am, it's running perfectly. All I need is my $300, and it's yours."

Gidget hung up on him. "That crook!" she shouted at a surprised Donna Magrette. "He stole our car!"

She called Dick Heidecker and explained the whole story to him. Dick said not to worry, he would mail her a check for $300 that day; they could worry about paying him back later. As soon as he hung up the phone, Dick called Shirley at Webster's to ask her how they could cover his check by tomorrow. Luckily, this was Shirley's pay day; Dick had enough left over from his last pay at London Fog to make up the difference. Shirley said she could make a bank deposit the next morning. Dick wrote a check and drove down to the post office to put it in the mail.

The moment Gidget received Dick's check, she called Joel again.

"Come on over with the money," he told her. Gidget persuaded Donna to drive her, but when they got to Joel's house he looked warily at the check from Dick Heidecker.

"It's not that I don't trust you, Gidget," he said, "but let's go get the check cashed first."

Gidget glared at him. "Why should I trust you?" she demanded. "For all I know, the car still doesn't work."

Joel shrugged. "You owe me $300 whether it works or not," he said. "It works, I've been driving it. If you want it, we get the check cashed first."

They went together to the base, where they cashed the check. Gidget handed $300 to Joel, and he gave her the keys to the Monte Carlo. The car started right away. As she backed out of Joel's driveway, she opened the window and called out, "You thief!"

Miraculously, the car did seem to run fine. Gidget began to examine the classified section of the Clarksville *Leaf-Chronicle* for a place to live. There were a number of apartments and trailers available for $200 a month. Gidget made telephones calls and visited some of the places. They were, consistently, run-down and dreary looking; some were downright dirty as well. She called Dick again and told him about her experience so far. Dick told her to look at more expensive places.

"See what they have for around $300," he told her. "I'll pay the difference if it's too much for you and David."

"Are you sure?" Gidget asked tentatively.

"Sure I'm sure. You have to find a nice place to live, that's all there is to it."

"But is it all right about the money?"

"Young lady," Dick said, "you listen to me. If I come down there and find you and David living in a dump, I will personally put you over my knee. Is that clear enough?"

Gidget smiled. "Yes, Richard," she said. "Thanks."

Now her search took on a whole new dimension. There were places in the $300 range which were quite appealing, including a furnished apartment that was closer to Fort Campbell. But it was small, and of course had no yard. Gidget wanted to visit some trailers, too. She saw an ad for one and went to visit it. To get there, she left Fort Campbell Boulevard at Tobacco Road, behind Allen's Fireworks. She drove for two miles, past modest low to middle income detached houses and large expanses of farm land to the American Village Mobile Home Park. It was an attractive park with paved, tree-lined streets. The trailer for rent had tan aluminum siding. It was immaculate on the outside, with grass all around and a large tree in front. Inside were spacious rooms con-

American Village Mobile Home Park in Clarksville, Tennessee.   *Ann Turnbull*

taining nice furniture in good condition. Gidget loved it. But the rent was $320.

It was time to call Dick Heidecker again. He chortled over the anxiety in Gidget's voice when she mentioned the extra $20, and told her to go ahead and rent the trailer. It sounded perfect for her and David, he said. Gidget told the man she would take it, and gave him the rent money for December. She bubbled over with enthusiasm as she described the trailer to Donna. It was completely furnished, she pointed out, so there was not much she had to do except move her clothes in, decorate it for Christmas, finish shopping for David's gifts, and wrap everything up. She had already done a great deal of shopping for David's Christmas. She had bought him a gold cross, a watch, an ID bracelet, and a T-shirt with a picture of David in uniform that she had made from a photograph taken at Fort Benning. She had not yet replaced David's lost wedding band, although she intended to one day. Now she bought a small Christmas tree and some inexpensive decorations so their new home would look festive. They had everything but a telephone, which was not yet hooked up.

On December 9, sitting contentedly in the mobile home, surrounded by her gifts for David, Gidget reread the last letter she had received from him before leaving Carroll County. It ended:

We found out some details about leaving the Sinai and coming home. On the 10th of December we are supposed to leave South Camp and go up to North Camp. We're getting there by bus. It's supposed to take a long time but I won't care because the next day I'll be home! We're supposed to get back to Fort Campbell somewhere around 1:30 in the morning. We'll turn in our weapons and gas masks. The people who live in the barracks will sign for their linen and rooms. They say we'll be done around 6 o'clock that morning. The CO says after that we should be off for 48 hours, that means we'll get Thursday, Friday, Saturday and Sunday off because we don't work on the weekend. I hope it works out that way, then it will give us that much time to be alone together.

Well, sweetheart, I thank God every night that I have such a beautiful lady as my wife. Believe me when I tell you that as soon as we are together I will make it up to you that we had to be apart so long. I will take you in my arms and let you know that you and I are forever. I love you.

Love you 4-ever-n-longer
David

CHAPTER 16

Flight From Egypt

In the early hours of Thursday, December 11, 1985, 250 soldiers from the 3rd Battalion prepared for final departure from the Sinai Desert. An equal number had left the week before in what was known as the "first rotation"; an equal number would leave the week after. In general, the soldiers assigned to this middle flight were the same men who had arrived on the middle flight five months earlier. Nearly half of them were in Alpha Company. There were a few last-minute switches. One married soldier, anxious to get back to his wife, was assigned to the middle flight but persuaded a single man, assigned to the first rotation, to change places with him. All changes had to be approved by the platoon sergeant.

The atmosphere at South Camp was noisy and festive, despite the fact that the soldiers assigned to the third rotation flight were still sleeping, or trying to. All of the baggage, other than carry-on, had already been packed up and sent to Cairo by truck. Soldiers took whatever they had forgotten and stuffed it into their carry-on bags, if they could. David Heidecker took his photographs and the news articles about the South Carroll Cavaliers from the wall above his bunk and pushed them into his bag. He wore the twenty-five cent ID coin from Wildwood, New Jersey, on a chain around his neck.

The soldiers were taken in buses from South Camp to the Ras Nasrani aerodome in the Sinai. For security reasons, American officials did not want to bring 250 soldiers in uniform through the Cairo airport. Therefore, they left South Camp wearing civilian clothes; they were scheduled to change in Cologne, West Germany, so that they would arrive at Fort Campbell in uniform. As the buses pulled away from South Camp, the men waved and shouted wildly, calling irreverent good-byes to fellow-soldiers, the barracks, the sand dunes, the Red Sea, and the Bedouins. The temperature was nearly eighty degrees; they all knew that winter would greet them in a day. The buses rang out with sounds

of happy anticipation, names of wives and girlfriends, even Christmas songs.
Almost every soldier wanted somebody else to guess what he would be doing
twenty-four hours from now: making love to his girl, eating a Big Mac, taking a bath, driving a Pontiac Firebird, sleeping in bed.

At Ras Nasrani, the soldiers disembarked from the buses and climbed
onto two Boeing 737's for the flight to Cairo. Their carry-on luggage was
stored in the 737 cargo holds for that flight. At Cairo, the men waited in the
airport for the beginning of their final flight home.

In the airport at Cairo, a twenty-year old private from Lake City,
Florida, named Eric Harrington could not find his passport. In a panic, he
repeatedly searched all of his pockets and his carry-on bag. The passport was
gone. He found his sergeant and told him his problem.

"Your passport is gone?" the sergeant asked in disbelief. "Where was
it?"

"It was in my back pocket," Harrington told him. "I moved it in my
front pocket on the other plane, and now it's gone."

"It can't be gone!" the sergeant insisted. He plunged his hands into
Harrington's front pocket, then his back pocket, then all other parts of his
uniform which might hold a tiny booklet. He opened Harrington's carry-on
bag and dumped its contents onto a bench along the wall. The sergeant and
Harrington searched through the pile of stuff item by item, tossing aside a
toothbrush, razors, an address book. They shook a magazine upside down
and tore open a brown bag containing after-shave lotion. No passport. The
sergeant sat down on the bench. He spoke very quietly.

"Eric, I'll have to tell the Colonel," he said. "Your passport's gone.
I don't think they'll let you travel without it."

Eric stared at the sergeant incredulously. "What am I gonna do?" he
asked.

"I don't know yet." The sergeant put his hand on Eric's shoulder.
"Wait here, I'll find out."

Eric sat down on the bench and slowly began to replace his personal
items in his carry-on bag. In the distance, he could see his sergeant talking
to the Colonel, the Colonel gesturing animatedly in his direction. The two
of them approached him rapidly.

"Are you Harrington?" the Colonel asked.

Eric stood up. "Yes, sir," he said. "I've lost my passport."

"So the sergeant tells me," the Colonel said. "Where was it?"

"I had it on the plane to here, but it's gone now," Eric said miserably.
"The sergeant and I looked everywhere. It's just gone."

"You know, Harrington," the Colonel said menacingly, "we have 250
soldiers going on this flight, and do you want to guess how many of them
do not have their passports at this moment?"

Eric Harrington stared unhappily at the floor. "No, sir," he murmured.

"One, Harrington!" the Colonel hollered. "One soldier out of 250, and you are that one! Damn it, what's your excuse?"

"Nothing, sir."

"Well, Harrington, I was looking forward to a full contingent arriving at Fort Campbell where, as you might imagine, there will be a celebration and other activities to welcome back the soldiers of the 101st who have been keeping the peace these many months, do you read me?"

"Yes, sir."

"And you will not be on that plane with us, Harrington, because you have managed to fuck up and *lose your passport* and it is *against the law* for you to travel from Egypt to the United States without a passport, do you get it?"

"Yes, sir."

"What's more, Harrington, because you managed to pull this dumb stunt at the last minute, it is now impossible to get another soldier from South Camp to take your place, and we will, therefore, arrive at Fort Campbell with an empty seat in the plane, do you understand that?"

"Yes, sir."

"In fact, Harrington, you will be lucky to get on the next plane out, which is one week from now, because it may just be that *that* plane is filled already and you *might* just be spending Christmas in the desert!"

"Yes, sir."

The Colonel stalked away. Eric sat down on the bench again. He had tears in his eyes. Christmas was less than two weeks away, and he had a wife and an infant son. What if he was stuck in the Middle East forever?

The sergeant sat down beside him and touched his arm. "Ease up, Harrington," he said. "The Colonel was just giving you a lot of bullshit about the next flight. They'll put you on the third flight home, and that leaves a week from today. You'll be home for Christmas."

Eric looked at him. "Really?"

"Sure. The Colonel just blew his stack because he wants the glory of bringing everybody back at once."

"What do I do now?" Eric wanted to know.

"You have to go to the American embassy in Cairo," the sergeant told him. "Tell them you lost your passport and you need a new one to leave on the final flight out next week. Then catch a military flight back to South Camp, and you'll be home in a week with the rest of us. Okay?"

Eric nodded. "All right," he said.

"Do you need money or anything?"

"No, I'm okay. Thanks."

"I'll see you at Fort Campbell in a week," the sergeant told him.

Eric picked up his carry-on bag and asked an airport guard how to find the American embassy.

One other soldier, who had a girlfriend in Cairo whom he had met during a three-day leave, decided he would rather spend the next week with his girl than as a bachelor in Fort Campbell. He obtained permission to remain in Cairo for seven days and to fly back on December 18. Now there were 248 soldiers waiting to come home.

The plane which was to bring the 248 soldiers home to Fort Campbell was not a military plane. It was a Douglas DC-8 operating as an international charter flight under contract with the Multinational Force and Observers, which was responsible for the contracting of air transport of MFO troop contingents. Technically, the aircraft was owned by International Air Leasing of Miami and was leased to and operated by Arrow Air of Miami, Florida. This particular plane had left McChord Air Force Base in the State of Washington the day before and had flown to Cairo by way of Gander, Newfoundland and Cologne, Germany.

At Cairo, the soldiers went through American Customs as part of an arrangement between the U.S. Army and U.S. Customs Service whereby American soldiers returning from the Sinai could clear customs in Egypt, before the long flight home, instead of doing it after they landed in the United States. All of the baggage had to be inspected, and was. There was then considerable difficulty in loading the plane because of the volume and weight of the baggage belonging to 248 soldiers who had been in the desert for five months. In the end, not all of the baggage could be squeezed into the front and rear cargo holds of the DC-8, and 41 duffle bags were left in Cairo, to be transported separately. The inside of the plane was crowded, too, because each soldier brought weapons, his uniform to be put on in Cologne, and normal carry-on items. The overhead racks were completely filled with carry-on items, and so were all the closets and the areas under the seats. Some military equipment protruded into aisles, and many of the passengers had to sit with their feet on top of bags that could not fit under the seats. A few had to hold their weapons on their laps.

None of this mattered, of course, to the soldiers who were now less than twenty-four hours from home, nor did the inordinate length of the flight still to come. On the contrary, the atmosphere inside the plane was convivial as well as boisterous. There was no room for dancing in the aisles, but there was plenty of calling back and forth, joking and laughter. David Heidecker, like many of the other soldiers on board, was in a state of near-euphoria at the thought of being less than a day away from the woman he loved, and only a week or so from seeing his mom and dad; neither crowded conditions nor a grueling trip could dampen his enthusiasm. A few of the soldiers noticed duct tape on some of the windows; when one man began to peel the tape, his seatmate shouted at him to stop, and the nearby passengers launched into a discussion of whether the plane was held together by tape or glue. They didn't care. They were on their way home, and it was almost Christmas.

The flight from Cairo, Egypt to Cologne, West Germany took five hours. At Cologne they had a two-hour layover. Everybody who wanted to got off the plane and wandered around the airport. There was nothing special to see or do, but they needed to stretch their legs. They also had to change into their uniforms. During this time, a crew change took place. The crew who now came on board was the same crew who had flown the same aircraft from McChord Air Force Base to Cologne the day before. The new captain was John Griffin, a forty-five year old resident of Miami. His first officer was Joseph Connelly, same age and city. The two of them and their flight engineer were all veterans of the U.S. Air Force. There were five flight attendants, based in New York. This same crew had operated the same aircraft on the first rotation flight from Cairo to Fort Campbell one week earlier, but that flight had refueled at Bangor, Maine, instead of Gander.

By the time the plane left Cologne, many of the energetic young soldiers were wearing out. They had travelled all day, and were now on a six-hour flight to Gander. There was some conversation on the plane about where Gander was. When a flight attendant said it was located in Newfoundland, Canada, there was grumbling about how long it was taking just to get to the United States and why it was necessary to make another stop. They had to land again, the flight attendant said, in order to refuel. There was more grumbling, and some requests for silence so that others could sleep. One soldier began to sing Silent Night. Several others told him they preferred silence to his singing; he switched to Rudolph the Red-Nosed Reindeer. Soldiers slept with their heads against the window, on the backs of their seats, or on each other; long legs protruded into the aisle. The plane crossed the Atlantic Ocean in the dark and landed on runway 4 at the Gander Airport at 5:35 a.m. Newfoundland Standard Time. It was December 12, 1985.

At Gander, they had a layover of a little over one hour. Most of the passengers woke up and went inside the airport. Some of them bought breakfast. Others perused the gift shops for last-minute trinkets to take home. Some called their families at Fort Campbell. David considered calling Gidget, but there were long lines for the pay phones; besides, he knew it was about 4:30 in the morning at Fort Campbell, and Gidget might not have a telephone yet. The announcement came for the passengers to board the plane. David and the others took their crowded seats for the last time; an air of subdued anticipation permeated the cabin of the DC-8 as they buckled their seat belts.

Glenn Blandford had begun his shift in the control tower at the Gander Airport at midnight. He was the only traffic controller on duty, which was normal for the midnight shift. It meant that he was working both air and ground control, which was okay at that time of night, although it required two different people in the daytime. This had been a slow night anyway, Blandford thought. There had been just three arrivals and one departure so far. An Ascot VC-10 had come in first, and later a Provincial 737. Then the Arrow Air DC-8 had landed on runway 04. No problems. Blandford had worked as an air traffic controller for fourteen years, all of it at Gander, which was an international airport operated by Transport Canada. Because of its strategic location in Newfoundland, near the easternmost tip of North America, it was a popular refueling stop for trans-Atlantic operators. Blandford heard a lot of foreign accents over his tower transmitter.

The early morning weather conditions at Gander were dominated by a low pressure system centered about 250 miles south of Greenland. Light snow and freezing rain had fallen intermittently since Blandford had come on duty. He saw snow clearing and sweeping operations in progress on the runways during the night. At 5:00 a.m., the runway foreman who was about to leave his shift had reported the runway conditions to the tower. Runway 04 and its reciprocal, 22, were forty percent bare and sixty percent rough ice, the foreman said. A truck was applying chemicals to the runway.

Blandford had instructed the DC-8 to park at Gate No. 8. Within minutes after the big plane had parked, he watched two trucks come out and begin refueling the DC-8. They were out there for about thirty-five minutes. When they finished, the flight engineer came down and signed for the fuel. He had a flashlight in his hand; Blandford could see him walking around the aircraft, apparently observing it from the ground. He needed the flashlight because it was still pitch dark. The crew did not request any servicing of the aircraft beyond removal of trash and wastewater. There was no request that the plane be de-iced.

It was a little after 6:30 when the Arrow Air DC-8 called Blandford.

"Gander Ground, Big A 950, we're going to Hopkinsville, Kentucky, and we'd like our clearance on request please."

Blandford responded, "Big A 950, no delay anticipated with the clearance, advise when ready to taxi."

"Ground Big A 950 is ready for taxi."

"Big A 950, runway 22, taxi via straight ahead Delta, right turn 13 to position and the winds are calm."

"Okay, it's runway 22 via Delta and runway 13."

As the DC-8 began its taxi along runway 13, Glenn Blandford had a Navaho twin engine plane on the radar. The Navaho was about twelve miles out, preparing for landing on runway 31. Runway 31 is the reciprocal of runway 13 at Gander — physically, an extension of it. The Arrow Air DC-8 was already on runway 13, taxiing out to make a right turn onto runway 22 for its takeoff. Blandford asked:

"Big A 950, I have traffic about twelve miles out there for runway 31, are you able to expedite the taxi on 13?"

"How would that affect our take-off, sir?"

"We should be able to get you off before they get down, that's just, I just want you to get clear of the runway, that's all."

"Okay."

"Go ahead."

Now Blandford heard from the Navaho twin engine. "Gander Tower good morning, it's November Lima Tango 351 with you."

Blandford acknowledged, "NLT 351 Gander Tower, runway 31, the winds are calm."

"Thank you."

Blandford turned his attention to the Arrow Air DC-8.

"Big A 950, be a right turn now on runway 22 to position, you are ready for take-off now."

"We're ready for take-off now, Big A 950."

"Big A 950, Gander Tower cleared for take-off on 22, winds are calm."

"Big A 950, you want us to go to the tower?"

"No, that's okay."

At 6:45, as the Navaho twin engine touched down on runway 31, the Arrow Air DC-8 left runway 22 on its final take-off. Glenn Blandford saw the plane become airborne. Because it was still dark outside, what he actually saw was the aircraft silhouetted by its lights. As it crossed the TransCanada Highway, which is less than a quarter of a mile from the departure end of runway 22, it appeared to level off. Blandford's eyes narrowed. The DC-8 could not have been more than 150 feet off the ground — probably more like 100 feet. It should be continuing to climb at that altitude, not leveling off. Blandford watched it disappear below his line of vision. At the same moment, he lost it on the radar. A second later, he saw a glow and then what looked like a fireball in the direction of Gander Lake. He heard the Navaho twin engine:

"Tower, it's 351, you seem to have an explosion off here to the west."

Glenn Blandford immediately telephoned the airport Crash-Fire Rescue services, and then the Royal Canadian Mounted Police.

It was 5:15 in the morning at Fort Campbell, Kentucky.

At Fort Campbell, company clerk Alan O'Sullivan was winding up all-night CQ duty. He was looking forward to the return of the rest of his company. There was a reason why he had not gone to the Sinai himself.

Early in the summer, he had requested a stateside swap to California; his request had been turned down so close to the date of Alpha Company's departure for Egypt that it was too late for him to get his passport. Alan was just as glad. His time in the Army was almost up; he would be getting out in a few months and going home to Nebraska, where he intended to go into police work.

During the night, Alan had acquired a new pet. Another soldier had come in with a cold, wet, little black kitten that he had found outside and deposited on Alan's desk.

"What's that?" Alan asked.

"I found it outside," the soldier said. "What can we do with it?"

Alan thought a minute. Pets were not allowed in the barracks, where he lived. Could he think of somebody who lived off base who might take in a little kitten for a while? He thought of Gidget Heidecker, whom he had seen recently while she was in the process of setting up her new home.

"Leave it here," he said. "I'll take care of it."

Throughout the night, he cared for the little animal, feeding it french fries and holding it on his lap. In the early hours of the morning, as he came off duty, he decided to drive out to Gidget's trailer, offer the kitten to her, and make sure she had a ride to the base for the welcoming ceremony. Several hundred soldiers were already in the 2nd Brigade dining facility. The gymnasium was decorated with streamers and "Welcome Home" banners; cooks prepared snacks and coffee for the welcoming ceremony which was planned for the soldiers returning from the Sinai. Alan drove out to Gidget's trailer where, a little after 6 o'clock in the morning, he was knocking on her door with the kitten in his arms. Gidget opened the door wearing her bathrobe.

"Alan?" She looked sleepily from behind the door.

Alan, who had been awake all night, stepped forward. "Hi, Gidget. Look, we found this kitten out in the cold, and we can't keep it in the barracks. I thought of you. Would you be willing to keep it for me for a while?"

Gidget looked at the kitten. "Sure, why not?" she said. "I don't think David will mind."

"I think the plane is a little late," Alan told her. "I don't have an exact time on it. Do you have a ride to the base later, or do you want me to hang around and take you?"

"Thanks, Donna's coming to get me," Gidget told him. She took the kitten in her arms. "I'll see you over there in a little while."

"Okay. Take good care of the little cat!"

Gidget closed the door and told herself to wake up. This was the day she had waited for. Everything was ready. The trailer looked immaculate. The kitchen was cheerful and stocked with food. A framed wedding picture stood on the bureau in the bedroom. Gidget had hung a bright new shower curtain in the red and white bathroom. A small live Christmas tree with decorations and lights stood in the living room with a pile of beautifully-wrapped presents underneath. Gidget was truly proud of the home she had created here, and exasperatingly anxious to show it to David. She also wanted desperately to look her very best. She stepped into the shower, bathed with perfumed soap, washed her long hair thoroughly. Afterwards she worked on her hair until she was satisfied. She put on her best slacks outfit, and did her makeup. It was about 8:00 a.m. when she heard a knock on the door. That would be Donna Magrette, coming to take her to the base.

Gidget opened the door to see that Donna was crying. Her face was white, her hair disheveled. For a moment, Gidget was speechless. Then she whispered, "What is it?"

Donna stumbled inside. "There's news reports that the plane crashed and everybody died," she blurted out.

Gidget stared at her. "What do you mean? What plane?"

"Their plane, the plane from the desert," Donna said. "It's on the radio."

Gidget helped Donna sit down on the love seat. She walked slowly into the kitchen, stunned, and took a soda from the refrigerator. She brought it back to the living room and handed it to Donna. "Drink some of this," she said.

Donna took a sip. "It's on more than one station, Gidget," she insisted.

Gidget sat down across from her. "Maybe it's a mistake," she said. "Maybe it's a different plane."

Donna looked at her. "Or there could be survivors after all," she suggested. "The news isn't always right."

Gidget thought a minute. "We should go to the base," she said. "They'll know what's going on."

Donna nodded. "You're right," she agreed. "Let's go to Fort Campbell."

The shock of Donna's anouncement had barely begun to register on Gidget. She took her purse and left the trailer with a sinking feeling. She and Donna made the ten-minute ride to Fort Campbell without speaking. Donna had her car radio turned on, but they heard no newscasts. They drove directly to the gymnasium. As they got out of the car, they saw a number of people milling around outside the building, in the cold. Gidget spotted Joel, the soldier who had sold David the Monte Carlo. She called out to him:

"Joel? What is it?"

Joel walked towards her. "The plane crashed, Gidget," he said. "I'm sorry."

Gidget began to cry quietly. She walked inside the gymnasium and saw groups of people standing about, many of them crying. Near the tables of doughnuts and coffee were a number of Army officers in dress uniform. There were also several chaplains. Gidget sat down on the lower level of the bleachers along one side of the gym and watched the crowd. Extra telephones were being brought into the gym and installed on the spot. A group of soldiers was setting up tables in a horseshoe arrangement to accommodate various health care professionals and Red Cross personnel. Somebody was attempting to pull a "Welcome Home" banner off the wall. Brigade Commander Colonel John Herrling approached the microphone on a makeshift stage; groups of people shouted at others to be quiet so they could hear.

Colonel Herrling stood quietly on the platform for a few moments. He took several deep breaths as he looked around the gymnasium. At last he tapped gently on the microphone to command attention. The Colonel cleared his throat and announced: "I have some very bad news. In fact, the announcement I'm about to make is tragic. This morning, the aircraft carrying the second increment of Task Force 3-502 back here to Fort Campbell crashed on takeoff from Gander Airport, Newfoundland. Reports from the Canadian air rescue services indicate there were no survivors. We are in the process of confirming the names of those manifested on the aircraft." Colonel Herrling paused. Everyone in the building appeared to be watching him. He continued. "Those families involved will be notified individually. We are sending representatives of the battalion and the brigade today. We will provide those families affected by tragedy with every possible help and assistance. I will do everything in my power to assist you at this time of need. As we get more information, we will pass it on to you. You have my sincere sympathy and my prayers. God bless you all."

Gidget got up from her seat in the bleachers and stumbled out of the gymnasium. Directly in front of her, coming her way, was Alan O'Sullivan. He put his arms around her and cried with her for a few minutes. At that point, Donna Magrette came running from the gym and grabbed Gidget from behind.

"Gidget, will you come home with me?" she cried. "I don't want to be alone!"

Gidget looked at Donna. She did not want to go back to the little yellow house in the country where she had spent her four weeks of married life with David. Gidget shook her head. "I can't, Donna," she whispered. "I want to go to David's and my home."

Donna was hysterical. "But what about me?" she was shrieking.

Gidget just stared at her. Then Alan said, "Donna, let me find somebody to go home with you. I'll get somebody for you."

He disappeared into the gym, and returned in a few minutes with a couple whom Donna knew. "Donna," he said. "These people want to go home with you and stay with you for a while. How will that be?"

Donna looked from one to the other. "Okay," she said, finally. "Thank you."

Alan put his arm around Gidget and walked her slowly to his car, which was some distance away. If Gidget had noticed, she would have seen that the base was in disarray. Nothing appeared to be the normal routine; evidence of emergency measures was everywhere. The bad news was constantly being told to someone else for the first time; people were moving mindlessly, oblivious to others around them. Alan was seriously afraid of their being hit by a car.

Gidget suddenly realized that her telephone was not yet hooked up in the trailer. She would need a phone to call people. When she mentioned this to Alan, he walked her to a telephone on the base which happened not to be in use. Gidget called her father in Carroll County. They had a quiet conversation. John Geisler said he would come to Fort Campbell. He said he would call Gidget's mother. Then he suggested to Gidget that she should be the one to call the Heideckers.

Dick Heidecker was in a wonderful mood. He had been at work at London Fog for several hours; he had already had breakfast and his regular coffee break with a doughnut and diet soda. He knew David would be back at Fort Campbell today; he was probably there already. He hoped David liked the trailer and wasn't upset about the expense. Dick was sure that Gidget had fixed it up beautifully by this time. David and Gidget probably were together at this moment, and David probably was begging Gidget to let him open just one of his Christmas presents early. Dick hoped Gidget would say yes, just as he and Shirley always had for so many Christmases. He wondered if David had finally stopped growing. He hadn't seen David, of course, since June when David and Gidget had left for Fort Campbell after their honeymoon; this was the longest David had ever been away from home. Dick and Shirley hadn't talked to him for a month or so, either, but they would call down there tonight, after David had had a chance to be alone with Gidget. And of course they would all be together for Christmas, which would be upon them in no time.

Dick heard somebody calling his name several times before he figured out that it was Larry, from the warehouse. Larry was saying that Dick had a telephone call, long distance from his daughter-in-law. Dick hurried towards the phone. He knew what it was: David had found out that the trailer was costing $320 a month, and was upset about the money. Gidget was calling to verify that Dick would pay the difference, and probably for reassurance. Or maybe David didn't mind at all about the money — maybe the two of them were just calling to say hello.

Dick took the telephone. "Hello?" he said.

He heard Gidget's voice. "Richard?"

"Hi, baby," Dick said. "What is it?"

"Richard, are you sitting down?"

"Sitting down? No, why?"

"Richard, you need to sit down."

Dick looked around. There was no place to sit, so he leaned against the wall instead. "Okay, I'm sitting," he lied. "What do you want to tell me?"

"It's bad news," Gidget said. "David died in a plane crash this morning on his way back from the Sinai."

Dick, leaning against the wall, heard the words but failed to understand them. "What?" he asked.

"They had a plane crash, Richard. David's plane home. They're saying that everyone was killed."

Dick gasped involuntarily. "Are you serious?" he asked, pathetically.

"Yes. I wanted to tell you myself before you heard it on TV. I'm really sorry." Gidget started to cry.

Dick said, "I'll get Shirley and we'll be right down." He got the address of the trailer and hung up the phone. He walked slowly towards the back of the warehouse and sat down on a bench. After a little while, he began to cry.

When Alan drove Gidget to her trailer, she was reluctant to go in at first. At Alan's gentle insistence, she unlocked the door and stepped inside. The rooms which had seemed so festive before now looked desolate and empty. The Christmas tree, Gidget now realized, was stupid; it would only die. And the presents underneath were pointless, too, since there would be nobody to open them. Gidget sat down on the loveseat and stared at Alan, who stood in the middle of the living room. She said, finally, "What do you think we're supposed to do, exactly?"

Alan sat down next to her. "Whatever you feel like," he told her. "I'm just here to keep you company."

Gidget looked at him. "I can't think what to do," she said.

"Are you hungry?" Alan asked.

Gidget shook her head. "Not at all," she said. "We do have a lot of food, though. Do you want any?"

Alan realized that he was hungry. He looked around the kitchen. It was well-stocked. He found a frozen pizza and put it in the oven. Gidget waited in the living room, wondering what to do. Soon Alan joined her, taking large bites of pepperoni pizza.

"Want some?" he asked.

Gidget shook her head. The thought of food nauseated her. Her mind began to wander. What kind of a plane crash had it been? Was it the kind where the plane came down, and then everybody burned alive? Could David have been trapped somewhere, conscious of his peril but unable to escape? Or had they all been killed instantly? Maybe David had been asleep when it happened; it was a long trip, after all. Did the plane roll over and over on its way down, so that people were somersaulting around inside? Or had the plane broken apart in mid-air so that the passengers actually crashed to their deaths outside the plane? Why would a military plane crash? Wasn't the 101st the best division in the world? Wouldn't they know how to fly a plane? Was David in heaven now? Did he miss her?

She heard Alan ask if it would be all right for him to take a little nap. He had been on duty all night, after all. She told him of course it was all right. He could go in the bedroom and sleep; that would be fine. Yes, she was sure. Alan went into the bedroom and went to sleep. Gidget picked up an old copy of the Clarksville *Leaf Chronical* that had been on the ground outside and tried to read the comics. After a while, she curled up on the loveseat and closed her eyes.

Sometime in the afternoon, Gidget awoke to a knock on the door. She called out to Alan, who got out of bed and came to the front door. He had been asleep for little more than an hour. Outside stood a lieutenant in dress greens who identified himself as Dennis Shanahan and asked if he could come in. Alan let him in. Lieutenant Shanahan told them he had been assigned to David Heidecker's family as the survival assistance officer, and that it was his unhappy job to make an official announcement.

Alan said, "Hey, you don't have to do that. We already know."

The lieutenant looked at Gidget, who nodded. Shanahan seemed relieved. "Okay," he said. "I'm supposed to make my speech anyway, but I won't. I'm very sorry."

Gidget said, "Thank you."

Shanahan explained to them that his job was to identify and inventory David's effects, such as money and property, to see that everything got to the right people, and to help the family through the mechanics of the system. Shanahan said that they would need help with financial matters, such as bank accounts that might need to be closed, or debts, if there were any, and that there would also be paper work for survivor benefits such as life insurance and other things. If Gidget did not choose to stay at Fort Campbell, there would be the logistics of moving. His job, Shanahan said, was to assist the family in any way possible.

Gidget asked him to sit down, and then she got up for the first time since she had returned that day, and went into the kitchen to get him a soft drink. It was good to have something to do, and besides, Dennis Shanahan seemed nice. She asked him if there was a different survival assistance officer for each family, and he told her there was. He asked about other surviving family members, and she told him about Dick and Shirley. She said they were on their way down, but it was a long drive and they probably wouldn't get here until the middle of the night. She asked Dennis if he knew any details about the plane crash, and he said no, but that there would surely be a detailed report on the evening news. Gidget asked Dennis where he was from, and he told her he was from Ohio and that he had gone to West Point. After a while, Dennis said he needed to get back to the base, but that he would be over the next morning to talk to David's parents. He left his telephone number in case Gidget needed anything in the meantime.

After Lieutenant Shanahan left, Gidget decided to take a shower. She was beginning to feel a little better. At first, it had been as if she couldn't move, couldn't do anything, but now she was beginning to feel like a human being. The shower felt good, except that every time she saw the pretty new shower curtain, it made her start to cry. When she finished her shower, she put on a clean slacks and sweater outfit. It wasn't as nice as the one she had had on this morning, but now it didn't make any difference.

There was a second knock on the door. Alan opened it to admit another soldier in dress greens. Neither Alan nor Gidget had ever seen him before. He stated his name and identified himself as the survival assistance officer for David Heidecker's family. As Alan and Gidget stared at him, he stood stiffly in front of the door and proceeded to announce, in a pompous manner, that it was his official duty to make the following statement. Staring straight at the wall behind Gidget and Alan, speaking as if the words were memorized, in phrases which alternately were monotonous or had inappropriate inflections, he announced that it was his duty to tell them that the aircraft en route from the Sinai Desert had crashed on takeoff at the Gander Airport at 0646 Newfoundland Standard Time which was 0516 in Fort Campbell, and that Army records stated that the passenger list included the name of PFC David Wayne Heidecker of Woodbine, Maryland. Before he could continue, Gidget interrupted:

"We know all that," she told the soldier. "And anyway, there was another survival assistance officer here before. He's the one assigned to David."

The soldier pulled himself up indignantly. "What do you mean, there was another officer here? *I'm* the survival assistance officer for Heidecker."

Alan, who was dressed in civilian clothes, stepped forward. He did not know this soldier and was not in a mood to be either patient or military. "Look, fella," he said. "There's been some kind of mix-up. Whatever it was, we already got the message and, to be honest with you, we don't want to hear it again."

The soldier looked deeply offended. "I'm doing my job," he said pompously.

"Well, you've done it," Alan told him. "Now get out."

The soldier hesitated, as if weighing the relative consequences of failing to complete his official announcement versus being punched in the nose by a survivor. Then he left.

Gidget looked at Alan in disbelief. "What an asshole!" she said.

Alan did an imitation of the soldier's posture, standing self-importantly against the door. Both of them broke into nervous laughter. Gidget walked over to the loveseat and sat down. She realized suddenly that she had just laughed for the first time today. Thank God for Alan, she thought. He was one of the nicest people she had ever met. Everybody in the company liked him. He was friendly and outgoing, polite to everybody, always thinking of ways to be helpful — and on top of that he was tall and handsome, self-possessed, able to move easily in any circle, as if he would fit anywhere. He was exactly the kind of friend you needed at a time like this. She and Alan looked at each other and smiled wanly.

At 9 o'clock in the morning at Fort Lewis, Washington, Pacific Time, Private Patrick Kenney had finished breakfast and his early morning routine. Back in the barracks, as he left to go to his assigned duties for the day, he heard a radio broadcast about a plane crash. He stepped into the brisk winter air outside, then stopped. The broadcast had said something about soldiers in the Sinai. He took a few more steps and stopped again. He thought the radio had mentioned the 101st Airborne. Patrick stood still in the cold. He knew that David Heidecker was expected home for Christmas. But wouldn't there be more than one plane coming back from the Sinai? He broke into a run to the nearest pay phone on base. He put change into the phone and dialed the Heideckers' number. There was no answer. He put his hands on his head. Could he remember Gidget's phone number in Carroll County? He thought he could. He put the change in again and dialed the number. He heard John Geisler answer the telephone.

"Hello?"

Patrick said, "Mr. Geisler? This is Patrick Kenney calling."

"Patrick? Where are you calling from?"

"I'm at Fort Lewis, sir, in Washington State. Look, the reason I'm calling, I know this is really silly. I heard a news story on the radio about a plane crash. That couldn't have been David's plane, could it?"

John Geisler paused. Then he said, "I'm sorry, Pat. It was David's plane."

Patrick hung up the telephone. A little while later his sergeant found him, still in the phone booth, gasping for breath and beating his hand against the clear glass.

* * * * *

Gladys Nunn drove along Liberty Road in Carroll County. She had finished a doctor's appointment and was on her way to her parents' house for dinner, because Jim was out with the boys that night. She had just passed South Carroll High School and the Winfield Community Volunteer Fire House when her radio station announced a news bulletin about the plane crash in Gander. The broadcast identified the flight as the one bringing soldiers from the 101st Airborne home to Fort Campbell, and said there were no survivors. The red Pinto left the road and stalled in a shallow ditch along the side of the highway. For a few minutes Gladys sat still, forcing herself to breathe deeply as she reconstructed what she had just heard. Finally, she started the car and was able to pull out of the ditch and back onto the road. She drove quickly to her parents' house and let herself in with her key; her father and mother were not yet home from work. She ran to the phone and dialed Donna Magrette's number. The line was busy. She called back, and Donna answered the telephone. Gladys suddenly realized that she had no idea what to say. Donna Magrette's husband, after all, would have been on the plane with David.

Hesitantly, Gladys said, "Donna?"

"Yes."

"Donna, this is Gladys, Gidget's friend from Maryland. I heard the radio. Is it — true?"

Donna said, "It's true."

Gladys said, "Oh, my God, I'm so sorry. Is Gidget there?"

"No, she moved into her own place last week."

"I know that, but I don't have any phone number there. Do you have it?"

"There's no phone there yet."

"Oh, God, what can I do?" Gladys beseeched. "Is there any way I can talk to Gidget?"

"Well, I could ride over there in a while and tell her you called," Donna volunteered. "She could call you back from another phone."

"Oh, would you do that? I'd appreciate it so much!"

"Sure, I'll do it," Donna said. "To tell you the truth, there's not a whole lot to do right now anyway. Will Gidget know where to call you back?"

"Tell her I'm at my parents. She knows their number."

Gladys sat down in a chair to wait for Gidget's call.

In the trailer in Clarksville, Gidget and Alan discussed the various alternatives for dinner. Gidget volunteered to cook. Alan offered to drive to get carry-out. Gidget said that was silly; there was plenty of food. They found some ground beef and made hamburgers.

It was time for the evening news on television. They talked about whether or not they should look at it, but they both knew they had to. Gidget turned it on. The plane crash was the lead story on the news. It was described as "the worst plane crash in military history." The broadcast also mentioned that this was the largest loss of life in one day for the 101st Airborne since D-Day. There were statistics on the number of people killed in 1985, which was characterized as the worst year in aviation history in terms of fatalities; this particular crash was called the eighth worst disaster in aviation history. A toll-free number was given for anyone who wanted to call Fort Campbell for information. But there were no pictures yet, and no word about when the bodies would be sent home for burial. Gidget turned off the TV.

There was another knock at the door. Gidget looked at Alan. "If that's another survival assistance officer, please get rid of him," she said. They both laughed nervously. Donna Magrette was at the door. She said Gladys had called and wanted Gidget to call her at her parents' house. Gidget thanked her for the message, and asked if she wanted to come in for a while. Donna said no, and left. Alan and Gidget set out in Alan's car to find the closest pay phone. It turned out to be in a fast food place on Fort Campbell Boulevard.

Gladys answered the phone. She said, "Gidge? Is it you?"

"It's me," Gidget told her.

"Are you okay?"

"Yes."

"Gidget, I'm so sorry."

"I know. I'm just glad to hear your voice."

Gladys said, "Gidget, I really wanted to come down. I didn't hear the news until this afternoon, and by then your dad and David's parents had already left. I couldn't find anybody until I finally reached your mother. She told me they were on their way already."

"I'll be glad when they get here," Gidget said.

"I really wanted to come, Gidget. You know that."

"I know," Gidget said. "Thanks. I'll probably be back in a few days. We'll see each other then."

She told Gladys about the two survival assistance officers. Gladys said that was the dumbest thing she had ever heard. Gidget said that a soldier named Alan was keeping her company; she didn't know what she'd do without him. Gladys told Gidget about the phone call she had received from David in the Sinai on November 18.

"Gidge, he was calling to find out what to bring you for Christmas. It was so sweet, you can't imagine!"

"Did you give him any suggestions?"

"Well, he asked me about a certain thing, but it's a surprise." Gladys stopped. "Of course, that wouldn't matter now, would it?"

"No."

"It was an Aztec statue. He wanted to know if you would like one."

"What did you tell him?"

"I said I thought you would. So he was going to bring it." Gladys
was quiet for a moment. "Gidget, I remember the last thing David said to
me. He said, I hope Jim loves you as much as Gidget and I do."

Now Gidget started to cry. She said, "Oh, Gladys."

Gladys was crying, too. "Gidge, I'm sorry. I should be trying to cheer
you up, not get you upset."

"It's okay, Gladys. I'm just glad to talk to you."

Afterwards, she and Alan drove around for a little while. Then they
went back to the trailer and watched television. Alan was tired. He had been
on duty the night before, and had had only a short nap today. Gidget decided
to sleep, too. She knew that her father and the Heideckers would arrive
sometime during the night; it would be best to get as much sleep as possible
before then. Gidget went to sleep in her bedroom and Alan stretched out on
the couch in the living room. It was still December 12.

As the car in which she was riding sped through the night, Shirley
Heidecker leaned against the door of the passenger side, sometimes looking
out the window. There was nothing to see, really; it was too dark. Shirley
just wanted to get there and straighten all of this out. She knew perfectly well
that David had walked away from that plane crash — *if* it had been his plane
that crashed in the first place. Everybody knew how crowded the skies were
nowadays; there was no way to tell which plane was which. And even if it
had been his plane, he might have missed it. David was good at missing things,
like school when he was in the 10th grade. Then he'd look at you so innocently,
not knowing how he could have failed to get where he was supposed to be,
you just couldn't be mad about it. This would have been like that. He was
probably goofing off in the airport, reading a sports magazine or something,
and didn't even hear the announcement to board the plane. Shirley hoped
he wouldn't be court-martialed or anything like that. Of course, Dick would
be able to get him out of trouble; he always had before. Even if David had
gotten on that plane, the very one they were talking about on the news, so
what? As agile as David was, he would have been the first person out of there.
He would have been able to open one of those emergency exit windows in
about a second, and luckily he was skinny enough to slide right through.
Besides, he was so strong; was she the only one who remembered that he had
played football with the Cavaliers his senior year, a championship team? David
was not lying in the rubble of any airplane crash in Canada. He was walking
around somewhere, maybe a little dazed; that was why he hadn't called
anybody. But that would be cleared up in a minute — he would be wearing
his dog tags, and they would find out at once who he was. In fact, he was
probably fine by now and had already talked to Gidget, since there was nobody
at their house in Carroll County to answer the phone. Maybe the Army had

even put him on another plane by now, and he was already in Clarksville. When they got there, he would probably open the door himself. He would put his long arms around her and Dick at the same time, and laugh and say, "Hi, Mom! Hi, Dad!"

If only Dick could get them there a little faster. Shirley looked over at him. He was doing the best he could, really. They didn't want to be stopped for speeding, or have an accident. And she knew Dick was upset. He really thought that David had been in the plane crash, and that he could have been killed. Dick wasn't sure about it, but he was afraid. And then there was John Geisler in the back seat, who seemed to be sleeping most of the time. Shirley didn't know what he thought; every time she said she was sure that David was fine, John just looked at her.

Shirley hadn't wanted to bother Aunt Ollie about this, not when it was probably a false alarm. Dick said they had to tell her — what if she heard a news broadcast on television? Shirley had refused to call, and so finally Dick himself called Aunt Ollie on the phone and gently told her the news. That was just before they got in the car and left Carroll County.

It was a long trip. Quite a bit of the time, no one said anything. A couple of times they stopped for coffee and hamburgers, just to keep going. Shirley had even done some of the driving, but Dick was doing most of it. For some reason, neither one of them felt a bit tired. They had left Carroll County so suddenly, stopping only to throw some clothes in a suitcase and get some money from the bank. Dick said he didn't know what they might run into down there; they should have extra money. It was good he'd thought of it, Shirley said to herself; David's birthday was on the fifteenth of December and they hadn't bought his presents yet. They'd need the money to buy things for David, now that they'd be seeing him sooner than they expected.

Once in a while Dick would turn on the car radio for a while. They could get some good country music down here, but then there were those damn news broadcasts every hour or half hour with the news about the plane. John said they should listen to the broadcasts, there might be some new facts or details, but Shirley didn't want to hear any more. Dick told John not to worry about it, they'd find out all the details soon enough.

They drove into Clarksville around four o'clock in the morning. Dick had directions to the trailer. It was easy; he went up Fort Campbell Boulevard to Tobacco Road, and then drove until they got to the American Village Mobile Home Park. John read him the directions so that he made the correct turns. Soon they were there. Dick pulled up next to the trailer and turned off the motor. There was a light outside, but they didn't see any lights inside. The three of them got out and walked to the door. Dick knocked, then tried the door. It was unlocked. He opened it and went in. Shirley was right behind him. In the dim light from outside, she could see a tall young man sleeping on the sofa. She ran over and touched him. Alan O'Sullivan opened his eyes and sat up. Shirley looked at him. Then she backed away and burst into tears. Dick put his arms around her as she cried softly on his shoulder.

For the next two hours, everybody sat in the living-room of the trailer — Dick and Shirley, John, Gidget, and Alan — and shared what little information they had. Gidget and Alan had the most to say, filling in the others on everything that had happened on the base, and even telling the story about the two survival assistance officers. John sat close to Gidget, trying to give her comfort. Dick had some questions, which Alan and Gidget did their best to answer. Shirley said nothing. And at dawn everybody stretched out somewhere in the cramped trailer and fell asleep.

CHAPTER 17

Farther Along

Tempted and tried, we're oft made to wonder
Why it should be thus all the day long,
While there are others living about us
Never molested, though in the wrong.

When death has come and taken our loved ones
It leaves our home so lonely and drear,
Then do we wonder why others prosper
Living so wicked year after year.

Farther along we'll know all about it,
Farther along we'll understand why;
Cheer up my brother, live in the sunshine
We'll understand it all, by and by.

"Farther Along," Traditional

They stayed in Clarksville for four more days. On Sunday, Gidget's mother arrived by plane and moved into the trailer, too. It was David's twenty-first birthday.

A perspective on the plane crash began to emerge from television news broadcasts. The Arrow Air DC-8 had been cleared for its right turn onto runway 22, the broadcasters said; it began its takeoff from a complete stop and reached its peak speed in less than a minute. Basically, the plane barely got off the ground. It rose 60 to 100 feet before it began to lose speed and crashed into trees on a grassy hill. The aircraft exploded on impact, said the newsmen, charring the surrounding woods, releasing jet fuel, and strewing debris for three-quarters of a mile. Altogether, the plane flew for less than a mile. It lay in crumpled pieces, the largest of which was a 20-foot portion of the fuselage with a small American flag painted on it.

Videotapes on the evening news showed makeshift shelters in Gander, where Canadians and Americans searched for the remains of passengers. It became clear from the news broadcasts that many bodies were not intact. An airport hangar became a temporary morgue where bodies lay in rows under sheets of plastic; they were all to be placed in aluminum coffins which the U.S. Air Force brought to Gander, and then transported to Dover Air Force Base.

There was considerable news commentary on the crash. Why were American soldiers flying in chartered planes, rather than military planes? Who was Arrow Air? Had deregulation of the airline industry had an adverse impact on safety? Should the United States continue to supply the bulk of the soldiers to the Sinai Peninsula, or were the Camp David Accords outdated? Was there a possibility of sabotage? In the midst of these speculations, CBS reported that a young private named Eric Harrington had just called his wife collect to say that he had missed the plane.

On Monday, December 16, President and Nancy Reagan came to Hangar 4 on the Fort Campbell airfield to participate in a memorial service for immediate family members. The Reagans were not novices at this. They had done it, in other locations, for the 241 Marines killed in a barracks bombing in Lebanon in 1983, and then for the 19 casualties of Granada. Gidget and Dick and Shirley sat in the front row of the makeshift chapel, where hot-air blowers provided a noisy background. After the ceremony, President Reagan came into the audience to speak personally to the family members. Gidget, who had begun to cry as the Army band played America the Beautiful, was suddenly confronted with the President of the United States. He put his arms around her and hugged her for a moment. Nancy Reagan said to her, "I'm so sorry." Gidget was able to manage an acknowledgment of sorts before they moved on to the next family. It took the President nearly an hour to speak to them all, but Gidget and those with her did not wait. They left the airfield and went back to the trailer.

That afternoon, Gidget packed a suitcase. The next morning, she said good-bye to Alan O'Sullivan, who told her she could keep the kitten if she wanted. She left the trailer in Clarksville for the last time as she and her father and the Heideckers piled into the car with the kitten, whom she had named Alan, and headed for Carroll County. Her mother flew home the same day.

Back on Bluebird Drive, Gidget found that her bedroom had been given away to her brother Johnny. She moved into Johnny's old room, which was smaller. There was a bed and a bureau, and just enough wall space for her 101st Airborne flag. She unpacked the few things she had brought back with her and slowly put them away.

On Gillis Road, the hill in front of the house was stark and frozen. The pine trees were still green, but the rest of the foliage was gone for the winter; naked trees stood sharply against the sky. Sometimes Dick would walk outside in the cold, and seated on one of the picnic benches, would gaze out across the county from the top of the hill. The panoramic view, so colorful in the spring and summer, scenic even in winter, now seemed empty; there was no joy in it.

By the end of December, only a few dozen soldiers had been identified and returned to their families. The rest remained at Dover, where the process continued. There were no estimates as to time, and the news reports were not encouraging. Days stretched into weeks as David's family, feeling themselves in limbo, went on one day at a time.

The Canadian Aviation Safety Board continued its investigation into the cause of the plane crash. The Board discovered immediately that the cockpit voice recorder had not operated properly and that the flight data recorder was obsolete and virtually useless. The destructiveness of the fire that had consumed much of the aircraft also impeded the investigation, as did the absence of survivors. For the Heideckers, and other families, the specific cause of the accident became incidental. Their sons and husbands, who had just spent five months in the Sinai Desert on an international peace-keeping mission, were men of the Screaming Eagles. Their first Commander, Major General W.C. Lee, had said in 1942:

> The 101st Airborne Division . . . has no history, but it has a rendezvous with destiny . . . [W]e shall be called upon to carry out operations of far-reaching military importance and we shall habitually go into action when the need is immediate and extreme. Let me call your attention to the fact that our badge is the great American eagle. This is a fitting emblem for a Division that will crush its enemies by falling upon them like a thunderbolt from the skies . . . .

But instead, the soldiers had themselves fallen like a thunderbolt, not to crush their enemies, but to be crushed, not like conquering heroes but like defenseless toys flung into a frozen inferno in an island in the Atlantic that had no connection with their lives. For the Heideckers, to whom America truly meant spacious skies and amber waves of grain, it was incomprehensible that David should have died in a civilian accident in a foreign country, three days before his twenty-first birthday. And so, finally, they lost interest in why the accident occurred, and simply mourned, quietly, for the little boy who had come to them quite by chance, and who had been taken from them the same way.

Before long, both Dick and Shirley went back to work. Dick needed to be occupied so he wouldn't dwell on the accident all the time. He also re-joined his bowling league. Shirley wanted the familiarity of her employment. She had recently been promoted to a more demanding position; that was fine with her. She would go to work as early as possible and stay there as long as she could. Webster Clothes helped to establish a scholarship in David's name. The fund would provide a college scholarship each year to a graduating senior from South Carroll High School, with the recipient to be selected by Dick and Shirley, Coach Parker, and the school principal.

The Army assigned the family a new survival assistance officer, Captain Sally Bock from Fort Meade, Maryland, the closest Army base to Carroll County. In her initial contact with the family, she told them that David had been promoted to the rank of Specialist 4th Class posthumously, that the promotion had been scheduled before his death. Captain Bock's main job vis-a-vis the Heideckers was to keep them advised of the identification process. In early January, there had been new speculation in news articles that some of the soldiers never would be identified and would be buried in a common grave. This was followed by a statement from the Army on January 10, which acknowledged that the identification of bodies had turned into a slow process and that only 115 soldiers had been identified so far, but added that "authorities are hopeful that modern identification procedures will make it possible to identify all but a few of the soldiers killed in the Gander crash." The Army had already acknowledged that, although regulations prohibited it, many of the men had been carrying their medical and dental records with them on the plane and the records had been destroyed in the crash.

For Shirley, in particular, the thought that David might never be iden-tified was intolerable. She could not bear to dwell on what the difficulties of identification told her about the condition of his body. In her mind, he was lying somewhere, in one piece, as if he were asleep. It was imperative that he come back to Maryland, where she could bury him and know where he was forever. Once she called Sally Bock.

"What's taking so long?" she demanded. "Is anybody working on this?"

Captain Bock spoke gently. "Mrs. Heidecker, we have people work-ing on this day and night," she said. "Believe me when I tell you that the Army is as anxious as you are to accomplish this."

"Well, I hope so," Shirley told her. "It seems to me it doesn't take a month or two to tell who is who."

Captain Bock hesitated. How could she tell this mother that her son's body must have been in pieces, scattered around a scene of death with parts of other bodies? She said, "I know how hard it is to be patient. We're doing the best we can."

The identification process had begun the day of the plane crash. Because the accident occurred in Canada, responsibility for identifying the remains belonged to the Canadian Aviation Safety Board. Members of the Board had arrived in Gander on December 12 to begin the process.

The Canadians agreed at the outset that all human remains would be transferred to Dover Air Force Base, where autopsies and identification would be carried out by the Armed Forces Institute of Pathology. Technically, the Canadian Aviation Safety Board would be in charge, although the Institute was part of the United States Department of Defense. As the bodies were collected within a few days of the accident, the United States moved them to the Port Mortuary at Dover.

Within a few days it became apparent that there were not enough body parts to account for 248 soldiers and 8 crew members. Obviously, not all of the remains had been removed from Gander. But by now, two feet of fresh snow had fallen on the crash site. The pathologists had two options: they could wait until spring for the snow to melt, or they could undertake some heroic effort to melt the snow. One of the drawbacks to the first option, apart from the interminable grief which it would inflict on some of the families, was that it would require security to be maintained in the area for several more months. There had to be a way to melt the snow. After a considerable number of trees were cleared, a large part of the crash area was enclosed with shelters. The snow was melted inside the shelters, and the search for bodies continued. That search included detailed examination of the sub-soil by hand with small trowels. All human remains were sent to Dover.

Identification was long and slow because of the severity of the crash and the intensity of the fire that followed. The pathologists used several methods of identification, including the matching of personal effects, finger prints, dental charts, and medical characteristics. In addition, they had physical anthropologists and a police artist who did facial reconstruction drawings. For the most difficult identifications, they used what they called an "exclusion matrix." This was explained by Colonel McMeeken, Director of the Armed Forces Institute of Pathology, in testimony before the Canadian Aviation Safety Board, as follows:

> Once we had made positive identification of all but eight by various means such as dental, finger prints and so forth, there were eight whose identity was quite difficult. There were some very good physical characteristics, but no single one of those characteristics provided identification. By putting them in an exclusion matrix and turning the coin, so to speak, and that is eliminating those

whose particular remains could not be, it was like putting together a puzzle. There was only one way that they
would fit, and that was our exclusion matrix.

In the end, the identification process took two and a half months.

On February 4, Captain Bock called Dick Heidecker to ask whether
David had owned a gold chain that he might have been wearing. Dick said yes.
Did this mean they had found somebody with a gold chain who might be David,
Dick asked? The Captain wasn't able to answer any questions. She was merely
communicating a question she had been told to ask. Two days later, Captain
Bock called the Heideckers' attorney. Could he find out whether or not David
had been circumcised? She was reluctant to ask the family directly. Their attorney went to the Johns Hopkins Hospital and looked at the records of
David's birth. He had been circumcised. The attorney passed that information
to Captain Bock. Did this mean they had a body that was circumcised, who
might be David? Captain Bock could not answer. On February 15, she called
Shirley to ask about David's hair color and his shoe size. She called Gidget the
same day for a specific description of the cross David might have been wearing.
    On Sunday, February 23, Captain Bock, in uniform, drove out to
Bluebird Drive. They had an identification. Because technically Gidget
Heidecker was David's next of kin, Army policy required that she be notified
first. But after Captain Bock left Gidget, she drove over to Gillis Road and
told Dick and Shirley that David's body had been identified.
    They had to make arrangements for David's burial. Captain Bock ex-
plained the procedure. David's body would come from Dover Air Force base
in a black limousine hearse. The driver would be from Dover, but there would
also be a soldier designated as body escort, and this could be somebody selected
by the family. Dick and Shirley and Gidget sat in the Heideckers' living-room
and talked. Why not ask the Army to send Alan O'Sullivan as the body escort?
He was somebody they had met who had known David. They agreed on that.
Shirley suggested they use the Burrier Funeral Home on Liberty Road. It was
right next to South Carroll High. They all agreed on that, too. They picked
the Geislers' church, Taylorsville United Methodist. Dick and Shirley already
had a lot at Woodlawn Cemetery on Liberty Road, about 20 miles east in
Baltimore County. Gidget said that was fine. They scheduled the funeral for
Saturday, March 1, six days away.
    Alan O'Sullivan was flown to Dover Air Force Base for an escort brief-
ing. He checked into the barracks on base, where he would spend the night.
He had always heard that there was no comparison between an Army barracks and an Air Force barracks, and now he could see it was true. This looked

like an expensive motel. There was carpeting on the floor; the rooms had television. The bathroom looked like the kind you got in a nice hotel instead of the kind you got in an Army barracks. Alan decided to take advantage of the luxury and go to sleep. This assignment was making him tense; he knew that it was his responsibility to keep things as smooth as they could be for David's family. He closed his eyes.

The next day, Alan rode to Maryland in a black limousine hearse which carried David's casket. He arrived at Burrier's late Wednesday afternoon. Alan thought it was strange that a funeral home would have that name, but he found out that it was actually the name of the family who owned it. Mr. Burrier sent his crew to carry the casket inside. They set it up at the end of a large room. Alan went over some paper work with Mr. Burrier. Then he put David's dog tags in his pocket for Gidget.

Captain Bock arrived at the funeral home and met Alan. She drove him to the Sandra Lee Motel, where she had made a reservation for him, and then to the Baltimore-Washington International Airport where he could rent a car. Alan was starving by the time he got back to the motel. He found a restaurant next door and went in. Their daily special was roast beef and baked potato. Alan ordered it. They were out of baked potatoes; Alan took french fries. He drank two beers and had banana pie for dessert. Feeling very much alone, he walked back to the Sandra Lee and went to sleep.

On Thursday morning, Gidget woke up resignedly. She knew David's body was in Carroll County. This was going to be the first day of a three-day funeral, really. Tonight from 7 to 9 they were supposed to be at Burrier's to receive people, and again tomorrow from 2 until 9. The services would be on Saturday. For Gidget, there was no role model for the part she was about to play. She had almost never been to a funeral in her life. She didn't know anybody her age who was a widow. Widows were supposed to be old, with grown children to support them. They wore frumpy black dresses, with veils to hide their faces. They were sad, but they had already lived most of their lives. What was an eighteen-year old widow supposed to do? Gidget's family didn't know, either. As her father said, they were going to have to wing it.

Somebody knocked at the door. Gidget opened it to find Alan O'Sullivan, wearing his dress greens and smiling cautiously at her.

"Alan, it's you!" Gidget threw her arms around his neck and hugged him. "Golly, I'm glad to see you. When did you get here?"

Alan stepped inside. "Yesterday," he told her. "I came with David."

Gidget nodded solemnly. "I know," she said. "All of us really appreciate it. Come on in."

Alan climbed the steps to the living-room and looked around. A medium-sized black kitten darted across the living-room rug. Alan stared at it. "Is that our kitten?" he asked.

"That's him," Gidget said. "I named him for you. Alan, meet Alan."

They laughed. "He's sure grown," Alan remarked. "Does he like it here?"

"Yup, he's pretty well adjusted," Gidget told him. "I don't think he misses Fort Campbell."

She offered Alan a soda, which he accepted eagerly. "Hey, I rented a car," he told Gidget. "Would you like to go over to the funeral home? I can take you there if you want."

Gidget thought a moment. She shook her head. "No, I'll wait until tonight," she said finally. "It'll be a long three days."

Alan reached into his pocket and took out David's dog tags. He handed them to Gidget. "Here," he said. "This is an official act, I guess, handing these to you."

Gidget looked at the tags. She was wondering why, if the Army had the tags, it had taken so long to identify David. She didn't want to think about what the answer had to be. She looked up at Alan. "Thanks," she said. She took the tags into the bedroom which she now occupied and put them in her bureau drawer. Then she went back into the living room where Alan was standing.

Gidget told him, "I have to do laundry and stuff like that for a while. There's our TV, and we rented a bunch of movies from the video store if you want to look at one while I'm working."

"Thanks," Alan said. He selected one and put it in the VCR. For the next two hours, he watched a movie while Gidget worked around the house, answered the telephone, and even greeted several visitors who came to the door. Later, he sat with her as they talked quietly about David, the past and the present. They took a walk in the cold, behind Gidget's house where the back yard met the woods next door, and talked about Alan's plans for the future.

Late in the afternoon, John, Kathy, and Johnny came home. They put together a simple dinner and Gidget asked what they thought she was supposed to wear to the funeral home.

"I think you should wear whatever you feel like wearing," her father told her.

"Good," Gidget said, "since I don't have an ugly black dress."

She put on a pair of dressy slacks and a nice sweater. Her father put on a suit, and Kathy wore a dress. After dinner, they all set out for the funeral home with Alan O'Sullivan.

Gidget had seen Burrier's hundreds of times in her life. It sat directly on Liberty Road, right next to South Carroll High School. She had even been inside once, the previous Tuesday when she and Shirley had come over to make arrangements with Mr. Burrier. Nevertheless, she was not prepared for the scene that awaited her. Inside the funeral home was a very large room with folding chairs set up at one end and in a few spots along both sides.

At the other end of the room was David's casket. It was a grey steel military casket draped with a large American flag. Behind the casket, on a wide shelf, was David's picture in a frame. A number of fancy flower arrangements stood on the shelf, including one sent by Gidget. Hers consisted of white carnations forming a cross. Her card said, "Love you 4-ever-n-longer."

Gidget walked slowly towards the casket and put her hand on top of it, touching the flag. She thought about how tall David had been; maybe that was why the casket seemed so big. She didn't think a lot about God, but now she began to pray silently. She prayed that David hadn't suffered. After the crash, she had had a recurring nightmare in which she had seen David's face right after the plane crash. In the dream, his face had looked shocked, but more than shocked: it had looked betrayed, as if he couldn't believe that he was about to be cheated out of the rest of his life — cheated out of going home to his wife, seeing his father and mother, having his own home and family, having children, going to football games, celebrating birthdays, growing old. In the dream, the face with the shocked look on it suddenly shattered into a million tiny pieces, all flying in different directions until the face no longer existed at all. Was that how it had been, Gidget wondered, or had everything happened too fast? Gidget stood there, touching the flag, and prayed that David hadn't suffered, that he was in heaven now, and that he had found peace.

She looked at the other flower arrangements. Dick and Shirley had sent red roses in a heart shape. John and Kathy had sent a Screaming Eagle of white flowers. There was an arrangement from Ken Parker and the football team, with a white ribbon that said "1983 Champions." There were other flowers from Gidget's mother, Webster Clothes, London Fog, Gladys and Jim. The flowers behind the flag-draped casket made a barrage of color at that end of the room.

The large room was filling up with people. Dick and Shirley were there, and Gidget's mother; soon there were many young people, friends of Gidget's and friends of David's. Half a dozen of his football teammates came. There were neighbors and family friends, the Langhages, Patrick Kenney's mother, even a few strangers who had read about David in the newspaper and wanted to extend their sympathy. Most of these people tried to say something comforting to Gidget. She thanked them, or tried to smile; it was hard for her to think what to say. After a while, she began to feel very tired. From time to time, she went downstairs with Gladys and her girlfriends. There was a soda machine, and they could sit around in a small lounge. Her father and Kathy stayed upstairs in the big room; they could greet people for a while. It felt a little like the parties they used to have in high school, where the kids went down to the club cellar and the parents stayed upstairs. Then Gidget would remember why they were there, and she would go upstairs for a while longer.

On Friday, Shirley slept as long as she could. At 2 o'clock in the afternoon, she and Dick drove over to Burrier's, where they were to receive people until 9 o'clock at night.

By now, Shirley had become accustomed to the sight of the flag-draped casket. She was able to look at it, even touch it, without reacting. Like Gidget, she was amazed at how big it seemed; to Shirley, the size of it proved that David's body must be intact. She was glad about that. As his mother, she knew, it was part of her job to protect David from harm. He had absolutely no business being on that plane, she thought, and she should never have allowed it. She really could have stopped him, if only she had not permitted him to finish high school one semester early. If she had made him stay the whole year, like the other students, he would not have gone into the service when he did. Maybe he should have gone to college after high school. Just because the Army offered educational benefits after the service was no reason why David had to go there. Why hadn't he picked the Navy, or the Air Force? Their men weren't in the Middle East at all. If he did have to go into the Army, why had he picked the Infantry, anyway? There were other things you could do in the Army; there was the Artillery, for instance. They didn't go to the Middle East, either; they just hung around the States doing K.P. or something safe. But the real problem, Shirley thought, was that he'd gone through basic training so smoothly. What if he had goofed up somewhere and been recycled at Fort Benning? Just one time, in one skill — that's all it would have taken to get him off the path to Fort Campbell and the Sinai and the second plane. But David had been too conscientious, too responsible, and that was Shirley's doing; she had tried to raise him that way. Now look where it had put him. What if he had lost his passport, like that other soldier who lost his and wasn't able to get on the plane? Hadn't she spent months and years teaching David to be careful with his things, to get where he was supposed to be on time? Silently, she told David she was sorry.

Aunt Ollie came over and took her hand. They walked over to some folding chairs and sat down. It was comforting, having Aunt Ollie nearby. Shirley thought, she knew I did my best, she knew I tried to raise David to get along in the world. She stopped caring who was coming to the funeral home to speak to her. She didn't want to see them. She just wanted to be with Aunt Ollie.

At 8:30 in the evening, Patrick Kenney came. He had flown that day from Fort Lewis, Washington, on special leave, and had come directly from Baltimore-Washington International Airport to Burrier's. Shirley saw him come in. She watched him stop as he saw the casket, and then walk slowly towards it. She saw him kneel down in front of the casket, his hands touching the flag. He was crying. After what seemed to be a long time, he stood up

The Geislers' church, Taylorsville United Methodist. *Ann Turnbull*

and looked around. He came over to Shirley and embraced her. Shirley held him for a little while. She suddenly felt stronger. Now she was ready to say good night to Aunt Ollie and go home with Dick.

Taylorsville United Methodist, a white wooden church with stained-glass windows and plain wooden pews, has a sign up front that announces the attendance and the offering for the day. On Saturday, March 1, the church was filled to overflowing as David's casket, still draped with the American flag, rested in front of the altar. The service was conducted by the Heideckers' minister from Ebenezer United Methodist and by an Army chaplain from Fort Campbell. At its conclusion, seven soldiers from the 101st Airborne, wearing dress greens with a white ascot containing the screaming eagle, stood and marched in small steps towards the casket. They lifted it with military precision and carried it out of the church and placed it into the hearse out front. TV cameramen filmed the congregation's exit from the church.

A Maryland state police car led the funeral procession down Liberty Road to Woodlawn Cemetery in Baltimore County, just half a mile from the Baltimore City line. Gidget sat between Dick and Shirley in the single limousine. At the cemetery, a military helicopter perched on a grassy knoll. David's gravesite was high on a hill. A green canopy was set up nearby with folding chairs underneath. Gidget took her place between Dick and Shirley in the front row. Her father, her mother, and Patrick occupied the remaining seats in front. Gidget observed silently that the green canopy offered no protection against the cold; she shivered in her jacket. The Army chaplain read the Twenty-Third Psalm and led the gathering in The Lord's Prayer. He announced that he was committing David's body to the ground, earth to earth, ashes to ashes, dust to dust. The pallbearers took their positions and slowly folded the flag that cloaked the grey casket. In the distance, seven soldiers fired their rifles three times each. Next to them, an Army bugler played Taps. One of the pallbearers handed the flag, now perfectly folded in the shape of a triangle, to an Army officer who had arrived by helicopter. The officer leaned over and gently gave it to Gidget. Captain Sally Bock immediately passed a second flag, already folded in the same triangular shape, to the officer. He gave it to Shirley. On command, the pallbearers marched down the hill, empty-handed.

Those who remained gathered together around the gravesite, shielding one another against a bitter cold wind that blew on the first day of March. Standing by the grave, Dick could see that David was being buried high on a hill. That pleased him; it would be like home. Down below, he could see and hear the heavy traffic of Liberty Road. That comforted him, too; even though the cemetery was twenty miles from home, it was on the most familiar road of David's life, and the road that went directly into Carroll County. "*I miss you, son,*" he thought. Dick looked around for Shirley. It was time to move on to a small gathering at John Geisler's house. The group was disbursing anyway; there was nothing left to do here. Dick leaned over and kissed Gidget on the cheek. He squeezed Patrick's shoulder. He waved to John and Kathy and Johnny. Then he took Shirley's arm and led her down the hill, toward their car.

It was over.

DAVID W HEIDECKER
SP4 US ARMY
DEC 15 1964 ✝ DEC 12 1985

Ann Turnbull

Woodlawn Cemetery.

EPILOGUE

In the year after the plane crash, Patrick Kenney received an honorable discharge from the Army and came back to Carroll County, where he got a job and rented an apartment. Gladys and Jim moved to Virginia. Chris Langhage entered the Air Force. Aunt Ollie Houghton moved to the home of another of her nephews, slightly closer to Gillis Road. Dick and Shirley and Gidget filed suit against Arrow Air, which had gone into bankruptcy shortly after the accident. They eventually settled out of court. The cause of the crash had not been finally determined, but a majority of the Canadian investigators believed that ice on the wings had been instrumental. Gidget went back to Clarksville, Tennessee, and enrolled in Austin Peay University, but she returned to Bluebird Drive within a few months. She bought a car. The blue Monte Carlo, which no longer ran, was parked at the top of the hill on Gillis Road. Eventually, Dick and Shirley gave it to Patrick. They contracted with a builder to complete the long-delayed addition to their house. Some months after the funeral they began to explore the possibility of adopting another boy.

At Fort Campbell Memorial Park, north of the post, a seven-foot copper statue of an Airborne soldier was erected with the names of the 248 military victims engraved in stone tablets around its base. The Pratt Museum at Fort Campbell displayed a colorful quilt made by a girl scout troop in Clarksville, containing one square with the name of each soldier. The first scholarship in David's name was awarded to Gary Myers, the captain of the football team and a two-way starter for the Cavaliers. In 1985, he scored nine touchdowns playing for the offense as tailback and had sixty-five total tackles playing for the defense as strong safety.

In the fall of 1986, a marker finally was placed on David's grave at Woodlawn Cemetery. It read:

DAVID W. HEIDECKER

SP4 US ARMY

DEC. 15, 1964 — DEC. 12, 1985

On December 12, 1986, one year after the accident, Dick and Shirley and Gidget visited the grave. Gidget took a red rose. Dick and Shirley took a small artificial Christmas tree. Afterwards, on Gillis Road, Dick Heidecker searched through a pile of cards and letters. He found one from Debbie Miller, the RICA teacher who had introduced him to David. It was exactly a year old. Dick sat down in the living-room and reread it:

> Dear Shirley and Dick,
> My teaching wasn't up to par this week, but the kids understood. He was one of them for a short while — they felt good that he had a loving family, a few wonderful years, and had made something out of his life — a new hero for them.
> Dennis Miller and I have been divorced for ten years — different lifestyles and goals — different commitments. The kids and I are still together trying to get this state to work miracles, which is so hard — so few really caring for so many. I feel so bad for you two — my heart goes out to you both. Thanks for doing such a wonderful job — I knew you would. A little love means a lot, especially to a RICA kid.
>
> Feeling your pain,
> Debbie Miller

Dick put the letter away carefully. He stepped outside and stood at the top of the hill, in the cold. Maybe, one day, he could hear again the sound of boys playing football or tag on the hill. There could be ruts in the ground from dirt bikes, a makeshift clubhouse down the road. In the spring, as flowers came, a young boy could help him mow the grass and trim the bushes. One Christmas, they could have a tree again, and presents. Another winter, a boy could run down the hill with great enthusiastic leaps, calling, "Dad! Dad! I shoveled a path for you, do you see it?" They could go for drives in the country, play catch, have snowball fights. Dick looked out from the top of the hill, above the pine trees. It was beginning to get dark. He turned and walked inside, where it was not as cold.

— THE END —

AUTHORS' ACKNOWLEDGEMENT

The authors gratefully acknowledge the cooperation of all those who made this book possible, especially the Heidecker family — Dick and Shirley and Gidget, and Aunt Ollie Houghton. Thanks also to Patrick Kenney, Gladys Nunn, and the Langhage family. We are grateful to the many people at RICA who shared with us their memories of David, as well as his written records, particularly Debbie Miller and Dr. Mel Klein, and to Barbara Skarf, who provided us with the earliest known photograph of David, taken at the institution. We thank South Carroll High School, who also gave us David's records, most particularly Coach Ken Parker and his wife Nancy, together with members of the 1983 Cavaliers and Coach Jerome Ellis. We are appreciative of the assistance of Gidget's father and mother, John Geisler and Linda Vogel, of her brother Johnny, and of Gidget herself for sharing with us her most personal memories as well as David's letters to her from Fort Benning, Fort Campbell, and the Sinai Desert. The authors acknowledge the assistance of the Canadian Aviation Safety Board, who sent us copies of its records and exhibits, and of Mr. Richard Johanneson of Steno Tran, who provided us with a complete transcript of testimony taken by the Board in Quebec in April, 1986, at its public inquiry into the airplane accident at Gander. Our thanks to members of the 101st Airborne Division (Air Assault) at Fort Campbell, Kentucky, especially Alan O'Sullivan, with special good wishes to Eric Harrington, who missed the plane.

Ann Turnbull
Joseph Wase